C000019200

FIRST PUBLISHED
IN GREAT BRITAIN 2001
COPYRIGHT
© JEFF FISHER 2001
THE MORAL RIGHT OF THE
AUTHOR HAS BEEN ASSERTED
BLOOMSBURY PUBLISHING PLC.
38 SOHO SQUARE
LONDON WID 3HB
A CIP CATALOGUE RECORD
FOR THIS BOOK IS
AVAILABLE FROM THE
BRITISH LIBRARY
ISBN 0 7475 5618 0
10 9 8 7 6 5 4 3 2 1
PRINTED BY
ST. EDMUNDSBURY PRESS
SUFFOLK

YOU START OUT
WITH NOTHING

YOU ATTEMPT A
MODEST LIVING
BY HARD WORK,
DECENCY, FRUGALITY,
AND INTEGRITY

YOU SCRUB THE
POOP DECK

YOU PAINT THE TROUSERS
ONTO AN ENDLESS LINE
OF PORCELAIN FIGURES

YOU HANDSTITCH
TINY PARTS OF
PIECES OF RUBBISH
TO OTHER BITS

YOU OFFICE

YOU PUSH YOURSELF
BEYOND THE LIMITS
OF HUMAN ENDURANCE

YOU REALIZE
YOUR MISTAKE

YOU MEAN TO MARRY
THE TREMENDOUSLY RICH
LADY KLIPPLOCH OF
MUDDERSCKHLASSEN

YOU CONSTRUCT AN
ELABORATE PERSONA,
INVOLVING DUTCH
ROYALTY, VINTAGE
CARS AND ADOPTED
MANNERISMS, PURELY
FROM FOUND OBJECTS

YOU CHARM, YOU
POLO TILL DAWN

HER FATHER, LORD
FOOTSTOOL, SETS
THE DOGS ON YOU

YOU WIN
£1,000,000,000,000,000.00

YOU SPEND IT

YOU EXPLOIT A
DEFENCELESS MINORITY

YOU ARE LYNCHED AND
BURNT IN THE STREET

YOU PAINT YOUR
MASTERPIECE

NO-ONE
WANTS IT

YOU GO INTO
INSURANCE

AN ENDLESS
STRING OF NATURAL
DISASTERS AND
MISPLACED DOUBLE
BUY-BACKS APPEARS
UNEXPECTEDLY
AT YOUR DOOR. YOU
CAN'T REMEMBER
WHY IT WAS, WHERE
YOU PUT IT, OR WHO THE HELL

YOU LOSE
THE PLOT

YOU OWE $1,000,000,
000,000,000,000,000,
000,000,000,000,000,
000,000,000,000,000,
000,000,000,000,000

YOU MAKE A
RUN FOR IT

YOU LUNCH

YOU ANNEX A TINY
FOREIGN ENCLAVE

YOU PILLAGE,
YOU PLUNDER

YOU CHANGE
YOUR IDENTITY

YOU FIND £1,000,
000,000,000,000,
000,000,000,000,
000,000,000,000,
000,000,000,000

YOU LIVE
LIKE A KING

YOU'RE ROBBED
AT KNIFEPOINT

YOU ATTEMPT
SELLING YOUR BODY

YOU GAMBLE

YOU SELL
YOUR MOTHER

YOU BECOME AN
APOLOGIST FOR
SOME APPALLING
FORM OF TOXIC WASTE

YOU SLEEP WITH
YOUR BOSS

YOU INVEST
IN ART

YOU WIN AT
THE TRACK

YOU BUY
PIG FUTURES

MALE 48
REQUIRES VAST
PERSONAL WEALTH
WILL DO ANYTHING
GBC. GIRLY. YLPAT.
HYLW. 164311226

YOU ADVERTISE

YOU SELL YOUR
SOUL TO THE DEVIL

HE DOESN'T PAY

YOU LITIGATE

YOU EXTRACT

YOU'RE RUN
OUT OF TOWN

YOU INHERIT £1,000,
000,000,000,000,000,
000,000,000,000,000,
000,000,000,000,000,
000,000,000,000,000

YOU LOSE IT

YOUR BANK ROBS
YOU AT KNIFEPOINT

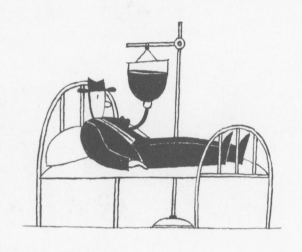

YOU ARE TAXED
MERCILESSLY

YOU INVENT AN
INDISPENSABLE GADGET

YOUR BOAT
COMES IN

YOUR BOAT
GOES OUT

YOU'RE DECLARED
BANKRUPT

YOU GO
DIRECTLY
TO JAIL

YOUR DEBT TO SOCIETY
PAID, YOU RETIRE TO A LIFE
OF CONTEMPLATION

INCREDIBLY ENOUGH,
BENEATH THE POTATOES,
YOU CHANCE UPON THE LOST
TOMB OF ZIB THE GOLDEN

A MULTITUDE OF SMALL CREATURES CARRIES YOU OFF TO THE LAND BEYOND THE CLOUDS WHERE YOU ARE DECLARED KING OF HEAVEN, FED FRESH FISH, CHOCOLATE CAKE & AS MUCH WINE AS YOU CAN DRINK.......

EVERYTHING GOES BLACK

*She's feisty ar[...]*
*a pow[...]*

# The Hot-Headed Virgin

Three sizzling, compelling romances from three
favourite Mills & Boon authors!

In May 2010 Mills & Boon bring you
two classic collections, each
featuring three favourite romances
by our bestselling authors

# CLAIMED BY THE SICILIAN
## by Kate Walker

*Sicilian Husband, Blackmailed Bride*
*The Sicilian's Red-Hot Revenge*
*The Sicilian's Wife*

# THE HOT-HEADED VIRGIN

*The Virgin's Price* by Melanie Milburne
*The Greek's Virgin* by Trish Morey
*The Italian Billionaire's Virgin*
by Christina Hollis

# The Hot-Headed Virgin

MELANIE MILBURNE

TRISH MOREY

CHRISTINA HOLLIS

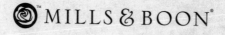

MILLS & BOON

First published in Great Britain 2010
Harlequin Mills & Boon Limited,
Eton House, 18-24 Paradise Road, Richmond, Surrey TW9 1SR

THE HOT-HEADED VIRGIN © by Harlequin Enterprises II B.V./S.à.r.l 2010

*The Virgin's Price, The Greek's Virgin* and *The Italian Billionaire's Virgin*
were first published in Great Britain by Harlequin Mills & Boon Limited in
separate, single volumes.

*The Virgin's Price* © Melanie Milburne 2006
*The Greek's Virgin* © Trish Morey 2006
*The Italian Billionaire's Virgin* © Christina Hollis 2006

ISBN: 978 0 263 88103 5

05-0510

Printed and bound in Spain
by Litografia Rosés S.A., Barcelona

# THE VIRGIN'S PRICE

BY
MELANIE MILBURNE

**Melanie Milburne** says: One of the greatest joys of being a writer is the process of falling in love with the characters and then watching as they fall in love with each other. I am an absolutely hopeless romantic. I fell in love with my husband on our second date and we even had a secret engagement, so you see it must have been destined for me to be a Mills & Boon author! The other great joy of being a romance writer is hearing from readers. You can hear all about the other things I do when I'm not writing and even drop me a line at: www.melaniemilburne.com.au.

Don't miss Melanie Milburne's exciting new novel, *The Mélendez Forgotten Marriage*, available in July 2010 from Mills & Boon® Modern™.

To my sisters, Coralie Margaret McNamara
and Jessie Isobel Bohannon. Thank you for your love
and support over the years. I love you both very dearly.

# CHAPTER ONE

'I CAN'T believe he wrote that about me!' Mia threw the morning's newspaper down in disgust, her grey eyes flashing with rage. 'It's the first real acting job I've had and he completely rubbishes it. My career will be over before it even starts.'

'I wouldn't take it too personally,' Shelley said as she reloaded the café dishwasher. 'Bryn Dwyer rubbishes just about everything. Did you hear him on drive-time radio yesterday? He made a complete fool of the person he was interviewing. It's how he gets the ratings he does. You either love him or you hate him.'

'Well, I *hate* him,' Mia said with feeling. 'I just wish I could have the chance to tell him to his arrogant, stuck-up face.'

'Yeah, well, you never know your luck,' Shelley said as she placed the washing powder in the compartment of the dishwasher. 'He was in here three mornings in a row last week, each time with a different woman. You should have seen the way Tony gushed all over him as if he was royalty. I nearly puked.'

*'In here?'* Mia's eyes began to sparkle with hope. 'Bryn Dwyer?'

Shelley straightened from the dishwasher. 'Listen, Mia, just remember you've only just started and Tony only gave you the job in the first place because I put in such a good word for you. If you so much as—'

'One cappuccino and a double decaf latte on table seven.' Tony Pretelli, the café owner, slapped the order on the counter and scooped up a plate of raisin toast on his way past. 'And make it snappy. Our favourite celebrity is here again this morning.'

'Uh-oh,' Shelley said as she took a quick peek over the counter.

'Who is it?' Mia asked as she peered over Shelley's shoulder. She whistled through her teeth when she caught a glimpse of a tall man with dark brown shiny hair and broad shoulders sitting chatting to an attractive brunette. 'Well, I'll be damned.'

Shelley grabbed her by the arm. 'Don't even think about it, Mia. You know what Tony's like. He'll fire you on the spot if you do anything to upset a customer, celebrity or not.'

Mia unpeeled the waitress's fingers and, giving her a sugar-sweet smile, reached for the coffees the barista on duty had just made. 'I think I'll risk it just this once. Anyway, it will be worth it to get back at that pompous jerk for giving me such a bad review.'

Shelley winced as Mia swept past with the coffees. 'I don't think I can watch this…'

Mia sauntered up to the table where Bryn Dwyer was seated with his back to her. It was a very broad back, she couldn't help noticing, and even though he was wearing a pale blue business shirt she could see the bunching of well-developed muscles through the expensive fabric. His shirt cuffs were rolled up at the wrists, revealing tanned forearms sprinkled with dark masculine hair, and an expensive silver watch on his left wrist. His hair was neither long nor short or straight or curly but somewhere in between, and was styled in a casual manner that suggested his long, tanned fingers had been used as its latest combing tool.

She didn't need to see his face; it had been splashed on the cover of just about every women's magazine for the past month as for the second year in a row he had been awarded the Bachelor of the Year title. His prime-time radio slot and popular weekly column in a Sydney broadsheet gave him the sort of fame and fortune most people only ever dreamed of, but even without that, he was a multimillionaire from some clever property investments he'd made all before he'd hit thirty-two or -three years or so ago.

Mia gave her reflection a quick glance in the mirrors above the booth section of the café on her way past, reassuring herself that he couldn't possibly recognise her from last night's performance. With her shoulder-length blonde hair scraped back in a high pony-tail and no make-up on she looked just like an ordinary café waitress. She gave a mischievous little smile as she mentally rehearsed an Irish accent; even better—a visiting-from-abroad café waitress.

'Top of the mornin' to you both. Now, what do we have here—a cappuccino and a double skinny decaf?' she lilted cheerily, as she hovered by Bryn's elbow.

'Mine is the decaf,' the brunette woman said with a friendly smile.

Mia reached over to place it in front of her and then turned to the woman's dark-haired companion, who hadn't even bothered to acknowledge her presence. 'And what is it that you will be having, sir?'

'The cappuccino,' he said without looking up from the document he was reading.

'One cappuccino coming up,' Mia said and proceeded to pour it into his lap.

'What the hell…?' Bryn sprang to his feet and tugged the fabric of his trousers away from his lukewarm groin.

'I'm terribly sorry, how very clumsy of me,' she said with no trace of sincerity. 'I'll get you another one straight away.'

'I don't want another one!' He glared down at her and then, narrowing his eyes a fraction, asked, 'Hey, don't I know you?'

She gave him a vacant look and began to turn away. 'Sorry, but I think you must be mistaken. I have never met you before.'

'You're that girl…' he stalled her with a very large, very firm hand on her arm '…the toilet-paper advertisement, right?'

Mia unhinged his fingers and dusted off her arm, shooting him an imperious look. 'I'm sorry, but you must have me mistaken for someone else.'

'I never forget a face and yours is certainly very—'

*'You are fired!'* Tony Pretelli bellowed as he strode towards them. 'Do you hear me, Mia Forrester? F.I.R.E.D. Fired. Now. Right now as of this very minute.'

'Mia Forrester?' Bryn frowned.

'Sorry, Mr Pretelli,' Mia said, momentarily forgetting to employ her Irish accent. 'I didn't mean to do it. It just slipped out of my hands.'

'I saw you, Mia; it didn't just slip out of your hands. You poured it on the poor man! Get your things and leave immediately,' Tony snarled at her and then, turning to Bryn, softened his tone to an obsequious level. 'Please accept my sincere apologies for the appalling behaviour of my staff— er—*ex*-staff member. I will see to it that she personally pays for the damage to your trousers. I'll organise another coffee for you immediately, and can I tempt you with a slice of our house speciality? It's a tiramisu and absolutely delicious—on the house, of course.'

'No, thank you,' Bryn said with a cool little on-off smile.

*Typical.* Mia gave a little snort. He looks down his nose at everybody. What a pompous jerk.

'But I would like a private word with your—er—ex-staff member,' Bryn added, training his dark blue gaze on her.

Mia's eyes widened in alarm and she started to step backwards. 'But I'm just leaving…'

'Not so fast, Miss Forrester,' he said, capturing her arm once more, his long fingers like a vice around her slim wrist. 'I'm sure your ex-employer won't mind if you humour me for a moment or two.'

Mia looked to Tony for help but he was already on his way back to the kitchen, shouting out another order from table five.

'I think I'll leave you to it,' the brunette woman said to Bryn before sending Mia a pleasant smile. 'I'm Annabelle Heyward, by the way, Miss Forrester. I'm Bryn Dwyer's publicist.'

'Poor you,' Mia muttered not quite under her breath as she took the older woman's hand with her free one. 'But I'm pleased to meet you. I'm sure you're a very nice person despite the company you keep.'

'Excuse me?' Bryn's dark brows met over his eyes.

'I'll call you later with the latest ratings, Bryn.' Annabelle gave him a little wave as she left the café, her eyes twinkling in amusement.

'Please let go of my arm,' Mia said through clenched teeth. 'Everyone is watching.'

'I don't care who is watching.' He glowered down at her darkly. 'I'd like to know why you think you can get away with tossing a cup of coffee in my lap.'

'I didn't get away with it,' she pointed out with a pert tilt of her chin. 'I got fired, remember?'

'And so you deserved to be. What the hell is the matter with you? What have I ever done to you, for God's sake?'

'How can you ask that?' she spat back, wrenching her arm from his, rubbing at her wrist where his fingers had been. 'Not only have I been fired from here, but I'm also sure I'm going to be dropped from Peach Pie Productions because of what you wrote in this morning's paper. It was my first real live theatre performance and you ruined it. The principal actor was sick and the director asked me to fill in for her and now my career is going to be finished because of you and your stupid opinion, which I'm sure is completely biased and—'

'Oh, *that* Mia Forrester,' he said, rubbing his chin thoughtfully.

Mia stared at him in outrage. What did he mean, *that* Mia Forrester?

'So you got a bad review,' he said dismissively. 'Get over it.'

*'Get over it?'* She stepped closer and jabbed him in the chest with her index finger. 'How about you get over this? You are the most arrogant, opinionated, chauvinistic smart alec I've ever met. You think you can say whatever you like or indeed write whatever insults you like but I am not going to allow you to get away with it. You have definitely picked the wrong person this time to make fun of. If I lose my understudy job over this, you are going to be very sorry. I will make sure of it.'

Bryn looked down at the little spitfire in front of him with increasing interest. When was the last time anyone had told him off, he wondered, really told him off, no-holds-barred? Most people—particularly women—bowed and scraped to his every whim, but she was something else again. She was all flashing grey eyes and swinging blonde pony-tail, looking more like a schoolgirl than the seductress she'd played so appallingly last night in Theodore Frankston's new play.

'You should stick to toilet-paper ads,' he said. 'Or have you ever thought about a career change?'

'Have you ever thought about a personality change?' she tossed back, her eyes like twin diamonds of sparkling fury.

Bryn suppressed a smile as he let his gaze run over her lazily. She had a neat figure, very trimmed and toned, and her skin had a healthy glow to it as if she was well used to outdoor activity. She wore no make-up but she had a fresh-faced beauty that was totally captivating. He couldn't help thinking she might be just the type of girl his great-aunt Agnes would approve of. It would be the perfect solution to a problem that had been worrying him for quite some time.

'Listen, Miss Forrester.' He took her to one side out of the way of the hearing of table six. 'I'm sorry you've lost your job here, but really, what's a talented actress like you doing in a place like this?'

She scowled at him. 'You didn't call me talented in your article this morning. You said, and I quote: "A pathetic attempt at portraying a *femme fatale* from a clearly inexperienced actress." Isn't that what you said?'

'It might have run something along those lines.'

'What?' She eyeballed him in fury. 'You don't even remember what you wrote about me?'

'Look.' He dragged a hand through his hair. 'I had a deadline to meet and I'd been out and it was late…'

'Are you telling me you were *drunk* when you wrote that column?'

'Of course not.' He glanced around to make sure no one had heard her fiery accusation. 'Will you keep your voice down? I can do without bad publicity right now.'

Mia straightened to her full height which still left her at a distinct disadvantage to his six-feet-three. 'Do you think I give a damn about your career when you've so cavalierly destroyed mine?'

He compressed his lips for a moment. 'Look, I'll strike a little deal with you.' He took out a business card and handed it to her. 'If you're dropped from the play, give me a call and I'll try and find some other work for you. OK?'

Mia tore the card into tiny pieces and, stepping on her tiptoes, reached to where his top button was undone and stuffed the pieces down his shirt. 'Thanks but no thanks,' she said crisply. 'And I'm going to tell all my friends not to listen to your radio programme ever again. And let me tell you I have a *lot* of friends.'

Bryn watched her flounce back to the kitchen, where, after a short interchange with one of the other waitresses, she scooped up a shoulder bag and left via a rear entrance, her pony-tail still swinging in fury.

He looked down at the neck of his shirt where the sharp little edges were digging into his skin and smiled.

Yes, Great-Aunt Agnes would most definitely approve.

He reached for his mobile and pressed in a few numbers. 'Annabelle, can you text me Theodore Frankston's number and the name and number of Mia Forrester's current agent?'

'What are you up to, Bryn?' Annabelle's tone was full of suspicion.

He waited until he was outside the café before responding. 'Listen, Annabelle, I've got a plan. You know how you said I needed to improve my image to encourage more female listeners? Well, this is a perfect way to do it.'

Annabelle gave a groan. 'This isn't another one of those publicity stunts that will make me cringe, is it? I really don't think I can cope with the fallout if you get involved with yet another married woman.'

'No, this isn't anything like that. And by the way Summer Riley was divorced, or as good as.'

'She was a slut, Bryn, and for the whole time you were involved with her your ratings slipped to an all-time low. Female listeners fell away in droves and we still haven't got them all back.'

'But that's exactly my point,' Bryn said. 'If I play my cards right with this I could overhaul my image within a matter of days. Think about it. What could be better right now than me having a whirlwind romance with a struggling actress I've just savaged in the Press? Women will love it. It's got that whole love-hate chemistry just like a Hollywood movie.'

'I can't believe I'm hearing this,' Annabelle muttered.

'No, listen, Annabelle,' he insisted. 'Women all over Sydney will tune in to hear how our relationship is going. It's perfect!'

'And how exactly are you going to convince Mia Forrester to have a relationship with you? Last time I looked you were wearing the cappuccino she tossed in your lap,' Annabelle pointed out with more than a hint of dryness.

'I have a strategy in mind that I think will do the trick. Text me those numbers as soon as you track them down. *Ciao.*'

A few minutes later Bryn phoned Theodore Frankston. It was a short conversation and very much to the point.

'It was a rotten review,' Theo growled when Bryn identified himself.

'It was a rotten performance,' Bryn returned. 'That girl was totally wrong for the role. What were you thinking, Theo? You should get rid of her immediately before your reputation is damaged any further.'

'And if I don't?'

'Then on air this afternoon I will warn my listeners to stay away from your play and stay at home and watch TV instead. Your little production company will lose all its sponsors before you can blink.'

'She's not going to like this,' Theo grumbled. 'I like the girl. She's a bit raw but I think with a little more work she'll improve.'

'I like her too,' Bryn said. 'Leave her to me. I've got big plans for her.'

'You're an arrogant bastard,' Theo said. 'Has anyone told you that lately?'

'As a matter of fact they have,' Bryn said with a lazy smile. 'And I liked it so much I can hardly wait until she tells me all over again.'

His phone call to Mia's agent was even more productive. He'd met Roberta Askinthorpe at various social events and although they had flirted occasionally nothing serious had come of it, but he knew she would do anything he asked.

'Long time no hear,' Roberta cooed at him. 'Are you ringing to apologise for that incendiary review you wrote about one of my favourite clients in this morning's paper?'

'Not exactly.'

Roberta laughed. 'No, the Bryn Dwyer I know would never apologise for his actions. What was I thinking?'

'I need you to do something for me, Roberta, but it has to remain a secret.'

'Your wish is my command, you know that, Bryn, darling.'

'I want you to temporarily take Mia Forrester off your books.'

'Why do you want me to do that? She's a real sweetie with bags of potential. I know Theodore's play was a bit out there for her but Sabina was sick at the last minute. Anyway, every actor needs stretching occasionally.'

'I have something else for her to do.'

'But how will I explain it to her?'

'Use my review as an excuse,' he suggested. 'It doesn't have to be permanent. You can take her on again later. I just need her to be without work and representation so she will agree to work for me for the time being.'

'I must say, this sounds very intriguing,' Roberta said. 'Don't tell me you've fallen for the girl?'

Bryn laughed off the suggestion. 'Come on, Roberta, you know me better than that. I'm not the falling-in-love type.'

'Perhaps not, but Mia Forrester is rather a pet,' Roberta pointed out. 'I wouldn't want to see her get hurt. What have you got planned?'

'Stay tuned and you'll find out,' he said. 'But remember this is between you and me.'

'I'll do it but I'm warning you it'll cost you dinner some time.'

'You're on,' he said. 'Dinner it is.'

'In Paris,' she added.

He smiled as he hung up the phone.

# CHAPTER TWO

THE telephone started to ring as soon as Mia entered her flat. She stared at it for a moment, wondering if she just ignored it she could put off the inevitable for a little while longer.

'Are you going to get that?' Gina, her flatmate, called out from the bathroom, her voice muffled by the sounds of tooth-brushing.

Mia picked up the phone. 'Mia? Is that you?' her younger sister Ellie's voice sounded in her ear.

'Hi, Ellie. Where are you calling from? Are you still in South America? This line is terrible.'

'I know…' Ellie said, breathing hard. 'Listen, Mia, I'm in trouble. Big trouble.'

Mia felt her insides drop between her knees. 'What's wrong? Where are you? What's happened?'

'I've been arrested.' Ellie let out a little sob.

Mia's eyes widened in shock and her grip on the phone became white-knuckled. '*Arrested!* What on earth for?'

'You know that rainforest-logging protest rally I've been involved with in Brazil? Well, I got arrested and I need bail money wired over to get me out of here.'

'*Oh, my God!*'

'Please don't call Mum and Dad,' Ellie said. 'I don't want to ruin their holiday with Jake and Ashleigh.'

'But we'll have to call them!' Mia insisted.

'No, Mia, please. Dad would have a heart attack on the spot, you know how his doctor told him to take things easy since that last scare.'

'But what about Jake? He'd gladly help out financially. I just know he would.'

'No, Mia. Please don't tell Ashleigh and Jake about this. Ashleigh will be hysterical and it will upset the kids. Promise me you won't tell.'

Mia was all too aware of her sister's fierce pride and had no choice but to reluctantly agree. 'All right, I promise.'

'Thanks, Mia. Just send me some money via my credit card. I've luckily still got that and my passport, although my backpack with my return ticket has been stolen.'

'How much money do you need?'

Ellie told her and Mia's stomach threatened to hit the floor this time. 'I'll send it as soon as I can,' she said. 'It might take me a couple of days to find that kind of money. I have a little in my account but not quite that much.'

'It's all right, I'll manage until you can get it to me,' Ellie said. 'I'm so sorry about this. Please don't tell anyone about it. Not even Gina. I don't want people to worry for nothing. This will all be sorted out in no time and I can't bear the embarrassment of having to explain it all ad nauseam when I get back.'

'What about the Australian Embassy? Should I call them and get them to help?'

'No, just do as I said, Mia,' Ellie said. 'Once that money's in my credit-card account there's a guy here who can help me. It's how things work over here.'

'I'm so worried about you…'

'Don't be, Mia. I'm fine, truly. Look, I've got to go. The guard's making a fuss about the length of the call. I had to bribe him with my last chocolate bar. I'll call you when I'm free. Love you.'

'Love you…'Mia stared at the dead phone, her heart sinking in despair. The amount of money Ellie needed wasn't huge but things had been tight lately and now, with her café job over, if Theodore didn't keep her with the company things could get rather desperate.

The phone rang again while she was still holding it and she answered it to find Theodore on the other end informing her of his decision to drop her from the company. He cut the conversation short as soon as she began to protest.

'Sorry, Mia. My investors are threatening to pull out on the deal after that review. Goodbye.'

She couldn't believe it. Her first foray into live theatre had come to an ignominious end. One bad review and she was back to waiting on tables full-time, except for the fact that, because of this morning's encounter with Bryn Dwyer, she no longer had any tables to wait on. And with Ellie's life in danger thousands of kilometres away she had to have money and fast.

She took a deep, calming breath. *Right, I just have to find another acting job,* she told herself firmly. No matter how small or demeaning it was, she *had* to find work.

She quickly dialled her agent but the conversation, like the one she'd just had with Theodore, was brusque and just as disheartening.

'What's wrong?' Gina asked on her way past a short time later. 'You look like you're about to murder someone.'

'I am,' Mia said, gritting her teeth as she searched for her car keys. 'I'm going to track down the person responsible for making me lose two jobs in one day and tell him exactly what I think of him.'

'You've been dropped from Peach Pie Productions?' Gina's eyes went wide.

Mia tossed one of the sofa cushions aside to retrieve her keys. 'Not just the company but the café as well, and as if that weren't enough my agent just made some pathetic excuse about being too busy to represent me any more. *Grrrrr!*'

'But why?' Gina asked. 'I thought you were brilliant last night, no matter what the review in this morning's paper said.'

'So you saw what he wrote, did you?' Mia asked, scowling furiously. 'God knows who else has seen it and completely written me off as an actor. I can just imagine what everyone is saying. I'm probably the laughing stock of the whole of Sydney by now. No one will ever offer me a role again and as for getting a new agent, who is going to take me on now?'

Gina did her best to be reassuring. 'Try not to worry, Mia, all actors get bad reviews from time to time. It comes with the territory. Maybe a new agent will be a good thing in the long run.'

Mia ground her teeth without answering. Her worries about Ellie made her anger towards Bryn Dwyer escalate to boiling point. He was responsible for this and he was going to pay—big time.

'But why did you lose your job at the café? I thought Tony liked having someone nearly famous working there part-time?'

She gave her flatmate another furious scowl. 'Because I tipped a cup of coffee in a customer's lap, that's why.'

'You mean…' Gina gave her a wide-eyed look '….*on purpose*?'

Mia lifted her head in proud defiance. 'He had it coming to him for writing such a horrible review.'

Gina's eyes nearly popped out of her head. 'You mean

you tipped a cup of coffee in Bryn Dwyer's lap? Bryn Dwyer, the Bachelor of the Year and multimillionaire playboy prince of radio?'

'That's the one.'

'Oh, my God, your career *is* over.'

'Not if I can help it,' Mia said determinedly, jangling her keys in her hand.

Gina gave her a worried look. 'What are you going to do?'

'Like I said—I'm going to see him and tell him exactly what I think of him. He told me to call him if I was dropped from the company, but I'm going to see him in person.'

'Do you think that's such a good idea? He probably has bodyguards or something. He had a stalker before. I remember reading about it in all the magazines. A crazy woman was following him for months, turning up wherever he was, threatening him all the time. His minders might think you're just like her and going to do him some harm.'

Mia gave her a glittering look over her shoulder as she opened the front door to leave. 'I *am* going to do him some harm,' she said. 'And I don't care who tries to stop me. The upsized egotist Bryn Dwyer has finally met his match. You just wait and see.'

The studios of Hot Spot FM were in the leafy suburb of Lane Cove. Mia parked in a side-street and approached the security check-in point.

'I'm here for a live interview with Bryn Dwyer,' she informed the attendant assertively. 'Mia Forrester. I'm an actor.'

The man looked down at his schedule for a moment. 'I'm afraid I don't have you marked down on my sheet. Are you sure your interview is for this afternoon?'

'Yes, I spoke with Mr Dwyer this morning over coffee,'

she said and, taking a risk added, 'He asked me to come and see him in person. Perhaps if you could call his studio and check, I'm sure he will verify it for you. We're—er—old friends.'

'Just a second.' The man pressed some numbers and had a brief conversation with the producer before he turned back to her and handed her a security pass through the booth window. 'Here's a security tag.' He activated the boom gate for her and added, 'Go right through, Miss Forrester; it's studio number five, the third one on the left. The producer will let you know when it's time for your interview. Mr Dwyer's been expecting you.'

Mia walked through with forced casualness while her brain was shooting off in all directions. What did he mean, Mr Dwyer was *expecting* her? How had he known she'd be storming over here to have it out with him?

The two-part studio was where the boom operator had indicated and one of the crew opened the door at her knock and ushered her through. Mia could see Bryn sitting in the transmitting studio next door, his headphones and mouthpiece in place. As if he sensed her presence he swung his chair around and mouthed 'hello' to her, his eyes glinting with something she couldn't quite identify.

She pursed her lips and, although she was seriously tempted to give him a very rude sign with one of her fingers, somehow she resisted the urge and sent him a frosty look instead.

'He's got one more song until the news and weather and then he'll be able to speak to you,' the producer informed her from where he was sitting behind his computer console.

'Thank you,' she said and took the chair he offered.

She could hear the sound of Bryn's deep, mellifluous voice as the show was broadcast around the studio. There was a seven-second delay, which she found a little unnerving because inside the glassed-in section she could see he had stopped speaking to swivel his chair to look at her again.

She gave him another cold look but just then she heard his voice announce his next guest.

'Right after the news and weather I will have with me the utterly gorgeous Mia Forrester, whom I met for the first time this morning when she accidentally spilt a cup of coffee in my lap. Hey, all you out there in radio-land, I'm in *love*.'

Mia's eyes went out on stalks as she sat forward on her chair, her stomach tripping over itself in alarm. What on earth was he doing?

He gave her a quick, confident grin and his voice continued, 'So call me after the news, all you lovers out there in listener-land, and tell me about your most romantic meeting.'

'On air in three minutes,' the producer informed Mia as he flicked another switch on his console.

'But I—' She clamped her mouth shut when she saw Bryn's lazy smile. *All right*, she thought. I'll do it. I'll go on radio and tell him exactly what I think of him. You just see if I won't.

She was led into Bryn's soundproof studio, fitted with a pair of headphones and seated opposite him in front of a microphone. She could hear the news segment coming to an end and then Bryn smiled as he spoke into his mouthpiece.

'Thank you for joining me in the studio this afternoon, Mia. This is Hot Spot FM and I have with me here the beautiful Mia Forrester, whom I met by accident this morning. And I can tell right my life will never be the same again. I'll take caller number four, who wants to tell us about how she met the love of her life. Hello, Jennifer from way out at Campbelltown. Tell us about your romantic meeting.'

Mia swallowed as a young woman's voice sounded in her

ears. 'Hi, Bryn and Mia. I met my husband when he ran into the back of my car at the traffic lights. I was so furious with him but after I'd vented my spleen I suddenly realised how gorgeous he was. He asked me out and the rest, as they say, is history.'

'Thanks, Jennifer, what a great story. Now we have Andy from Castle Hill on the line. Hi, Andy; how did you meet the love of your life?'

This time a male voice sounded in Mia's ears. 'I met my fiancée when she waxed my legs in preparation for a triathlon I was competing in.'

'No kidding?' Bryn said, winking at Mia. 'So how many waxes did it take to ask her out?'

'Five, but it was worth the pain.'

Bryn laughed. 'Way to go, Andy. Who says men have no sense of romance? Now I think it's Mia's turn to tell you about how she met me this morning. Mia?'

Mia met his dark blue gaze and tightened her mouth. 'I met Bryn Dwyer in the café where up until this morning I was employed part-time. But as a result of my—er—spilling a cup of coffee in his lap I lost my job on the spot and—'

'And lost her heart as well, isn't that right, sweetheart?'

'I—'

'You know the number.' Bryn cut her off as he addressed his listeners. 'Call in and tell us if you agree with the concept of love at first sight.' He took the first caller.

Mia listened with one ear as she tried to make sense of what was going on. Was this some kind of joke? What the hell was he playing at, pretending he'd fallen in love with her?

The switchboard was buzzing with incoming calls and the producer gave Bryn a thumbs-up sign from the studio next door, his face beaming.

'Now we have Sharon from sunny Seaforth, who has a question for Mia,' Bryn said. 'Go ahead, Sharon.'

'Mia, did you feel an instant attraction for Bryn or did it take a few minutes before you realised you were falling in love with him?'

'I…' Mia caught the gleam in Bryn's dark gaze and sent him a blistering glare. 'No, not instantly…it was more of a slow realisation that here was a man who would stop at nothing to get his way and—'

'See how well she knows me already?' Bryn cut her off again. 'How about a question from Corinne? Go ahead, Corinne.'

'Mia, I was wondering if you are worried about falling in love with one of Sydney's notorious playboys. What if he lets you down?'

'I don't think he'll let me down,' Mia said, finally catching on and hatching a vengeful little plot of her own. She gave Bryn a beguiling smile and added, 'Not now that we're planning to get married as soon as possible. He proposed to me this morning and I said yes.'

Within seconds the switchboard was jammed with calls and the producer gave the signal for the next bracket of music to be played.

Mia waited until she was sure they were off air. 'What the hell do you think you're doing? I'm not in love with you!'

'I know,' Bryn said, leaning back in his chair to survey her outraged features. 'But the listeners don't know that and neither does my producer.'

'You mean…' she glanced at the still beaming producer in the studio next door and then back at Bryn '…you mean they think it's…*real*?'

'Of course they think it's real.'

'Are you crazy or something?'

'Not crazy, just hungry for more ratings.' A segment of advertisements began to play as he continued, 'I thought since you ruined a pair of Armani trousers this morning the very least you could do was give my ratings a boost by pretending to be in love with me for a week or two.' He pressed another button. 'But that bit about marriage was total overkill. It'll be all over the papers tomorrow.'

Mia felt her heart give an extra beat. 'The papers?'

'Yep. Journalists love this sort of stuff. Celebrity playboy meets perfect match.' He smiled a white-toothed smile. 'But we can go along with it for a while. What do you think?'

'I think you're a jerk, that's what I think. I lost my job because of you.'

'I told you you're wasted in the café; you could do much better than that.'

'Not the café, although that was bad enough,' she bit out through clenched teeth. 'I was dropped from Peach Pie Productions this morning. Theodore Frankston saw your review and decided to pull me out completely. Then I spoke to my agent who told me she was too busy to represent me properly but I know it was because of your stupid review.'

'Too bad.'

'It's worse than bad. I have bills to pay.' *And I need a heck of a lot of money to get my sister out of trouble*, she wanted to insert but stopped herself just in time. 'I've not long moved into a flat with a friend. How am I going to meet my commitments when I no longer have a job and no agent to find me a new one?'

'Ah, but you do have a job,' he said. 'I just gave you one.'

She frowned at him in confusion. 'What are you talking about?'

He leaned forward in his chair until his knees were almost touching hers. Mia hadn't realised how very dark his eyes were until that moment and she felt her tummy do a funny little moth-like flutter as she was pulled into their deep, ocean-blue depths.

'I want you to act the role of my devoted fiancée,' he said. 'I would have settled for girlfriend but, since you mentioned the M word in front of two-point-four million listeners, I'm afraid we'll have to run with that role instead.'

*'Your fiancée?'* She gasped. *'You want me to pretend to be your fiancée?'*

He flicked a glance at the monitor and pressed another button before he sat back in his seat. 'You're an actor, right?'

She gave him a resentful look. 'Yes, but according to this morning's paper not a very good one.'

'Here's your chance to prove me wrong,' he said. 'If you can convince the Press and my listeners that you are indeed in love with me then I'll take back everything I said. I'll pay you, of course. What was Frankston's company giving you?'

She told him and he gave a snort. 'What a joke. No wonder you didn't put your heart into that role. I'll pay you four times that much, plus expenses.'

'Expenses?'

'Hang on a minute.' He turned his headphones back on and began to speak on air. 'You heard it first on Hot Spot FM. Bryn Dwyer the confirmed bachelor is in love with a little lady who has promised to be his wife. You know the number. Give me a call to congratulate me. This is one very happy man.'

Mia sat silently fuming. This was getting ridiculous. Surely he didn't expect her to take him seriously?

She chewed her lip for a moment.

It *was* a lot of money he was offering. Besides, it might only be for a week or two, maybe a couple of months at the most. And it would certainly solve Ellie's problems, which was her biggest priority right now. And she was an actor, so it shouldn't be a problem playing the role, but still…

She stole a covert look at him as he chatted with another caller. He was smiling, which made his eyes crinkle up at the edges in a rather attractive way.

'So what do you say?' he said as he went off air again.

'What if I don't agree to this?' she said, not wanting to feed his ego by sounding too keen.

He shifted his lips from side to side as if he was thinking about a suitable plan of action. Mia felt distinctly uneasy. She felt as if she was now under his control and she didn't like it one little bit. She had come storming to the studio to tell him what she thought of him but somehow he had turned the tables on her.

'There were witnesses to your assault on my person this morning,' he said into the little silence. 'And, like you, I have a lot of friends, several of them with impressive law degrees. All it would take is one phone call and you could be in very hot water, even hotter than the liquid you tossed in my lap.'

Mia's throat moved up and down. Surely he wouldn't press charges if she didn't fall in with his plans?

She met his midnight-blue eyes and swallowed again,

Yes. He would.

She lowered her gaze. 'You mentioned something about expenses…'

'Yes. You'll need to have nice clothes and get your hair done occasionally. I don't expect you to pay for that out of your own pocket. I'll make sure you have a substantial clothing and grooming allowance. So have we got a deal?'

'How long do you expect me to play this role for you?'

'Not long; a week or two, maybe longer.'

She narrowed her eyes at him. 'How much longer?'

'What say we give it a month at the most and then we'll call it off?'

'What will happen to your ratings then?'

He gave her another grin. 'They'll probably increase due to my heartbroken state. Everyone will feel sorry for me being dumped.'

Mia rolled her eyes.

'I'm off air in thirty minutes,' he said, flicking another switch. 'Wait for me in the cafeteria and we'll go somewhere where we can have another chat about the deal. But in the meantime, don't let the cat out of the bag. I don't want anyone at the studio to suspect this is a stunt.'

'What about your publicist?'

'I'll tell her only what she needs to hear but no one else is to know, not even your family and friends.'

'I can't lie to my family and friends!'

'You're not lying, Mia. You're acting. There's a difference.'

She opened her mouth but he went back on air before she could get a single word of protest out. She blew out a breath of frustration and, snatching up her bag, made her way to the cafeteria she'd seen on her way in.

# CHAPTER THREE

MIA was almost relieved when Bryn finally joined her half an hour later. She'd been practically besieged by staff rushing up to congratulate her on her impending marriage to Sydney's crown prince of the airwaves.

'Sorry about that,' he said as he led her to an office down the hall. He smiled at her as he pushed open the door marked with his name. 'See what a sensation you've caused?'

'*I've* caused?' Mia swung around to glare at him once they were alone inside. 'If you hadn't rubbished me the way you did none of this would have happened.'

'You were the one who told everyone we were engaged,' he pointed out.

'I only did that to get back at you for saying we'd fallen in love this morning.' She gave him a disparaging glare and added, 'As if I'd ever fall in love with someone like you.'

'I don't know why you're so upset,' he said. 'Your season with Theodore would have ended in two weeks anyway—then what were you going to do? Wait on tables until something else turned up? I'm doing you a favour, Mia. I'm giving you the sort of exposure most wannabe actors would give a right arm for. Your face will be on every national paper tomorrow. The Press will want interviews, magazines will carry your picture on their covers and before you know it every film or theatre producer in town will be begging you to audition for them. You'll have agents falling over themselves to represent you.'

Mia frowned as she thought about it. It certainly would get her name out there, but at what cost? How would she ever explain it to her family?

'I don't like the idea of being used as a marketing ploy, especially without consultation with me first,' she said. 'And I don't appreciate being blackmailed.'

'Yes, well, I don't appreciate having my groin soaked with hot coffee,' he returned with a glint in his eyes.

Mia's eyes went to his groin. He was leaning against his desk, his long legs outstretched, the fabric of his trousers pulled tight over his…

She wrenched her gaze away and forced herself to meet his laughing blue eyes. 'I'm sure no permanent damage was done and even if it was I'm sure the rest would do you good. It's a wonder it hasn't dropped off by now from overuse.'

'Maybe you should check it out just to make sure it's still on active service,' he suggested with a lift of an eyebrow.

She gave him a withering look and folded her arms across her chest. 'I don't think so.'

He laughed and pushed himself away from the desk to stand right in front of her. He tipped up her chin with one long finger and looked into her eyes. 'You've got such an expressive little face. I can't stop looking at you. Those big grey eyes of yours remind me of a stormy afternoon sky, one minute dark and brooding, the next flashing with lightning sparks of fury.'

Mia held her breath as he began to trace his thumb across her bottom lip, back and forth, back and forth until she could feel her mouth tingling. She knew she should have at least made a token effort to move out of his reach but somehow his touch was totally mesmerising. Her heart began to hammer behind her chest as he placed his hand on her hip and brought her even closer.

'Wh-what are you doing?' she croaked.

He held her firm, his long fingers splayed over the slim curve of her hip, his mouth tilted in a little smile. 'I thought we should get this bit over with in private. That way when we have to do it in public it won't feel so strange. It's like a rehearsal, if you like.'

'A rehearsal?' She gave a quick nervous swallow. 'A rehearsal for what?'

His head came down, hovering just above hers, his warm, hint-of-mint breath brushing over her lips as he said in a deep, spine-tingling voice, 'We need to rehearse the kiss scenes we'll be expected to play in public.'

Her stomach gave an unexpected lurch. 'K-kiss scenes?'

His mouth moved a little closer, his chest so close now she could feel the deep rumble of his voice against her breasts when he spoke. 'Yes, you know—where I put my mouth on yours and you kiss me back.'

'I know what a kiss scene is but I—' Mia began but before she could get the full sentence out, his mouth had come down and settled firmly on hers.

It was a shock to feel his lips moving over hers so persuasively. She'd had every intention of fighting him but somehow as soon as those firm, warm lips connected with hers she felt an electric charge rush through her as if some sort of visceral energy was passing from his body to hers. Before she knew it she was responding to him, her mouth opening at the first sweep of his tongue. He entered her mouth with a toe-curling thrust that sent a riot of sensations through her body from her breasts to her thighs. It was madness but she just couldn't help it. She kept reminding herself how much she hated him but what she was feeling in his arms took over the rational, cool-headed, thinking part of her brain. Every part of her body reacted to him. She could feel the prickling tension in her breasts as he brought her even harder up against his chest and deepened the kiss. She could even feel her inner thighs quivering at the thought of what was pressing so insistently just above them. She had never been so thoroughly kissed in her entire life and this was just a rehearsal! God knew how she would cope with the real thing.

*But none of this is real*, she told herself sternly. It's an act, a publicity stunt for him to increase his ratings. It has nothing to do with reality, nothing to do with real feelings and responses.

It was an act.

Bryn lifted his head and looked down at her flushed features. 'Wow, I think I might have to take back everything I said in my column. That was an Oscar-winning performance. No one would ever think you weren't in love with me after that.'

Mia eased herself out of his hold, her eyes flashing with rage. 'If you think I'm going to be manhandled by you whenever you feel like it then you're in for a big shock.'

'It's only a performance, just like any other,' he said. 'Besides, you kissed the leading man last night, not very convincingly in my opinion, but then maybe he had bad breath or something.'

'He did not have bad breath.'

'Then what was the problem? Didn't you like the guy?'

'Actors don't have to like the person they're playing opposite, which is just as well, as I can't think of a person I hate more than you.'

'What a professional challenge this will be for you, then,'

he observed with a mocking smile playing about his mouth. 'Convincing the public you're in love with me when all the time you really hate my guts.'

'I can do it,' she bit out with pride-fuelled determination. 'I'll show you I'm not the inexperienced, pathetic actor you apparently think I am.'

'Good,' he said. 'We'll start with public performance number one this evening. I'll send a car for you at seven. Wear something glamorous and sexy.'

'I don't have anything glamorous and sexy.'

He reached for his wallet and, opening it, peeled off a thick wad of notes and handed it to her. 'Buy something.'

Mia stared at the money without touching it.

'Go on,' he said. 'It's part of the deal, remember?'

'I don't want your disgusting money. I'd rather wear rags than take anything off you.'

He tugged her towards him and with a deftness that left her completely breathless he tucked the wad of notes down the front of her cotton top right between her heaving breasts.

'When I say go and buy something sexy and glamorous I mean it, Mia. Got that? You're playing a role for me and I expect and indeed am paying you to give a brilliant performance.'

Mia gave him a fulminating glare as she retrieved the money out of her top and stuffed it in the back pocket of her jeans. 'I might have to act my heart out in public but when we're alone I'm still going to hate you with every bone in my body. Got that?'

'Loud and clear,' he said, holding the door open for her. 'Come on, I'll walk you to your car.'

'I can find my own way.' She made to brush past but he put out an arm to stop her. She jerked back from the feel of his muscled arm against the softness of her breasts.

Her eyes locked with his and her heart gave an extra beat at the diamond-sharp glitter in his dark gaze.

'Don't fight me, Mia, because when I fight, I fight dirty. You'd be wise to remember that.'

'Tell me something I don't already know,' she tossed back. 'You're an unscrupulous playboy with nothing better to do with your time than manipulate people to do what you want. How pathetic.'

'I'll tell you what's pathetic,' he said, a thread of anger beginning to tighten his voice. 'Your little attempt at pay-back this morning was a childish impulse that clearly demonstrates how ill-suited you are for anything other than those ridiculous toilet-paper ads you've done in the past.'

Mia clenched her fists by her sides. 'Why don't you just go ahead and sue me? Go on. I dare you.'

'Don't tempt me, little lady. How long do you think it would take you to find another job if I tell the truth about what really happened this morning? There isn't an agent who would take you on and you damn well know it. You reputation as a hot-headed little prima donna would make anyone think twice about representing you.'

Mia tried to outstare him but something about the rigid set of his jaw warned her against pitting her puny strength against his. He was a man used to having things his way and anyone in the way would be ruthlessly disposed of with whatever means he had available. She knew she would never find work in the industry again if he put his mind to it. He had connections and in the acting world that meant everything. One bad word and her reputation would be ruined. One bad review was enough. How much worse would it be if he took it into his mind to totally alienate her future career prospects?

She lowered her eyes and though it irked her intolerably

she made no demur as he took her hand and led her out of his office through the building and the grounds until they came to her car.

'See you tonight,' he said, stepping back from the car as she started the engine.

'See you in hell,' she muttered darkly as she backed out.

Bryn watched her roar away in a clang of clutch and gears, her smooth cheeks still bright pink with outraged colour.

Once she was out of sight he ran his tongue over his lips. He could still taste the summer-strawberry flavour of her soft mouth where it had been pressed against his. Even his chest felt as if she were still up against it, her slender curves fitting so neatly against him as if she were tailor-made for him. Holding her close had triggered a deep pulse of desire that even now he could feel thudding insistently in his blood. He couldn't remember a time when he'd felt so turned on by a woman.

He gave himself a mental shake. He didn't believe in love at first sight. He didn't believe in romantic love at all. The term 'love' was all too often used when the word 'lust' would have been much more appropriate. Lust at first sight; now, there was a concept he could get his head around.

He was *in lust* with Mia Forrester.

That was more like it.

Lust he could handle.

But even so, a tiny frown closed the distance between his eyebrows as he turned and walked back to the studio building.

# CHAPTER FOUR

'OH, MY God, is it true?' Gina gasped as soon as Mia walked through the door of their tiny flat in Neutral Bay. 'I listened to you on the radio. Are you *really* engaged to him?'

'Um…well…you know…I…it…we…'

'It's just *soooo* romantic!' Gina gushed. 'I thought you hated him and now you're going to be married. Talk about a whirlwind affair. Can I be bridesmaid?'

'I'm not…sure what plans we will be making about that just yet,' Mia said, hating Bryn all over again for making her lie to her closest friend. 'It's all happened so fast. My feet haven't touched the ground yet.'

'How did it happen? I mean, did you just suddenly realise he was the man of your dreams? Was it truly love at first sight?'

Mia had to dig deeply into her acting repertoire to sound anywhere near convincing. 'I went there to tell him what I thought of him but as soon as I saw him sitting there…I couldn't control my reaction. It was…unbelievable.'

'God, I wish some gorgeous guy would sweep me off my feet like that,' Gina said. 'And think of how rich and famous he is. You'll never have to worry about the rent again.'

'His money doesn't matter to me in the slightest,' Mia lied.

The truth was, Bryn Dwyer's money was the only reason

she was doing this, to help Ellie, otherwise she would have told him exactly where to put his stupid fiancée role with considerable relish. She'd already deposited the wad of money he'd given her into her sister's credit-card account, which had in some way made her feel a little less compromised about what she was doing in playing the role he'd assigned her. At least it would tide her sister over until she could get her hands on some more.

'I'm sure his money doesn't matter to you but every little bit helps,' Gina responded pragmatically. 'So when are you seeing him again?'

Mia glanced at her watch and felt her stomach clench in panic at how she was going to be ready in time. 'In about two hours.'

'Two hours?' Gina looked aghast. 'But you haven't even done your hair!'

'Can I borrow that black evening dress of yours?' Mia asked as she kicked off her shoes and released her pony-tail.

'Which one? The one with the diamanté halter-neck or the one with the split up the thigh?'

'Which do you think is sexier?'

Gina scrunched her face up as she thought about it. 'Definitely the split—besides, you've got the legs for it.'

Mia stared at her reflection an hour and forty-five minutes later. There was no trace of the struggling and out-of-work actor now. In her place was a sophisticated vision in close-fitting black satin, her blonde hair scooped up in a casual but still elegant twist on top of her head, the glittering drop earrings she'd borrowed off Gina giving the final touch of glamour.

'Wow…you look fabulous. Bryn is going to fall in love with you all over again when he sees you,' Gina said.

Mia stifled a cynical little laugh. Bryn Dwyer didn't seem

to be the type to fall in love with anybody but himself. The Press had been full of his numerous relationships, none of them lasting more than a week or two. And no wonder, she thought uncharitably. With his ego the size it was, there wouldn't be room for anyone else's in any of his relationships.

'That's him!' Gina whispered as the doorbell sounded. She scooped up the evening bag she'd lent Mia and ushered her towards the door.

Mia flicked a loose tendril out of her eye and opened the door to find a man dressed in a chauffeur's uniform standing there.

'Good evening, Miss Forrester. My name is Henry. I'm Mr Dwyer's driver. I have been instructed to take you to him for this evening's event. He had another commitment but told me to tell you he will meet you there.'

Mia saw Gina's eyes go out on stalks but she herself was not so impressed by such opulent wealth. She hated unnecessary displays of prosperity and couldn't help feeling Bryn had done it deliberately to remind her of his power over her. She inwardly fumed as she wondered what his other commitment had been— no doubt a quick dalliance with one of his numerous lovers.

She gave the driver a pleasant smile and followed him out to the stretch limousine and turned around in her seat to give the awestruck Gina a little fingertip wave once Henry had settled her inside.

A few minutes later they were travelling across the Harbour Bridge into the city, the summer sun still high in the sky, casting a golden glow over the high-rise buildings. There were numerous yachts out, their white sails in perfect accord with the sail-like structure of the Sydney Opera House, which sparkled in the bright sunshine.

Within a short time Henry drove into the sweeping driveway of one of the premier hotels, where a host of paparazzi were already gathered in anticipation as one of the hotel staff stepped forward to open her door.

Mia had to rely on what she'd learnt in a role play workshop she'd done a few months back. She stepped out of the vehicle as if she were royalty, smiling graciously for the flashing cameras as she made her way across the red carpet to the ostentatious foyer.

The ceiling was dripping with crystal chandeliers, the marbled floor beneath her high-heeled feet was polished to perfection and huge, fragrant floral arrangements dominated the centre table in front of the grand, sweeping staircase.

A journalist thrust a microphone in her face. 'Miss Forrester, tell us how it feels to have won the heart of Sydney's most confirmed bachelor.'

She smiled sweetly and answered in a breathy tone. 'It feels absolutely wonderful.'

'You are the envy of the young and single female population of Sydney,' another one said. 'No one ever thought he would commit. Can you tell us your secret?'

'There is no secret about love,' she said. 'It takes you by surprise when you're least expecting it.'

'Is it true you met by accident?' a female reporter asked.

'Yes…' Mia gave a coy smile. 'I accidentally spilt a cup of coffee in his lap.'

'Is there any truth in the rumour that Mr Dwyer's comments in this morning's paper in regard to your performance in Theodore Frankston's latest production precipitated your—er—little accident?'

'No, of course not…as I said, it was an accident. It just slipped out of my hand,' Mia lied with increasing confidence. 'It was only when he stood up that I realised who he was and…well…I was overwhelmed by my feelings, as indeed he was too.'

'There has been some suggestion that this is all a publicity stunt,' another journalist said. 'Do you have any comment to make?'

'Yes.' She looked towards the television camera, giving her lashes a little flutter before she continued in the same breathy tone. 'I would like to say to all those sceptics out there that there is such a thing as love at first sight. Bryn and I are living proof of it. As soon as we met it was like…kismet.' She was on a roll and continued with a hand pressed to her bosom. 'I could almost hear the angels singing.' She gave a dreamy sigh. 'I can't wait until we're married. It's like a dream come true.'

'Er—thank you, Miss Forrester.' The journalist turned to the camera. 'Well, you've heard it straight from the filly's mouth, so to speak. To those who've just tuned in, Sydney's twice-in-a-row Bachelor of the Year has finally met his match. The official engagement of Miss Mia Forrester and Mr Bryn Dwyer has made headlines around the country.'

Mia turned as a hand touched her on the elbow.

'This way, Miss Forrester,' a hotel staff member said as he directed her towards the staircase. 'Mr Dwyer will be here shortly. The ballroom is on the first floor.'

Mia picked up the tiny train on her dress and glided up the stairs as the cameras flashed behind her. It occurred to her then that she was quite enjoying herself. She hadn't expected to but somehow she was relishing the role of Bryn's fiancée. She was particularly pleased with her portrayal of a star-struck *ingénue*. Who said she couldn't act?

The ballroom was decked out with pink and blue balloons and streamers, the arc of tables beautifully and elegantly set for dinner around a small dance floor.

The other guests had already assembled and were enjoying

their pre-dinner drinks as the waiters began to lead them to their tables.

'You're on table one,' the same staff member informed her. 'Come this way.'

Mia followed him to the table where some of the guests were already seated. They sprang to their feet as she approached and congratulated her effusively.

'Such wonderful news!'

'I always knew he'd do it some day.'

'But you're gorgeous! No wonder he was instantly smitten.'

Mia lapped it up. She felt like a Hollywood movie star. She smiled and took each hand in turn, doing her best to memorise names and faces as each person introduced themselves.

'Here, sit next to me.' An older woman called Jocey Myers patted the seat beside her. 'Bryn will be here soon.'

'Thank you.' Mia sat down and settled her gown around her.

'He's probably visiting his great-aunt,' Jocey said in an undertone. 'Has he told you about her?'

Mia wasn't sure how to answer. She was supposed to be his fiancée. Surely a fiancée would know just about everything about the man she was about to marry. 'Um…yes…'

'She's not expected to live much longer, poor dear,' Jocey went on. 'He doesn't know I know. I only found out by accident, as my mother-in-law is in the same palliative-care unit.' She leaned towards Mia conspiratorially. 'No one at the station knows, of course; it just wouldn't go with the image, now, would it?'

'Er—no…'

Mia frowned as she took in the information about Bryn's relative. She felt as if she'd done him a disservice, assuming he'd been off with one of his lovers when instead he had been sitting by the bedside of a terminally ill relative.

She thought of her own elderly relatives, the extended family that she so adored, uncles and aunts, great-uncles and great-aunts and her three remaining grandparents. They had filled her life with such amazing love and security and given true meaning to the word family.

Jocey tapped her on the shoulder. 'Ah. here he is now.'

Mia turned to see Bryn approach the table, his tall, commanding stance turning every head in the room. He bent down and, before she could do anything to counteract it, pressed a lingering kiss to her mouth.

'How's my beautiful fiancée this evening?'

She gave him a tight smile without answering, but she sent him a message with her eyes which she hoped no one else could see.

His mouth tilted as he tapped her gently on the tip of her nose with the end of one long finger. 'I can see you're speechless with love for me. How adorably sweet.'

'You lucky dog.' One of the older men thumped Bryn on the shoulder on his way past to the drinks waiter.

'I told you it would happen eventually,' another guest said.

'I thoroughly approve,' one of the other women said. 'You should have seen how she handled the media. A natural, if you ask me.'

'How *did* you handle the media?' Bryn asked softly as he sat down beside her.

Mia couldn't help feeling a little ashamed of her earlier behaviour with the Press. She'd come across as an empty-headed, star-struck bimbo. If only she'd known he was visiting his dying relative. Now she just felt silly and childish.

'It was a piece of cake,' she whispered back.

'Good girl,' he said and reached for his glass. 'I'd hate for this children's charity to be spoilt by a bad Press release.'

Mia stiffened in her seat. *Children's charity?* She glanced towards the podium, where a brightly festooned sign portrayed the emblem of the charity for kids with cancer. Bryn's name was printed there as principle sponsor and another wave of shame passed through her from head to toe.

'What's wrong?' he asked. 'You look a little flustered.'

Mia bent her head and stared at her cutlery. 'I'm not the least bit flustered.'

'Why are you blushing?'

'I'm not blushing,' she denied even as her face felt as if it was going to explode with heat. 'It's hot in here.'

'Let's go get some air,' he said and drew her to her feet.

She had no choice but to go with him. The other guests looked on indulgently as he escorted her from the ballroom, a couple of cameras flashing at them as they went past.

He waited until he'd led her into a quiet alcove out of the way of the Press. 'I'm sorry I was late. I had something to see to.'

'Why didn't you tell me you were visiting your great-aunt?'

He frowned down at her, his dark eyes narrowing into slits. 'Who told you about my great-aunt?'

'Jocey Myers.'

His features darkened and Mia noticed his hands begin to clench by his sides. 'She had no right to do that.'

'I think she had the right to tell me the important details of your life and background,' she said. 'I can't act this role if I don't know who the other principle character is.'

'You don't need to know me. This is all an act. Just run with the script I gave you.'

'The script you gave me has some very big gaps in it,' she said. 'I can't do this convincingly if I don't know who you are as a person. No one will believe I have fallen in love with you unless I can prove I know who you really are.'

Bryn thought about it for a moment. 'All right, I'll fill you in on some details but they are to go no further. Understood?'

She nodded.

'Right, then.' He took a breath and wondered where to start. 'My parents were killed when I was seven. I hardly remember what they looked like now. My great-aunt Agnes stepped in and brought me up. End of story.'

Mia frowned. 'But surely—'

'I don't remember, OK?' His eyes hardened as they lasered hers. 'Now let's go back and do what we're here to do.'

'What exactly are we here to do?' she asked as she trotted to keep up with his long strides.

'We're here to raise a hundred thousand dollars for the Children's Cancer Ward at St Patrick's.'

She stared at his back as he started back towards the ballroom. 'Wait!' She tugged on his arm and he turned to face her. 'What do you want me to do?'

He looked down at her mouth for a moment before he tore his gaze away. 'I told you this afternoon. I want you to act the role of the devoted fiancée. Did you happen to cover that at stage school?'

She lifted her chin. 'That was in Tricky Relationships 101.'

He threw back his head and laughed.

'What's so funny?' she asked. 'You don't think I can do tricky relationships?'

He placed a casual arm around her shoulders as he led her back into the ballroom. 'I'm beginning to think I've seriously underestimated your acting ability.'

'I told you I can act,' she said through a forced smile as someone stopped to take their photo.

'So you did but up until today I hadn't seen you do it very convincingly.'

'I was going on instinct rather than experience in Theo's play. I just needed more time to get my head around the role. I was the understudy, remember,' she said.

He stopped in his tracks to look down at her, a small frown beetling his brows. 'So what you're saying is you've never actually been in love?'

'Um…no…' She shifted her gaze. 'I've had a few close calls but nothing very serious.'

'Have you lived with anyone before?'

'No…'

'Been engaged before?'

She rolled her eyes at him. 'No, of course not. In case it has escaped your notice, most women these days prefer to be in love with the man they've agreed to marry.'

He gave her a thoughtful look that seemed to go on and on for endless seconds, his dark blue eyes steady on hers.

Mia began to brace herself for his next question. Here it comes, she thought.

The big one.

Have You Slept With Anyone Before?

'I think you'll enjoy the rest of the evening,' he finally said. 'Do you like dancing?'

It wasn't the question she'd been expecting and it took her a moment to register what he'd asked. 'Oh, yes…I love dancing…'

Bryn glanced down at her when she wasn't looking his way. She had dressed beautifully for the evening, the clinging black satin showing off every toned curve of her slight frame. Her bright and intelligent grey eyes were highlighted by a smoky eye-shadow and eyeliner and her soft mouth glistened with a camellia-pink lip-gloss.

There was an ingenuous air about her he found incredibly

alluring. So many women he'd been involved with in the past had been so street-smart and worldly he'd found it grating after a while. He knew his money and status had been the draw card in such relationships, but Mia had no interest in him either as a person or for what he could give her in terms of money or prestige. She was with him under sufferance and he knew as soon as they were alone again she would take the very first opportunity to remind him of it.

His gut gave a tiny twinge of guilt as he thought of the conversation he'd had with his great-aunt earlier that evening. He'd hated lying to the one person who had stood by him all of his life, but it had been worth it to see the sheer joy on her pain-ravaged face as he'd confirmed his engagement. He wasn't sure if she would believe him at first but somehow she had. He'd told her as soon as he'd met Mia he'd found the woman of his dreams. It was after all more or less the truth. Mia Forrester was exactly the stuff male dreams were made of.

'Oh, my darling boy!' Agnes had clutched his hand in both of her frail ones in delight. 'I'm so pleased. At first I thought it must have been a publicity stunt or a way to get me to change my will. I know you weren't happy about my conditions but I couldn't risk you throwing yourself away on someone who was only after you for your money. And, besides, your parents wouldn't have wanted you to be this bitter for so long.'

Bryn inwardly grimaced at the thought of how his great-aunt's will was written. It was a lot of money, not that he needed it personally, of course, but he wasn't going to stand by and see the person responsible for his parents' death inherit the lot. That was taking forgiveness way too far.

'You're exactly like your father,' his great-aunt continued. 'He fell in love with your mother the very first time he met her. It was so romantic.' She gave a heartfelt sigh and added, 'I have dreamed of this moment. I have wanted this for you for so long, for you to settle down with a nice girl instead of those money-hungry ones you usually date. I heard her on the radio with you this afternoon—she sounds so sweet. When can I meet her?'

'I'll bring her to see you tomorrow,' he found himself promising, hoping his acting fiancée would agree to it.

'That would be wonderful; I can hardly wait to see her. I'm sure she's absolutely perfect for you.'

Bryn bent down and kissed her papery cheek as he made to leave. 'Yes,' he said, a funny flutter coming and going in his chest as he brought Mia Forrester's feisty little heart-shaped face to mind. 'She is perfect. Absolutely perfect.'

The first course was being served as they came back into the ballroom. Mia sat down with considerable relief when Bryn's arm slipped from around her shoulders as he turned to speak to the person on his right. Having him so physically close was deeply unsettling, for ever since he'd kissed her that afternoon her awareness of him had lifted to an almost intolerable level. All her senses were finely tuned to pick up on his every movement or gesture. When she turned her head towards her left shoulder she could even smell his cologne on her skin where his arm had lain. She knew she'd have to get used to having him touch her in public but each time he did so she felt as if another part of her was being made more vulnerable to him.

She reached for her wine glass and felt his leg brush against hers. She tried to edge away but his hand came down on the middle of her thigh. The weight of his fingers felt like a scorch through the thin fabric of her gown. And her heart began to pick up its pace when he turned to speak to her, his dark blue eyes steady on hers.

'Everything all right, sweetheart?'

'F-fine…just fine…' She moistened her lips and forced herself not to flinch away when his hand moved upwards a fraction.

He leaned closer to whisper in her ear, 'Relax.'

'I am relaxed.'

'No, you're not. You're as tense as a trip-wire.'

'Only because your hand is where it shouldn't be,' she said, smiling inanely as someone took their photo.

'I'm your fiancé. I'm supposed to touch you.'

'In public—yes.'

'This is in public. In fact, it couldn't be more public. There are at least five hundred people in this room.'

'It's not public under the table,' Mia pointed out tightly.

He gave her a lazy smile and took his hand off her thigh to place it on the nape of her neck, his long, warm fingers toying with the silky tendrils of her hair. 'Is that better?'

A shiver of reaction passed right through her from the top of her head to her toes. She forced herself to maintain eye contact, knowing that people were watching, but it was increasingly difficult to disguise her reaction to him. She hoped he would assume she was simply acting but something about his smile suggested he was well aware of the effect he was having on her.

'Let's dance,' he suggested after a little silence.

Mia was glad of an excuse to move out of his embrace, but it wasn't until she was on the dance floor with his arms pulling her into his rock-hard body that she realised she had just stepped out of a sizzling frying-pan and straight into the leaping flames of a fire she had no hope of controlling.

There wasn't even room for air between their bodies as he turned her into a quick-stepping waltz. She was pressed to him from chest to thigh, the thin, close-fitting fabric of her gown no barrier to the searing heat of his body. Her breasts were pushed up against him and he took full advantage of it by dipping his gaze over their creamy curves.

Mia felt her skin tingle from the burning heat in his eyes, and her stomach did a nervous little flip turn when she felt the unmistakable evidence of his growing erection against her belly.

'Maybe this wasn't such a good idea…' she said, trying not to blush but knowing she was failing miserably.

'Why?' He skilfully turned her in his arms and brought her even closer. 'I'm enjoying myself.'

She gave him a caustic look while her back was turned to the tables. 'No doubt you are but let me tell you I am not.'

'I thought you said you liked dancing?'

'This is not dancing, this is making out in front of an audience!' she hissed back.

'You want to go somewhere more private?'

'I don't want to go anywhere with you.'

'Careful, Mia, there are cameras everywhere. We have a deal, remember? Now, stop looking at me as if you're going to take me apart piece by piece and kiss me instead.'

She gave him a recalcitrant look. 'I am not going to kiss you.'

His dark eyes held hers challengingly. 'Yes you are.'

She elevated her chin defiantly. 'Make me. I dare you.'

'It will be my pleasure,' he said and tugging her up hard against him brought his mouth down on hers.

# CHAPTER FIVE

MIA was determined not to respond to his kiss but her awareness of the rest of the guests watching made it difficult for her to put her resistance into action. She began to kiss him back and told herself she'd had no other choice, but another part of her wondered if she would have responded anyway, audience or not.

His kiss softened and she felt herself being carried away by the swell of passion his searching tongue evoked as it entered the warm, moist cave of her mouth. She heard her soft sigh mingle with his and something hot and liquid seemed to burst deep inside her, running through her in a flowing tide that melted her to the core. Her chest was thrumming with a build-up of unfamiliar emotion, an acute neediness she had never experienced before. It frightened her at the same time as it intrigued her. How could someone she hated so much provoke such intense reactions in her body? Had she no control over her responses to him? Was it lust or something much more dangerous?

Bryn stepped back from her and looked down at her flushed face for a long moment, seemingly unaware that the band was still halfway through a song. Other couples were dancing around them but Mia felt as if time had come to a halt right where they were standing facing each other. She ran her tongue over her lips and her chest fluttered again when she saw his eyes dip to her mouth, lingering there for several pulsing seconds.

'We should get back to the table,' he said, his eyes dark and unreadable when they slowly came back to hers.

'Yes…yes…we should…'

He took her arm and, sliding his hand down its slender length, curled his fingers around hers and led her back without another word.

The rest of the meal passed without incident, although Mia felt as if her face was going to crack from smiling all the time. Guest after guest approached her to congratulate her on taming the wild heart of Bryn Dwyer, and, while she thanked them each in turn, she found by the end of the evening she was totally exhausted by the pretence. It seemed wrong to be deliberately misleading everyone; she felt terribly compromised saying one thing while, indeed, the very opposite was true.

Acting a role had never been so challenging. She'd played some awkward parts in the past, things she hadn't felt well prepared for and somehow struggled through, but nothing had ever been like this.

Dancing with Bryn was the hardest, for while she was sitting next to him at the table at least she could turn her head to talk to someone else, distracting herself with pleasant conversation, but each time he led her back to the dance floor she felt the pulse of his body against hers and the blood began to pound heavily through her veins. Circling the floor with his arms around her, held close to his hard male body, she had no way of protecting herself from his magnetic attraction. She fought it constantly, but each look he gave her made her heart race, each time his thigh brushed one of hers she felt the shock waves of reaction rush up her spine, and every time he smiled that devastatingly handsome smile she felt another chink of her armour fall away.

It annoyed her that he was so effortlessly attractive. There wasn't a woman in the room, old or young, who didn't simper up at him in open adoration and the last thing she wanted was to join their number.

'Time to leave,' Bryn said a little later as the ball began to draw to a close. 'I saw that big yawn of yours.'

'It's been a long day,' she said, his fingers curling around hers as he drew her to her feet.

'And it's not over yet.'

'What do you mean, it's not over yet?' she asked with a little frown.

Bryn just smiled as another camera snapped in front of them. Mia forced her fixed lips into a smile as he led her from the room and down the sweeping staircase, waiting until they were in the back of the limousine before repeating her question. 'What do you mean, the night isn't over? I'm tired and I want to go home.'

Bryn leaned forward and closed the sliding glass panel that separated them from the driver. 'There's something I need to discuss with you. I thought we could go back to my place, where we won't be disturbed.'

She stiffened in her seat. 'I don't want to go anywhere with you. Take me home. *Now.*'

'We'll be in private so you don't need to worry about me having my wicked way with you.'

She gave him a cynical glance. 'You expect me to believe that after the dirty dancing and under-the-table groping routine?'

'You've got great legs,' he said. 'I was just wondering if they felt as good as they looked.'

She rolled her eyes scathingly. 'I can't imagine how you have acquired your Don Juan reputation if that's any indication of the pick-up lines you resort to.'

'It wasn't a pick-up line, it was the truth. You do have a fabulous figure.' He reached for her hand and ran his finger down the length of her bare ring finger. 'Now that we're engaged you need an engagement ring. I have one at my house.'

'How very convenient,' she scoffed. 'I bet you say that to all the girls.'

He ignored her comment and stroked her finger again. 'I want you to wear it.'

She snatched her tingling hand out of his grasp. 'I can just imagine your taste in jewellery—no doubt it's as overbearing and pretentious as you.'

The line of his mouth tightened. 'Actually I think you might be pleasantly surprised.'

'I doubt it.'

'Let's wait and see,' he said and for the rest of the journey remained silent.

Mia sat back in her seat and scowled. She was tired and wanted the safety and security of her own little flat and the familiar, friendly face of Gina, not the company of a man who made her feel as if she was on the edge of a precipitous cliff all the time. No matter how hard she tried to resist his dark good looks she found the pace of her heartbeat increasing every time she met his fathomless blue eyes.

She turned her head away from his silent figure and looked out at the lights fringing the water as Henry drove them along the Cahill Expressway towards the eastern suburbs.

Her sleepy eyes struggled to stay open with the soporific

motion of the luxury vehicle. She fought to keep them from closing but in the end she gave up and let her eyelids drift downwards...

Bryn looked down at the silky head resting on his lap, one of her hands on his thigh, her small, neat fingers splayed against him. He watched the in and out of her breathing, the slight movement of her chest lifting the creamy curves of her breasts tantalisingly. Her body was totally relaxed against him; gone was the stiff, defiant little firebrand with her quick-witted tongue, and in her place was a young woman who was breathtakingly beautiful now that the earlier tension had left her body. She had a sweet vulnerability about her, as if she had slipped to his lap in unconscious trust that he would do nothing to harm or exploit her.

He gently tucked a strand of hair off her cheek and secured it behind the small shell of her ear, her soft murmur as he did so making his chest feel a little strange, as if someone had caught him with a tiny fish hook deep inside and given it a quick little tug before just as swiftly releasing him.

He sighed and wondered if he was doing the right thing after all. He was used to women who were happy to play by the rules he set down, took what he offered and were grateful for whatever time and attention he afforded them. Mia Forrester, however, was not likely to appreciate what he had in mind for her and it bothered him. It bothered him a great deal. But he had to find a way to convince her to go along with his plans. Time was running out and this was the only way he could see to solve the dilemma he was in.

Mia woke up as soon as the car came to a halt.

'Hello, sleepyhead.' His glinting eyes met hers, his mouth tilted in a little smile.

She struggled upright, appalled that she had draped herself all over him. She looked outside and saw they were in the driveway of an imposing-looking mansion in the exclusive suburb of Point Piper.

'Is this your house?'

'Yes. Come inside and I'll show you around.'

Mia got out of the car reluctantly. Pretending to be his fiancée in public was one thing; coming back to his house and being alone with him was something else again. She didn't trust him not to insist on another kissing rehearsal. How would she be able to keep a clear head if he decided to take things even further? She was already in over her head as it was. He was exactly the sort of man she'd actively avoided all her dating life. He was too self-assured and too experienced for her to keep at arm's length. She just didn't know how to handle men like him.

Bryn opened the soundproof panel and addressed the driver. 'You can go home now, Henry, I'll see that Miss Forrester gets home.'

'Thank you, Mr Dwyer.' He took off his cap at Mia and added, 'Miss Forrester. Enjoy the rest of your evening.'

'Thank you.'

Mia waited until the driver had left before turning on Bryn. 'I thought I told you I didn't want to come back here with you. I'm tired and I want to go home.'

'You can sleep in tomorrow. It's not as if you have to get up for work.'

'Thanks to you,' she said with an embittered look.

'You can't tell me you enjoyed working in that café, Mia,' he said as he opened the door and ushered her in. 'It was a pittance of a wage and you had to be polite to obnoxious people all day, which I can only assume from what I've seen of you so far was incredibly difficult, if not at times impossible.'

'Not all of them were obnoxious,' she countered with a nar-
row-eyed glare.

He shrugged himself out of his jacket and tossed it to one
side before reaching to loosen his tie. 'Would you like a drink?'

'No.'

He led the way to a sumptuous lounge with stunning views
over the harbour. Two luxurious caramel-coloured leather
sofas dominated the room, the floor was covered with deep
cream carpet and the walls adorned with original paintings
from some well-known Australian and international artists.
There was a well-appointed bar at one end of the room and
an impressive-looking sound and entertainment system along
the far wall.

Mia stood looking out at the view rather than meet Bryn's
dark eyes. 'How long have you lived here?' she asked.

She heard the chink of a glass behind her. 'A couple of
years or so. I wanted a place where the Press can't hound me
all the time.'

She turned around to look at him in puzzlement. 'I thought
you actively courted the Press. Isn't that the whole reason I'm
playing this role for you, to increase your ratings?'

He took a sip of his drink before answering. 'It's one of
the reasons you are here.'

She gave him a wary look, her heart beginning to thud
unevenly. 'You mean there's more than one?'

He put his glass down and came to stand in front of her.
Mia tried to step away but the backs of her legs came up
against one of the sofas. She drew in a sharp little breath as
she brought her gaze up to his. His eyes were so dark she felt
as if she was staring into the moonless midnight sky.

'When you poured that coffee in my lap this morning I
thought it would be a good opportunity to give my ratings a

boost by pretending to have a whirlwind romance with you, and it worked. The public fell for it, hook line and sinker. Annabelle called me earlier with the ratings for this afternoon's show and they were absolutely phenomenal. The stuff the Press releases tomorrow will ramp them up even more. But it's not the only reason I have for wanting you to act this role for me a little longer.'

Mia waited for him to go on, wondering what other reason he could have for continuing this ridiculous charade. She wanted it to stop before things got out of hand. She already felt as if she'd stepped over some sort of invisible barrier after he'd kissed her, not once but three times. She wasn't even sure if what she was doing was even acting any more. The more time she spent with him the more the lines blurred between what was real and what was fantasy.

'Jocey mentioned my great-aunt Agnes to you this evening,' he said after a small pause.

'Yes…'

'She's my only living relative and I owe her a great deal.' He let out a small sigh and scored a rough pathway through the dark brown silk of his hair before adding, 'She hasn't got long to live and I would give anything to make her last few weeks of life as happy as they can possibly be.'

Mia was surprised by the sincerity in his voice, he sounded as if he really cared for his great aunt.

*Truly* cared.

She found it difficult to fit his public persona as a thirty-three-year-old filthy rich playboy with a reputation for shallow, short-lived relationships with the man in front of her, who obviously cared very deeply for an ageing relative.

'I'm sorry about your great-aunt's health,' she said softly. 'It must be an awful time for you both.'

His gaze meshed with hers once more. 'My great-aunt's only wish is to see me happily settled. She sacrificed her chance at marriage in order to raise me when my parents died so suddenly when I was a child. She gave up everything for me.'

Mia swallowed at the sudden intensity of his blue-black gaze.

'You see, Mia, a simple engagement might be enough for the Press and the public, but it is not going to be enough for Agnes.'

'I-it's not?'

He shook his head gravely. 'No. What she wants more than anything in the world before she dies is to see me officially married.'

'M-married?' she gulped. 'Officially?'

'Yes, in front of witnesses, preferably in a church and legally binding.'

'You surely don't expect me to…' She found it impossible to finish the sentence in case by saying it out loud it would somehow make it inescapably true.

'I'm asking you to marry me, Mia,' he said, confirming her worst fears.

She stared at him open-mouthed. Surely she'd misheard him. He couldn't possibly have…

'Of course, I don't expect you to do it for nothing,' he went on evenly. 'I will pay you a lump sum up front and a generous allowance for as long as the marriage continues.'

'You want me to marry you? For real?' She gawped at him incredulously. 'You mean you're actually *serious* about this?'

He frowned at her stupefied expression. 'I'm not asking you to jump off the harbour bridge, Mia, just to wear my ring until such time as it is no longer necessary.'

Mia's stomach felt as if she'd just jumped off Centrepoint

Tower, which was a whole lot taller than the harbour bridge. How could she possibly consent to marrying a man she hated? And even worse—for money?

'But marriage?' she asked again, shaking her head in disbelief.

'Yes, as in vows and rings and stuff.'

'Marriage is a whole lot more than vows and rings and stuff,' she said. 'It's a legally binding agreement between two people who are supposed to love one another and promise to do so until death parts them.'

'So we're not exactly up to scratch on all the particulars but we can still pull this off,' he said.

'You sound as if you're discussing some sort of business proposal.'

'That's exactly what I'm discussing. A business proposal.'

Mia frowned as she tried to take it all in. 'You mean this won't really be a real marriage?'

'It will be real in the sense that it will be official and legal. I can't risk someone uncovering it as a sham but as for us being a normal couple...' he hesitated for a fraction of a second before adding, 'well, of course it won't be real.'

She moistened her bone-dry lips. 'So we won't be...you know...'

His dark eyes met hers. 'Having sex?'

'Yes...'

'Not unless you want to.'

Mia felt her cheeks burning but forced herself to hold his gaze. 'Of course I don't want to!'

His expression was contemplative as he held her gaze for several moments before he responded. 'Fine; however, I must insist that for the duration of our marriage you refrain from sleeping with anyone else. I wouldn't want anyone to suspect things are not normal between us if you are seen with someone other than me.'

She gave him a pointed look. 'Do I get to insist on the same rule for you?'

'I will do my best to be discreet if the need should arise.'

'Then I insist on the same for myself. I, too, can be discreet.'

'As you wish, but let me tell you if you put one step wrong I will be extremely angry. I don't want my great-aunt to be upset by any rumours of impropriety.'

'She won't be upset by me,' Mia said confidently. 'At least I don't have any empty-headed bimbos in my background.'

He gave her a droll look. 'As of today I have finished with empty-headed bimbos. You are now, for all intents and purposes, the love of my life, and I expect you to maintain that illusion for as long as is necessary.'

'And I thought my four years at stage school were challenging,' Mia muttered resentfully.

'The challenging part for you will be controlling your propensity for insulting me at every opportunity.'

She gave a cynical snort. 'That's rich coming from the High Priest of Insults. If you weren't such a pompous jerk I wouldn't find it so challenging.'

'If you weren't such an uptight little cat you would see I'm nothing like the public image I project,' he clipped back.

She folded her arms across her chest, her expression full of scorn. 'I suppose you're going to tell me you're really nothing like the Bryn Dwyer the public has come to love and hate. Oh, please. Spare me the violins. Anyone can see you're a self-serving egotist who would stop at nothing to achieve his ends. This crazy scheme of yours to hoodwink your great-aunt is a case in point. What kind of man would openly lie to a little old lady by marrying a woman he has absolutely no feelings for?'

'I happen to love my great-aunt very dearly and I would do anything to make her last days happy, even if it means temporarily tying myself to a shrill little shrew to prove it.'

'Shrill little shrew, am I, now?' She glared at him. 'Well, let me tell you I don't think too much of you either. You're hardly what I'd call the ultimate choice in husband material.'

'You don't have to think much of me,' he said. 'All I want you to do is marry me. We'll sort the feelings end of it out later.'

'I don't have any feelings where you're concerned other than unmitigated dislike.'

'Good. You'd be best to keep it that way. I wouldn't want to complicate things any further with you forming an emotional attachment to me.'

'Where exactly did you go for your ego-enhancement surgery?' she quipped in return. 'Was it horrendously expensive?'

Bryn struggled to hold back his amusement but in the end gave up. His face cracked on a smile. 'I think you are definitely wasted as a serious actor. You have a real future in comedy.'

'Yes, well, this little farce is definitely running along those lines. You're asking me to act a role that is totally immoral. Acting in front of an audience is one thing but acting in front of a dying old lady is another. And marriage! It just doesn't seem right.'

'It will make her happy. That's all I want.'

'I don't want to do this, Bryn; you can't force me.'

He held her gaze for an uncomfortable pause. Mia felt as if she was being slowly but steadily backed into a tight corner. She even wondered if it had been wise to mention the word force. She could see the steely determination in his darker than night eyes and her stomach felt as if something with tiny clawed feet had just scuttled across it.

The sudden silence was like a third presence in the room,

brooding and somehow menacing, making the fine hairs on the back of her neck lift one by one.

'I'm hoping it won't have to come to me actually forcing you,' he said. 'At this point in time I'm simply asking you to help me bring a small measure of happiness to an old woman who sacrificed her own to raise me. I am willing to pay you well. I know it will be difficult for you. I also know you hate me, but I can't help feeling you are the one person my great-aunt will take to. She heard us on the radio this afternoon; she already thinks you're perfect for me. There are plenty of women I could ask to play this role, but I know my aunt well enough to know that the only one she will accept as the real thing is you.'

Mia tried not to think of how she was going to explain all of this to her family or friends. Instead she thought about an old lady who had sacrificed her life to raise a child who had been devastated by the loss of his parents. She thought too of the little boy of seven who had suffered such a tragic loss. A little boy with dark brown hair and deep blue eyes, a little boy who had become a man who, as far as she could make out, hid his childhood pain behind a façade of cocksure arrogance.

It wasn't as if it was going to be a real marriage, she did her best to reassure herself. After all, actors did this stuff all the time. God, how many times had Julia Roberts been married on screen? It meant nothing.

It was all an act.

A role to play.

Temporarily.

But still…

'Can I have some time to think about it?' she asked. 'This is totally surreal. I can't quite get my head around it.'

'Of course,' he said. 'But I'd like you to meet my great-aunt tomorrow; it will perhaps help you to make up your mind.'

She captured her bottom lip for a moment. 'What if I don't agree to marry you?'

His eyes locked down on hers. 'Then you'll be throwing away a fortune.'

Mia gave a tiny swallow. 'Exactly how big a fortune?'

He named a sum that sent a shock wave through her brain. Mia came from a comfortable background and had never really wanted for anything in her life, but the amount of money he was willing to pay was unbelievably generous. The money he'd already given her had helped ease Ellie's situation fractionally but if she could send her thousands it would mean her sister would be out of danger for good.

But marrying Bryn Dwyer?

'If you do decide to take up this offer there will be some legal documents to sign,' he said into the silence, 'a prenuptial agreement and so forth. And, as I mentioned in the car earlier, as my fiancée I'd like you to wear an engagement ring.'

Mia watched as he went across the room to where a large painting was hanging. He shifted it to one side as he activated the code on the concealed safe set in the wall and, opening the safe, took out a blue velvet box before closing it again and repositioning the painting.

He brought the box over to her, took out a solitaire diamond engagement ring and handed it to her.

'It was my mother's,' he informed her.

Mia turned the white-gold ring in her fingers, staring down at the simple perfection of the diamond.

'Try it on,' he said.

She slipped it on her ring finger, not sure whether to be surprised or spooked by the perfect fit. It was nothing like she'd been expecting. There was nothing ostentatious or flashy about it. It was simply a beautiful ring that had once been worn by his mother, a woman who had been torn from his life when he was a small, vulnerable child.

'If you don't like it we can choose something else,' he said into the silence.

'No…no, I like it…it's…beautiful…' Tears welled in her eyes and her throat felt tight, but she wasn't sure why she was feeling so emotional.

'It's not worth a lot of money but it's one of the few things I have left of my mother,' he said, turning away to hunt for his car keys. 'Come on, I'd better take you home. It's nearly three a.m.'

Mia followed him out of the house in silence, the ring on her finger tying her to him in a way no priceless jewel could do.

*It's just a stupid old ring*, she chided herself, but somehow whenever she looked down at the diamond winking up at her she felt as if something elemental had just taken place in their relationship.

He didn't speak on the journey back to her flat. Mia stole covert glances at him from time to time but his expression was closed. She could see the lines of tiredness around his eyes and wondered what sort of day he had ahead. She knew that working in radio was not just a simple matter of turning up for the time he was on air but that hours of research and preparation had to be put in before and after. She also knew it was a fickle business. A radio personality could be the flavour of the month only to be cast aside the next. Ratings were everything and contracts were cancelled or renewed on what they revealed. But Bryn hardly needed the money. He was a multimillionaire, so whatever satisfaction he got from having his own prime-time show must be motivated by something other than monetary reward. Fame? Prestige? Power? Or was it the desire to be known as something other than who he really was?

'I'll call you later,' Bryn said as he pulled up in front of her flat.

Mia didn't answer. She got out of the car when he opened her door and with her head down began to move towards her front door.

'Mia.'

She stopped as his hand came down on her shoulder and slowly turned around to face him.

'You did a good job tonight,' he said. 'Thank you.'

Her chin lifted in pride. 'So you're finally admitting I can act, then, are you?'

He bent down and pressed a soft kiss to the corner of her mouth. 'That's what I'm paying you to do,' he said as he straightened. 'Goodnight.'

She watched from her window as he drove away, her fingers absently playing with the ring he'd given her, a small worried frown taking up residence on her forehead.

Yes, he was paying her to act, but what if she forgot her script and began to make up her own?

A script that wasn't for the temporary season he had in mind but for much longer?

# CHAPTER SIX

'OH, MY God, look at this!' Gina thrust the morning's paper at Mia. 'And this one…and look at this magazine! You're famous!'

Mia looked at the articles spread out before her and forced a stiff smile to her face. 'Hey, I don't look so bad, do I?'

'You look absolutely gorgeous and the Press loved you,' Gina answered. 'Here, listen to this:

The beautiful Mia Forrester, a struggling part-time actor and former café waitress has stolen the heart of Sydney radio personality and multimillionaire Bryn Dwyer, in a whirlwind romance that has to be seen to be believed. Miss Forrester is a radiant young woman who clearly has taken to her role as Bryn Dwyer's future wife with enthusiasm. It is rumoured that the wedding will take place within a matter of weeks. The young couple dined and danced the night away at the St Patrick's Children's Charity Ball before spending the night together at Mr Dwyer's Point Piper mansion.'

'I did not spend the night with him!' Mia said indignantly and then, seeing her friend's raised brows, hastily tacked on, 'or at least not the whole night.'

'I know that but it just goes to show you can't believe everything you read in the Press, now, can you?'

Mia lowered her gaze to the photo spread and answered with more than a hint of irony, 'No, you certainly cannot.'

Gina put her chin on her hand and sighed. 'You know, I really envy you, Mia. You're so lucky you haven't had a string of disastrous love affairs in your past like me. That's just so special these days when just about everyone jumps into bed on the first date. Your honeymoon will be so romantic, the memory of your first time together will be something you'll treasure all your married life.'

Mia felt a hot, trickling sensation low down in her belly at the thought of the possibility of Bryn Dwyer becoming her lover.

She hadn't intentionally held back from conducting a sexual relationship with previous boyfriends but neither had she rushed into anything she hadn't felt ready for. She'd always believed making love should be about exactly that— making love, not having sex just for the sake of it. She knew it was perhaps a little old fashioned, but a part of her was proud that she had maintained her standards in spite of peer and popular-culture pressure.

One of her friends had been very ill with a sexually transmitted disease as a teenager and it had made Mia all the more determined to wait until she was absolutely sure it was the right step to take. Besides, she had never been in love with anyone, at least not seriously enough to consider committing herself physically.

Gina gave another dreamy sigh as she flicked through the rest of the articles. 'He's just so gorgeous—look at the way he's smiling at you in this picture. I don't think I've ever seen a man more in love.'

Mia looked over her friend's shoulder and frowned. It was

strange, as she was supposed to be the professional actor, but Gina was right; Bryn Dwyer had given a truly brilliant performance as a man totally smitten by love.

'What did your parents think of your news?' Gina asked.

Mia faltered over her reply. 'Um…I haven't actually called them yet…time differences and so on. I'll probably email them later today.'

'What about Ellie? When does she get back from her wilderness trek in the Amazon?'

Mia carefully avoided her flatmate's eyes. She hated lying but Ellie had expressly asked her not to tell anyone. As much as she wanted to break her promise, deep down she understood Ellie's motivations. News had a habit of travelling and if her parents got wind of the danger Ellie was in it could trigger another heart attack for their father. It was going to be bad enough when they got to hear of Mia's impending marriage.

'I'm not sure,' she said evasively. 'She said something about staying on for a little longer. You know Ellie, if there's a crusade she can put her name to, she will.'

'It seems a shame none of your family is here to celebrate your engagement with you.' Gina closed the paper. 'Wouldn't it be absolutely awful if they didn't get back in time for the wedding?'

*It would be wonderful*, Mia thought privately; that way I won't have to stretch my acting capabilities to the limit. But as she responded verbally she had to yet again draw deeply on her acting experience to sound genuine. 'You know something, Gina, I've always sort of dreamed of a private wedding. The only person I want there is the man I love. If the church was full to the rafters I'm sure I wouldn't even notice a single soul except for the one waiting for me at the altar.'

'You're right.' Gina smiled. 'Who cares who is there as

long as your future husband is there, ready and waiting? But I insist on being there—I wouldn't miss it for the world.'

Mia gave her a smile, even though her jaw ached with the effort. 'It will be nice to have you there, Gina; after all, who else is going to catch the bouquet?'

Mia watched from her window as Bryn arrived in front of her flat a short time later in a powerful red Maserati. He unfolded himself from the driver's seat, the casual clothes he was wearing highlighting his height and lean, athletic build as he strode towards her front door. She opened the door at his firm knock and tried not to be overwhelmed by his disturbing presence as he stepped inside.

His eyes ran over her but before she could mumble a single word of greeting Gina came bounding out of her room.

'Wow! I can't believe it's really you.' She stuck out her hand to him. 'I'm Mia's flatmate, Gina. I've been dying to meet you. I absolutely *adore* your show and your column. I'm a huge fan and so are all our friends, but most especially Mia, she never misses your show, right, Mia?'

Mia stretched her lips into a semblance of a smile. 'That's right.'

Bryn smiled as he drew Mia closer, stooping to press a long, searing kiss to her mouth. He lifted his head and looked into her eyes. 'That's what I like to hear—the woman I love is my biggest fan.'

Mia had to wait until they were in the car and on their way before she could vent her spleen. 'Did you have to be so…so completely over-the-top? I'm sure you embarrassed Gina by kissing me like that. It was totally unnecessary. A simple peck would have done.'

He sent her a sideways glance, his eyes glinting darkly.

'I'm not a simple-peck sort of guy. If I'm going to kiss someone I'm going to damn well do it properly.'

Mia felt a fluttery feeling between her thighs at his statement. She was already well aware of his kissing skill and couldn't help wondering what it would be like to experience his whole lovemaking repertoire. She imagined he would be a demanding but consummate lover who would take his partner to the very heights of sensual experience.

Her gaze strayed to his hands where they rested on the steering wheel, her skin tightening all over at the thought of those long, tanned fingers touching her intimately. How would it feel to have him stroke her…?

Bryn caught the tail end of her glance, noting her heightened colour and the agitated look on her face. 'If you're feeling a bit nervous about meeting my great-aunt, don't be. I'm sure you'll take to her immediately; she's that sort of person.'

'I'm not nervous…' she said and began chewing at her bottom lip.

He sent her one more thoughtful look but she had turned her head and was looking out of the window, her fingers playing absently with the engagement ring on her hand.

The private palliative-care unit Agnes Dwyer was residing in had a peaceful atmosphere and was beautifully landscaped with sweet-smelling roses that could be viewed from every window.

Bryn's great-aunt was in a room overlooking a trickling fountain adorned with cupids and dolphins, the sound of wind chimes signalling the movement of the summer breeze across the exquisite garden.

Mia looked at the emaciated figure lying on the bed, the sunken eyes closed, the hollow papery cheeks speaking of a life long lived and now coming to its inevitable end.

Her heart contracted painfully as she glanced up at Bryn.

His expression, unguarded for a fraction of a second revealed the depth of his emotions at the loss he must soon face.

'Aunt Aggie,' he said softly, taking his great-aunt's hand in his.

Mia watched as the old woman's eyes opened and gradually focused.

'Oh, darling…you caught me napping.' She struggled upright with Bryn's gentle, solicitous help and met Mia's clear grey gaze at the end of the bed. 'Come here, my dear, and let me look at you. My eyes are not as good as they used to be.'

Mia stepped forward and took the thin hand that had reached for hers. 'Hello.'

'My, oh, my, but you're gorgeous,' Agnes said. 'One of the nurses brought in the papers this morning but you are even more beautiful than the photographs in them.'

'Thank you,' Mia said shyly.

Agnes smiled. 'You are just as I hoped Bryn's future wife would be.'

'I—I am?'

'Yes, indeed. I so wanted him to find someone genuine. You have a big heart; I can see it in those big grey eyes of yours. You are perfect for him.'

Mia felt the daggers of guilt prod at her sharply. She could barely stand to look into the old woman's eyes in case she saw the truth about her relationship with her great-nephew.

'I—I'm glad you think so…' she said, lowering her gaze and hating herself for yet another lie as she added, 'He's perfect for me too.'

'I knew it would be this way. His parents were the same, you know. When my nephew first met Bryn's mother it was love at first sight.' The old woman gave a sad little sigh. 'But they didn't get the chance to live the life they should have had together…'

Mia could sense Bryn's discomfiture at his great-aunt's disclosure and her heart went out to him again for what he must have suffered. She felt uncomfortable with the way she had judged him so rashly; it didn't seem right to have written him off as a self-serving playboy, given what he'd been through. No wonder he lived life so shallowly when life had let him down so early.

'It was a long time ago,' he inserted gruffly.

'I know, darling, but now that I am facing…well, you know what I'm facing…I can't help feeling that I could have done more for you.'

'That's totally ridiculous and you know it,' he said. 'You've been the most wonderful support. I couldn't have asked for a better guardian.'

'But I wasn't the real thing, was I?' Agnes said. 'I was just a substitute for the real thing. I could never be enough. I could never be your parents, no matter how much I tried to be.'

'Please don't say that…' Bryn said, squeezing her hand gently.

'Darling, darling boy,' Agnes sighed and, giving his hand an affectionate pat, turned her head to Mia. 'You will have to take over from me, sweet child, and love him when I'm gone. It won't be long now…'

Mia swallowed the solid lump of emotion in her throat. She could feel the sting of tears at the backs of her eyes and her chest felt as if someone had clamped it in a vice. Guilt assailed her and passed over her skin like a scalding burn.

'I will love him…for you and for me…' she said softly. 'He's a wonderful man…'

'I'm so very glad you think so,' Agnes said through misty eyes. 'Very few people know the real Bryn, but I can rest in peace now that I know he has found someone who loves him for who he really is. It's not easy being in the public eye, but then you'd know all about that, being an actor yourself.'

'I'm not a very good one, I'm afraid…' Mia said with downcast eyes.

'Your modesty is delightful,' Agnes said. 'But perhaps Bryn was right when he wrote that review, although he was a very naughty boy to put it quite the way he did.' She sent her great-nephew a mock-reproving glance before turning back to Mia. 'You were miscast. You have a delightful air of innocence about you which is so rare these days.'

Mia wondered just how innocent Bryn's great-aunt would consider her if she knew what was really going on between her and Bryn.

'We mustn't tire you,' Bryn said to his great-aunt. 'We'll leave you to rest for now. I'll pop by again later.'

'Thank you, darling.' Agnes took Mia's hand again and gave it a tiny squeeze. 'You probably haven't even had time to discuss when you're getting married but personally I'm not a great believer in long engagements. In this day and age, when practically everyone is cohabiting, what is the point? Besides, I haven't got much time left. It would be a dream come true to see my Bryn happily married. I know it's a lot to ask, but I do so want to be there on your special day if it's at all possible.'

'I want you to be there too,' Mia said, swiping at an escaping tear.

Bryn slipped his arm around her waist and drew her closer as he addressed his great-aunt. 'We'll let you know as soon as we have a date set.'

'Thank you, darling…I'm sorry to be such a bother.'

Bryn stooped down to kiss his great-aunt's cheek. 'You could never be a bother. Now, have a good rest and I'll see you later.'

Mia slipped out of Bryn's embrace to kiss his elderly relative, her eyes bright with tears as she straightened. 'It was lovely to meet you.'

'You have made me so very happy,' Agnes said. 'I cannot think of a more wonderful partner for Bryn.'

Mia was blubbering uncontrollably by the time they got back to where Bryn had parked his car. She began to hunt for a tissue when he pressed a clean white handkerchief into her hand, his expression thoughtful as his dark blue eyes met her streaming ones.

'I'm sorry…' she choked out. 'I just can't help it…'

'It's all right,' he said and drew her up against him, his hand going to the back of her head to bring her head to his chest.

'It's just so sad…' she sniffed. 'I don't know how you can bear it…it reminds me of when my granny died…I still feel emotional every time I see someone with grey hair and it's been seven years.'

Bryn kept stroking his fingers through her hair, his chest feeling a little strange as he breathed in the fragrance of her light but unforgettable perfume.

Mia lifted her head to look up at him, her eyes red-rimmed and swollen and her bottom lip still trembling with emotion. 'I feel so guilty lying to her… I know you're going to think this is really weird, or dumb even, but I wish we *had* fallen in love…' She gave another little sniff and added, 'I wish this was really true and not just an act.'

Bryn stared down at her uptilted face and felt another gear shift in his chest. Something warm and indefinable began to slowly spread and then fill him inside as he thought about being loved for real by her.

The only person he had ever felt truly loved by since he'd

lost his parents was his great-aunt. The truth was, he hadn't always been that lovable. Although he'd always denied it, he had been seriously traumatised by his parents' death. He had never been able to find it within himself to forgive the person responsible for taking his parents from him.

He'd been a lonely, angry child and his behaviour throughout his childhood and adolescence had been nothing short of deplorable. Even as an adult he'd been selfish and arrogant, riding roughshod over people with a ruthless disregard for their feelings. To a very large degree his bad-boy image had propelled him into the success he'd experienced and most of the time he played it to the hilt. The public expected him to be cutting and sarcastic, it was his trademark, but it wasn't who he really was or indeed who he really wanted to be.

'Does this mean you've decided to go ahead with our marriage?' he asked after a little pause.

'I don't see how I can possibly say no,' she answered somewhat grimly. 'Agnes is dying…it seems so unfair not to grant her this last wish, even if it is all an act.' She bit her lip and then released it to add uncertainly, 'I guess I can see it through for a week or two…'

'We have to see this through, Mia, no matter how compromised each of us feels. I don't want her to know this is all an act. It would destroy her.'

'I know…' she said and eased herself out of his embrace. 'I just feel uncomfortable… I'm being paid to be your wife. It just seems so…so…you know…terribly tacky.'

'You're thinking too much,' he said as he unlocked the car. 'It's just money and I have plenty, so you don't need to worry on that score. Think of it as any other acting job. I'm sure every actor has been assigned roles that aren't quite to their taste, but they do it for the money.'

Mia frowned as she got in and fastened her seat belt. It wasn't the money she was really worried about, she knew he had plenty and what he was paying her would hardly make a dent in it, and it would certainly solve her sister's dilemma. It was what he couldn't give her that worried her more. She was being paid to pretend to love a man she had previously thought unlovable, but somehow as he'd held her a few moments ago she had felt a tiny flicker of something deep inside, as if something was trying to make its way out to the surface but was being blocked in some way.

She sneaked a glance at him as he drove out of the car park. His expression was mostly inscrutable except for the tiny glitter of sadness she thought she could see in his dark eyes. But, as if he sensed her looking at him, he reached for his sunglasses on the dashboard and put them on his face and she was shut out once more.

# CHAPTER SEVEN

THE next few days passed in a whirlwind of activity that left Mia spinning. There was legal work to be dealt with and, although she felt uncomfortable signing documents that were so legally binding, she did it for the sake of Bryn's great-aunt. She just couldn't stop thinking about the older woman's life coming to an end and how it would impact on Bryn. She was his last living relative. Once she died there would be no one else but him. His final link with his parents would be gone.

As far as she could tell he had spoken to no one about his dying relative. Jocey Myers had only found out by a quirk of fate. There had been nothing mentioned in any of the newspaper articles about Agnes Dwyer's role in his life and certainly no mention of the tragic loss of his parents when he was a child. She wondered if he did it deliberately, as Jocey had suggested, to keep his hard-as-nails image in place or whether there was some other reason.

The Press went wild when the news broke of their impending marriage; requests for interviews flew thick and fast and wherever she went paparazzi followed, hoping for a candid shot of Bryn Dwyer's intended bride.

It made Mia totally rethink her life-long dream to be

famous. Now fame was becoming a reality she found she hated it. She couldn't do the most basic things without being followed; even going for her morning run or thrice-weekly visits to the gym became an exercise of subterfuge in order to escape the intrusion of journalists and cameras.

Bryn, on the other hand, seemed to take it all in his stride. He insisted they dine out regularly and she was forced to put on a bright smile and accompany him to yet another high-profile restaurant.

'I don't know how you stand this,' she said at the end of the second week of their engagement. They were in a harbour-side restaurant and had only been seated for three minutes when a rush of fans had come up for autographs and impromptu phone-camera photos.

'It'll soon pass,' he reassured her. 'Once we're married they'll leave us alone.'

'I certainly hope so…' She toyed with the stem of her glass agitatedly as the *maître d'* ushered the last of the lingering diners back to their tables.

Bryn gave her a quizzical look. 'I thought your goal in life was to be famous. Isn't that what every actor wants?'

She let out a tiny sigh. 'There's fame and there's fame. I guess I didn't really think about it too much…you know… how it would be if I ever made it into the big time.'

'How long have you wanted to be an actor?' he asked.

He watched as her mouth tilted engagingly, his chest feeling that little fish hook tug again. 'I think I was about four or five years old,' she said. 'I'm a middle child and apparently I was always trying to be the centre of attention. It was the Christmas pageant when I was in kindergarten that finally decided it for me. I was cast as the front end of a donkey in the nativity play and that was it. I decided I wanted to be on stage. I went to ballet and tap classes and gymnastics and joined the school swimming team and then a junior drama club when I could finally persuade my parents to pay for it. My poor mum was run off her feet ferrying me back and forth to everything.'

'Tell me about your family.'

'Well…' She smiled fondly as she met his eyes. 'My mum and dad have been happily married for nearly thirty years. They are wonderful, just as parents should be. I have a sister, Ashleigh, a year older than me, who's married to Jake and they have a son and a little daughter. I adore them. I have a younger sister, Ellie, who's adopted. She's fantastic.'

'So you're a close family?'

Mia gave him a very direct look. 'There's nothing I wouldn't do for my family. I would give my life up for any one of them at a moment's notice.'

He returned her look for a lengthy period before asking, 'Have you told them about us?'

She chewed her lip for a moment and lowered her gaze. 'My younger sister is…somewhere in the wilds of the Amazon. My parents are overseas at the moment with Jake and Ashleigh and the kids, so I haven't got around to it. I'm not sure I want them to rush home for a wedding that's not really real. Apart from a quick visit to London a few years ago, this is the first European trip my parents have had since they were married, so I didn't want to ruin it for them.'

'I hardly think attending their daughter's wedding is going to ruin their holiday,' Bryn said.

Mia looked up at him with a slight frown. 'But it's not as if it's a proper wedding. What would be the point? Besides, as soon as your great-aunt…' she faltered over the words '…passes away the marriage will be annulled.'

He gave her another lengthy look, his eyes very dark as they held hers. 'What if my great-aunt doesn't die in the next few weeks?'

Her hands gripped the edges of the seat. 'Wh-what do you mean?'

'I was speaking to her oncologist earlier today,' he said. 'Her condition has improved remarkably since she heard the news of our engagement. Her spirits have lifted and she's making a real effort to eat again; the last bout of chemotherapy hit her hard but she's put on a bit of weight and has more energy.'

'But that's a good thing, surely?' Then at his wry look she stumbled on, 'I mean…for your great-aunt, that is…maybe it's not so good for me…us…well, you know what I mean…'

'Of course it's a good thing for Agnes, but it may mean we will have to continue our charade for a bit longer than I initially expected.'

Mia lowered her gaze to her wine glass as she considered the possibility of being married to him for months on end. The very last thing she wanted was to hurry up his great-aunt's death, but living with a man as his wife for several months was just asking for trouble, especially with a man like Bryn. She was already fighting an attraction to him that was threatening to get out of hand.

'How…how long do you think we'll have to stay married?' she asked after a little silence.

He picked up his wine glass and took a sip before answering. 'It's hard to put a time on it. Three or four months.'

She swallowed thickly. 'That's a long time…'

His mouth twisted. 'It's not such a long time when you're the one who is terminally ill.'

'No...no, I guess not...'

He reached into his top pocket and handed her a card with the name of one of Sydney's top bridal designers on it. 'I've organised an open account for you to purchase what you need. I've also deposited funds in your bank account which you will no doubt need to draw on in preparation for our wedding.'

Mia found it a little unsettling for him to be discussing their marriage in such terms. She couldn't help wondering what it would have been like planning a proper wedding, with both parties excited at celebrating the most important day of their lives. Her sister Ashleigh's wedding to Jake after four long years of separation had been one of the most moving experiences she'd ever had. There hadn't been a dry eye in the house and even now, more than a year later, the photos of that special day still brought tears to Mia's eyes.

How different would her wedding day be? She'd be marrying a man who was using her as a career hoist, not to mention colluding with him in fooling his dying great-aunt that her greatest wish for him had come true.

But then, she reminded herself, she had her own reasons for going through with it. Her sister, for one thing, but then there were those feelings that kept her awake at night. Feelings she really had no business feeling...

'After the wedding we will be going on a short honeymoon,' he announced into the silence.

'A honeymoon?' She stared at him, her heart thudding in alarm. 'Whatever for?'

'All newly married couples go on a honeymoon.'

'I know, but surely in our case it's not necessary. I mean, what would be the point?'

'It will be a good opportunity for us to get to know one

another a little better out of the way of the Press,' he said, and then added with a teasing grin, 'You never know, you might even start to like me a bit.'

She gave him a castigating look without answering.

'There is something else we need to discuss about our living arrangements,' he said after another tiny but telling pause.

Her gaze flicked nervously back to his dark and unwavering one. 'I get to have my own room, right?' she asked.

'If you want one.'

She blinked at him. 'What do you mean, if I want one? Of course I want one!'

'There is the perplexing little matter of my housekeeper,' he said. 'She comes in three times a week.'

'So…what are you saying?'

'If Marita sees two beds being used instead of one she'll immediately suspect something is up and it will be all over the papers the next morning.'

'Can't you pay her to keep quiet or something?' she asked hopefully.

He shook his head. 'There are very few people I would trust even under payment.'

'I don't suppose you could dismiss your housekeeper…I mean, I can cook and clean if you want me to.'

'I have no intention of dismissing my housekeeper. She has a young family to support.'

'So what are you suggesting? That we play musical beds or something on the days your housekeeper is there?'

'I don't know. I haven't thought it through.' He gave her a sexy grin and added, 'Who knows, you might have decided to sleep with me by the time we are married.'

She looked at him incredulously. 'You surely don't think I'd take things *that* far?'

'I will leave that decision entirely up to you. The agreement we made is that this will be a paper marriage but if you at any time wish to change your mind about consummating it, I will be perfectly happy to do so.'

'Just because we will be sharing a house temporarily doesn't mean we will be sharing anything else, housekeeper or no housekeeper,' she said with force.

He gave a casual shrug and reached for his wine. 'There are plenty of women in your position who would jump at the chance to share my bed and my body.'

'And I'm quite sure legions of them have, but you can forget about putting my name in your little black book. I'm not interested.'

'I promise to keep my hands to myself as long as you promise the same.'

She sent him a frosty look. 'You seem very confident I'll be tempted by you.'

He smiled wickedly. 'You have been so far. Every time we've kissed you've got all hot and bothered.'

'I was acting!'

His smile tilted even further. 'Maybe, but when you kissed Clete Schussler on stage that night it didn't look half as convincing as when you've kissed me.'

Mia wasn't sure how to defend herself. Clete Schussler was undoubtedly a damn good kisser but, acting or not, he was not quite in the same league as Bryn Dwyer. Was any man?

'It was first-night nerves,' she said. 'I'd only ever been the understudy. We had six weeks of rehearsal but I hadn't kissed him before.'

'I'd only met you a few hours before I kissed you for the first time, and as far as I'm concerned we did a much better job.'

Mia was inclined to agree with him but didn't want to give

his already oversized ego another boost. She gave him a stony look instead and remained silent.

Bryn smiled at her brooding expression. 'Come now, Mia. Admit it. You might not like me all that much but you are very definitely attracted to me.'

She rolled her eyes disdainfully. 'You'd have to try a whole lot harder to get me to agree to a physical relationship with you. No one's managed it so far and…' She stopped when she realised what she'd inadvertently revealed.

He frowned at her in puzzlement. 'No one's managed what so far?'

'Um…' Her cheeks flared with heat and she had to look away from his probing gaze.

Bryn leaned forward a fraction, his expression becoming incredulous as realisation dawned. 'You mean you've never actually had sex?'

She didn't answer.

'You're what…twenty-four years old and you've *never*—?'

'Will you keep your voice down?' she hissed back at him. 'Someone will hear you.'

He sat back in his chair and shook his head in amazement. 'I can't believe it.' He gave a quick self-deprecating laugh. 'I employ a virgin to act as my wife. Hell, I must be out of my mind.'

She gave him a resentful scowl. 'I don't know why you're making such a big deal about it. Anyway, most men still maintain the double standard by having sex indiscriminately until they decide they want to choose a wife and future mother of their children, then they want someone who hasn't been around the block too many times.'

'No wonder you couldn't act that role,' he said. 'I was right after all. You didn't have a clue how to play a seductress.'

'I do know what goes on, you know,' she said. 'I'm not totally clueless.'

His midnight-blue gaze twinkled. 'So you've gone south solo a few times to see how things work?'

Hot colour flooded her face but she forced herself to hold his taunting look. 'That's none of your business.'

He gave a soft laugh at her discomfiture. 'Don't be embarrassed. I think it's delightful. It shows you're not a total prude.'

'There's nothing prudish about being selective with whom you share your body, especially these days. You don't know what you might catch.'

'No, indeed there isn't, but you surely can't have had a lack of opportunity. You're a beautiful-looking young woman with a great body. You must have been fighting men off for years.'

Mia berated herself for reacting to his compliments but she just couldn't help feeling a glow of warmth as his words washed over her. She disguised her reaction by saying airily, 'I've had a few boyfriends.'

'But no one has ever tempted you to sleep with them?'

She met his eyes once more. 'No one so far.'

He gave her an unreadable little smile as he signalled to the waiter for the bill. 'Then I guess the road is wide open to me.'

She hitched her chin up a fraction as he drew her to her feet. 'Better men than you have tried and failed,' she informed him coldly.

His eyes were alight with challenge. 'No, what you mean is, better men than me have tried and given up. I don't believe in giving up. If I want something, I make damned sure I get it.'

'Not this time,' she said with overblown confidence. 'If you don't keep to your side of the deal I won't be obliged to keep to mine.' She drew in a breath and tacked on recklessly, 'I will go to the Press with the truth about our relationship. Then what will your great-aunt think of you? She'll know you lied to her when she was most vulnerable, and no matter what your motive was, I don't think she will forgive you.'

His eyes started to smoulder as they held hers. 'If you do that I will be forced to play dirty with you, Mia. Don't make me show you how ruthless I can be.'

She didn't get a chance to respond, for he grasped her hand and practically dragged her out of the restaurant and over to his car.

'Get in,' he bit out as he opened the passenger door.

She got in but only because people were starting to look at them, and she didn't want to create a scene. She sat stiffly in her seat and watched as he strode around to the driver's side, his expression dark with simmering anger.

He waited until they were on their way before he spoke, his voice chillingly hard and determined. 'I swear to God, Mia, if my great-aunt's last weeks or months of life are ruined by you leaking something to the Press you will seriously regret it. I'll make sure of it. I'll throw everything at you. You will never work again—in any industry. Don't think I wouldn't or couldn't do it, for I can, and I will.'

Mia felt deeply ashamed of her impulsive threat but there was no way her pride would allow her to show it. 'I'm not scared of you,' she tossed back. 'You can threaten me all you like but I'm not scared.'

'Then perhaps you should be,' he said. 'Didn't you read the fine print on those documents I sent for you to sign?'

She felt an icy shiver pass over her skin. She had read the documents but only briefly. The legal terms had been offputting enough, but when Gina had come home unexpectedly and started to peer over her shoulder Mia had hastily signed the highlighted sections and stuffed the documents back in the return express envelope and posted it.

'Let me refresh your memory,' he continued when she didn't respond. 'There is a clause on page five that states that if you, the undersigned, at any point during the duration of our marriage reveal intimate information about our relationship to the Press or anyone else, you will have to repay all monies already allocated to you as well as the legal fees in the subsequent defamation case I will immediately activate with my legal advisors.' He sent her a quick, brittle glance and continued in the same chilling tone, 'In case the legalese is a bit hard for you to understand, let me put it in layperson's terms: I am going to take you to the cleaners.'

Mia compressed her lips as she thought about how much money might be involved. It was a daunting scenario and one she was going to have to do her very best to avoid. Her parents were comfortably well off but certainly not in Bryn's league and, while her brother-in-law, Jake, was extremely wealthy, she didn't want to involve him in a public fight that could turn out to be very nasty. And until Ellie was out of danger she had no choice but to play by the rules.

Bryn's fierce loyalty to his only living relative was certainly admirable and perhaps a clue to whom he really was as a person, but she didn't like the thought of being on the receiving end of his wrath if things didn't go according to plan.

'Anyone could have heard you in there,' he said into the tight silence. 'You know the deal. In public we are like any other normal couple in love, if you want to pick a fight with me then please have the sense to do so while we are in private.'

'I won't go to the Press if you stick to your side of the deal. You can pay me to be your wife but there's no amount of money on this earth that I would accept to become your lover,' she said stiffly.

'Fine.' He shoved the car into top gear. 'But as I said, if you ever change your mind just let me know.'

She gave a scornful snort. 'As if.'

His eyes clashed with hers for a brief moment. It was hardly more than a fraction of a second but Mia had to turn away.

She felt herself being thrust back in her seat as he floored the throttle—the atmosphere crackled with tension and her stomach gave a funny little quiver when he drawled, 'We'll see.'

# CHAPTER EIGHT

Two days before the wedding Mia visited Agnes at the palliative-care unit. She had deliberated over it for days, wondering if it was wise to see the old lady without Bryn present, but the temptation to find out more about his background from the person who knew him best was far too tempting to resist. She didn't tell Bryn about her intention to visit his great-aunt the night before when they'd had dinner together in yet another of Sydney's premier restaurants. For days after their terse exchange when she'd threatened to go to the Press he had been distant and formal with her in private, although whenever they were in public he acted the role of attentive fiancé with his usual and somewhat unnerving expertise. For all his charming smiles and spine-tingling touches when others were looking, Mia knew he was still angry with her, and she also knew, if she was truly honest with herself, she really couldn't blame him. He wanted his great-aunt's last weeks of life to be as happy as possible, and she had threatened to jeopardise his plans, with what would appear to him a callous disregard on her part for what his great-aunt would feel on hearing such a revelation.

The nurse on duty led the way to Agnes Dwyer's room and,

after announcing to the old lady she had a visitor, she gave Mia a quick smile and closed the door on her exit.

'Mia, my dear, what a wonderful surprise! How lovely to see you,' she greeted her with a warm smile. 'I thought you'd be far too busy organising your wedding to take time out to visit me.'

Mia came towards the bed and held out the bright red, orange and pink gerberas she'd brought with her. 'These are for you…I thought you might like something colourful for your room.'

'They're gorgeous, my dear. What a lovely gesture. Most people give me dull, old-lady-type flowers. I'm fed up with lavender and lily of the valley. These are marvellously cheery. I'll get the nurse to put them in water. Now, come and tell me how the wedding plans are going.' She patted the bed beside her. 'Sit next to me here…go on, I won't bite.'

Mia perched on the edge of the bed and the old woman reached for her hand. 'I was hoping you'd come to visit me,' she said. 'Bryn comes in twice a day but I wanted to speak to you privately.'

'Y-you did?'

'Yes,' Agnes said. 'I thought it would be nice for us to have a little woman-to-woman chat.'

'Oh…'

A small silence fell into the room. Mia could hear the rattle of a tea trolley further down the corridor, and further away the sound of a relaxation CD playing in another patient's room.

Agnes finally spoke. 'Bryn won't be an easy man to live with, Mia. I feel I should warn you, since it's really my fault you're rushing into marriage so quickly. You haven't had time to get to know him properly. I know you love him, that's more than obvious, and he very clearly is devoted to you, but you might find things tough going once the first rush of love passes.'

Mia remained silent, her heart doing a funny hit-and-miss beat in her chest.

'I always knew it would take a very special woman to melt the ice around Bryn's heart,' the old woman said. 'He's been so guarded for so long. He has never let his emotions rule his heart before. I'm so very glad he found you.'

'Thank you…' Mia said softly, her eyes falling away from the unwavering gaze of Bryn's only relative.

'You see, Mia, Bryn has never really come to terms with his parents' death…'

'It was an accident, wasn't it?' Mia inserted into the silence.

'Yes, but it wasn't really anyone's fault,' the old woman said. 'The young driver of the car that hit my nephew and his wife head on lost control on a bend. He'd only had his licence a short time. He wasn't speeding and the inquest found that no alcohol or drugs were involved. It was just one of those accidents that wouldn't have even happened if Bryn's parents had driven past just a few seconds later.' She shook her head sadly. 'It's hard to imagine how different things would have been just for the sake of a few seconds…'

Mia swallowed the lump of emotion clogging her throat. 'You've given up so much for Bryn…'

'Yes, that's true, but he needed me and I was happy to step into his parents' role. He was such an unhappy little boy. What Bryn needed was his parents, but due to circumstances beyond our control he could never have them. He has harboured such ill feeling towards that poor man for most of his life. Forgiveness is something he finds very hard. I guess you could call him stubborn.' She gave Mia a little smile. 'No doubt you'll come up against his strong will from time to time.'

'I'm sure I'll be able to handle it,' Mia said. 'I'm pretty strong-willed myself.'

'You will need to be, my dear. Bryn can be a wonderful friend but a powerful and deadly enemy. But I am sure with your gentle love you will be able to help him let go of the past and find it in himself to forgive.'

'I'll do my best,' Mia promised.

Agnes gave her hand a little squeeze. 'Are you excited about the wedding?'

'Um…nervous really…'

'That's understandable. It's been such a rush.' She gave a little sigh. 'I wish I had more time allotted me, then you would have had more time to prepare for your life together. It doesn't seem fair for you to be fast-tracked into marriage without the time to plan things properly.'

'It's fine…really,' Mia reassured her. 'It's what Bryn and I both want.'

'You know, Mia, I was in love once,' Agnes said softly. 'It happened late in life; I was so excited. We were going to be married but when Bryn's parents were tragically killed my fiancé wasn't keen on having an instant family. He gave me a choice. It was either him or Bryn.'

'And you chose Bryn…'

'Yes. But then I had to act as if I was no longer in love with my fiancé. It took some doing, I can assure you, especially when after a few months he married someone else and had a child with her. I was heartbroken but I had to carry on.'

Mia felt the sting of tears at the backs of her eyes for what both Bryn and his great-aunt had been through. How had she coped with losing the man she loved? And how had Bryn as a child so small and defenceless coped with such a terrible loss without it leaving permanent scars?

'Bryn shut down emotionally after his parents died,' Agnes went on sadly. 'I tried to ease him out of it but I'm afraid he resisted all my attempts to get him to talk about it. It was as if his parents had been permanently erased from his mind. He never mentioned them. He still doesn't. Even the photos I kept about the place would disappear without explanation. I gave up in the end.'

'He speaks so fondly of you…'

'Yes, he's a darling, but as I said you'll have your work cut out for you. I never thought he'd ever settle down. No one did. It's a miracle it happened while I was still alive to see it.'

Mia moistened her lips self-consciously. 'Yes…it is…'

'I can't tell you how much it means to me to see him so happy at last,' the old woman went on. 'I am so excited about the wedding. I am living for the day.'

Mia gave a tight swallow. 'So am—' Her words faded as a tall figure suddenly appeared in the doorway.

'Is this a private meeting or can anyone join in?' Bryn asked as he entered the room.

'Bryn, darling, you're early,' Agnes greeted him warmly. 'Look at the lovely flowers Mia brought me.'

Mia watched as he stooped to press a kiss to his great-aunt's cheek, trying to work out if he had overheard any of their conversation. She could imagine he would be very annoyed to find her discussing his past with his only living relative. How long had he been standing there?

'And how is my gorgeous fiancée?' He turned and pulled her into his embrace, lowering his head to place a scorching kiss on her lips.

She forced herself to meet his glinting dark gaze once he'd lifted his mouth from hers. 'Hi…'

He held her look for what seemed a very long time before he turned back to his great-aunt. 'Are you all set for the wedding?'

'Yes, dear,' Agnes responded. 'The nurse is coming with me, as you arranged. I can hardly wait.'

Bryn took Mia's hand and tucked it through his arm, looking down at her with an inscrutable expression on his face. 'Nor can I, isn't that right, sweetheart?'

'Um…that's right…' Mia gave a shaky smile.

Bryn waited until they were outside in the car park before he spoke, his tone and frown accusatory. 'Why didn't you tell me you were coming to visit my great-aunt?'

'It was a last-minute decision,' she said, lowering her gaze. 'I thought she might like some flowers.'

'What did you talk about?'

'Not much…the wedding arrangements and stuff…'

His frown increased at her evasive answer. 'You weren't tempted to act on your threat to spill the beans?'

'No, of course not.' She looked up at him. 'I didn't even mean it when I said it, much less intend to ever act on it. I was angry at you. I would never do anything to upset her.'

His eyes were hard as they clashed with hers. 'You'd better be telling me the truth.'

'I am telling you the truth but if you don't stop glaring at me like that your great-aunt along with the staff around here might draw their own conclusions about the true state of our relationship,' she warned him.

He let out his breath in a ragged stream, his mouth tilting wryly. 'You're right. I must have pre-wedding nerves or something.'

'It's not too late to call it off,' she said, fiddling with her car keys in an effort to avoid his eyes again. 'I'm sure Agnes would understand if you told her the truth.'

'No.' His tone was implacable. 'Our marriage is going

ahead come hell or high water. It's what she wants more than anything. Besides, Annabelle rang me just before I arrived here and told me my latest ratings. My popularity is at an all-time high. If we pulled the plug now it would destroy my credibility and totally ruin my career.'

She gave him a haughty look as she unlocked her car. 'I hope you're not expecting empathy from me if that should ever happen.'

'It's not going to happen, Mia,' he said with steely determination. 'Because we are going to be husband and wife in forty-eight hours, and like I just said to Agnes: I can hardly wait.'

'You look absolutely beautiful,' Gina gushed as Mia put the final touches to her bridal make-up two days later. 'I can't wait to see Bryn's face when he sees you.'

Mia gave herself a critical look in the mirror. The skirt of the white satin and tulle gown was voluminous and emphasised her slim waist, and the close-fitting strapless top showcased her upper body to maximum effect. Her make-up was subtle but highlighted her clear grey eyes and the creamy texture of her skin. Gina had done her hair for her, setting it in Velcro rollers first before arranging it on top of her head in a sophisticated style that made her feel like a princess.

'I guess I look OK,' she admitted grudgingly.

'More than OK,' Gina said, then added with a tiny sigh, 'But it's a pity your family aren't here to see you.'

Mia pretended to be concentrating on attaching her veil rather than meet her friend's eyes. It had been the hardest thing she'd had to do so far when she'd called her parents the previous night and told them she was getting married the following day. In many ways it had been the performance of her life. She had managed to convince her entire family that it was the real deal, including Ellie, who had called her from Brazil saying she was going to be released in forty-eight hours thanks to Mia's efforts on her behalf.

Mia had told each of them of her whirlwind love affair with Bryn and how very happy she was. Her parents had initially been disappointed that she had left it so late to tell them but when she explained her reasons they understood her concern that they have the holiday they had planned for so long without interruption.

Ashleigh, so much in love with her own husband, was an easy person to convince. She had fallen in love with Jake Marriott at first sight, so there was no way she would have ever questioned Mia's story.

'I think that's Henry now,' Gina said, peering out of the window.

Mia took a steadying breath as she reached for the bouquet of white roses, her stomach turning over in trepidation.

There was no way out now.

She was going to be married to Bryn Dwyer within the hour.

Officially.

Legally.

Temporarily.

'Ready?' Gina asked with a huge excited grin.

Mia smiled until it hurt. 'I'm ready.'

Bryn turned to watch Mia walk up the aisle; she had refused his offer of someone to give her away in the absence of her father and decided to do it all by herself with just her flatmate as bridesmaid.

He caught the eye of his great-aunt, who was sitting with a nurse in attendance. The sheer joy on her frail, pale face was all he had ever hoped for and it made him a little less guilt-stricken about how he'd engineered his relationship with Mia.

From the very first moment his eyes had clashed with Mia's in that café, he had wanted her. And when she'd come to the station and bawled him out he had wanted her even more. He liked her fighting spirit. He liked the way she stood up to him defiantly when every other woman would have given in. He also liked her soft heart; the way she had openly cried when she met his great-aunt for the first time had touched him very deeply. And though he knew it was probably terribly chauvinistic of him, he couldn't help but feel pleased she hadn't slept around. It seemed likely she would be less inclined to be indiscreet with someone else, but on the other hand it meant he would have his work cut out for him convincing her to sleep with him, which he very much wanted her to do. He had thought of nothing else; his desire for her throbbed constantly in his blood, until he could barely think about anything else. He saw her as a particular challenge, and the one thing he liked in life was a stiff challenge. She hated him and he looked forward to the challenge of making her fall for him just like every other woman had in the past. It had nothing to do with his feelings. He had no intention of complicating his life with emotions that could only come to grief. He liked her, of course; who wouldn't? She was feisty and quick-witted and when she wasn't tearing strips off him her personality was sweet and caring.

He looked down as Mia came and stood next to him, the scent of her flowery perfume filling his nostrils, her tentative smile as she met his gaze through the film of her veil making his throat feel unusually tight. He cleared it discreetly and faced the front, straightening his shoulders and taking a breath as the priest began the ceremony in a solemn, authoritative tone.

'Dearly beloved, we are gathered here…'

# CHAPTER NINE

MIA stood very still as Bryn turned to lift her veil from her face at the priest's command to kiss the bride. His dark gaze meshed with hers for an infinitesimal pause before he lowered his mouth to hers. A soft sigh escaped from her lips and disappeared into the warmth of his mouth as it covered hers in a lingering, passionate kiss that sent rivers of sensation through her body.

*You're not acting*, a little voice inside her head began to taunt her but she refused to acknowledge it. Of course she was acting! That was what Bryn was paying her to do, to convince the world that she was in love with him when the very opposite was true.

She hated him.

*No, you don't.* That same little voice was back and even more insistent this time.

'I do.'

Mia hadn't realised she had spoken the words out loud until she saw the quizzical look on Bryn's face as he straightened from kissing her.

'We've already said that bit,' he whispered with a teasing little smile.

'I—I know...I was just...' She gave up in relief when the

priest announced the signing of the register would take place before the bride and groom would exit the cathedral.

Once the register was signed and some photos taken, they made their way back down the aisle to the strains of Handel's music, the congregation and interested bystanders swelling towards them as they stepped out into the warm summer sunshine.

The reception was held at the same hotel as the ball had been, the room beautifully and lavishly decorated, and the champagne flowing freely by the time they arrived from having the official photographs taken.

Speeches and toasts were made, the cake was cut and the bridal waltz performed, cameras still flashing madly until it was finally time for Bryn and Mia to leave.

Gina had a tussle over the bouquet with several other young women but she was victorious in the end, although the bouquet she held proudly aloft was suspiciously short of a few blooms.

The ever-present journalists pressed forward as Bryn helped Mia into his car, their microphones outstretched. 'Where's the honeymoon going to be, Mr Dwyer?' one of them asked.

'How long will you be away?' another pushed in.

'No comment,' Bryn said and closed Mia's door. He waved to everyone before he got in the driver's seat and leaning across gave Mia a long, sensual kiss for the benefit of the cameras.

Mia was already feeling a bit light-headed from all the champagne she'd consumed and his kiss made her head spin even more. She sank against him, her senses reeling at the erotic message being communicated by his lips and tongue.

He lifted his head and, smiling once more for the Press, he gunned the engine and they were away, balloons and tin cans and streamers trailing in their wake, the shaving-foam message 'Just Married' scrawled all over the back window.

'How are you holding up?' Bryn asked the silent figure beside him a few minutes later.

She sent him a rueful sideways glance. 'My face aches from smiling all the time.'

He gave a soft chuckle of laughter. 'Yeah, so does mine.' He glanced in the rear-view mirror at the bouncing cans and pulled over to the side of the road to remove them, placing them in a rubbish bin on the pavement before getting back in behind the wheel and easing the car into the traffic.

Mia stared down at the two rings on her left hand. It hardly seemed real that she was sitting next to a man she hadn't even met in person a little over a month ago. And now she was going on a honeymoon with him to his private retreat in the Queensland Sunshine Coast town of Noosa.

'Do you think the Press will follow us?' she asked to fill the little silence.

'I shouldn't think so,' he answered. 'I think now the wedding has come and gone their interest will die down. It has to. All they were really interested in was whether or not we were really getting married. No one thought I would ever do it.'

Mia gave her rings another twirl, not trusting herself to chance a glance his way. 'Your great-aunt seemed to be very happy for you.'

'Yes, she was.' His eyes flicked to her briefly. 'I guess I should thank you for playing the role so well. You must have acted the beautiful-bride part before. You were a natural.'

'I've been to a lot of weddings,' she said and then added in a self-deprecating tone, 'besides, the priest tells you what to say. It's hardly challenging. It's like having an Autocue to prompt you.'

He smiled as he took the turn to the domestic terminal. 'I guess the challenging bit is yet to come.'

Mia decided not to respond. She'd been steadily panicking about the bit to come all day and wondered how in the world she was going to negotiate her way through it.

Ever since she'd spoken with his great-aunt Mia had felt increasingly confused about her feelings towards him. She could still taste his kiss on her lips and it worried her that once they were alone she wouldn't have the resolve to keep her growing attraction to him under control. He was hard enough to resist while she hated him. How much more tempting would he be if she started to like him?

*But you do like him,* the little voice in her head returned. She tried to block it but it kept on filling her head with nonsense.

*You're in love with him.*

*You want to spend the rest of your life with him.*

*You want to have his children.*

She clutched at her bag with both hands, staring down at the rings on her finger that bound her to him.

It couldn't possibly be true. How could she love a man who had destroyed her career with a few words he'd written, thinking nothing of it, as if it were a simple game of sport?

She was just falling under his sensual spell like every other silly woman who didn't have a measure of self-control. She would just have to try harder to avoid becoming yet another of his conquests.

Falling in love with Bryn Dwyer was too dangerous.

Their relationship was temporary.

She had to remember that.

'Come on, Mia.' Bryn's voice broke through her reverie as he opened her door a few minutes later. 'Our plane leaves in forty minutes. We need to check in before the flight closes.'

* * *

The flight to Maroochydore took an hour and a half and Mia was glad that for most of it she had slept. She woke just as they were coming in to land, the lights of the coastal town situated on the south bank of the Maroochy River twinkling in the clear night air.

Bryn had organised a hire car for them and as soon as the luggage was collected he began the thirty-minute drive north to Noosa.

'Have you been to Noosa before?' he asked once they were on their way.

'Yes, but it was quite a while ago, ten years at least. We came on a family holiday,' she answered. 'It might have completely changed by now.'

'That's what so nice about it up here,' he said. 'It never really changes. Sure, there've been developments up and down the river and along the coast, but nothing like the massive high-rises on the Gold Coast. Noosa National Park is a great place to walk through. You can even do a beach crawl if you want. There are quiet, shady bays or great surf spots, so whatever your mood you can usually find somewhere to relax.'

'I remember the national park. My sister Ashleigh hated the long walks my parents kept taking us on. Ellie wanted to stop and look at every bit of wildlife and I kept running on ahead, driving my parents crazy in case I got lost, which I seem to recall I did on more than one occasion.'

'You must have been a cute kid,' he said after a little pause. 'I envy your family life. It must have been wonderful having such a loving environment to grow up in.'

'It wasn't always fun and games,' she said. 'I love my sisters but we fought a lot when we were younger. I guess all kids do.'

There was another lengthy silence.

'I often wondered what it would have been like to have a brother or a sister.'

She looked at him. 'It must have been very hard growing up without your parents.'

'It was. But I learned to cope. My great-aunt did the best she could but I wasn't the easiest person to be around at times.'

'Do you have any photos of your parents?'

'I guess I have them somewhere.'

'Why don't you have them out on show?'

'I'm not the sentimental type,' he said. 'It's in the past and I'm only interested in the future.'

Mia decided to step out on a limb. 'Your great-aunt said you used to hide any photos of your parents when she put them out. Why did you do that?'

He gave her a hard little glance. 'You sound as if the two of you had a very cosy chat.'

'I just wanted to find out a bit more about the man I was marrying.'

'And did she enlighten you?'

Mia frowned at his sharpened tone. 'There's no need to be so defensive.'

'I'm not being defensive. I just don't appreciate you interfering in things that don't concern you.'

'I think I have the right to know what has made you the way you are.'

'Why? So you can reform me, to make me more user-friendly?'

'You're way beyond reform,' she snapped back irritably. 'I wouldn't even bother trying.'

'Good. Then at least we know where we both stand.'

Mia frowned as she sat back in her seat with a sigh of frustration. He was like a closed book. As soon as she tried to prise open the pages he would just as quickly snap them shut. She knew he was hurting—she could almost feel it coming off him whenever the subject of his childhood was raised. It was like an aura surrounding him. He didn't trust life not to hit him from the left field again when he was least expecting it.

He reminded her of Ashleigh's gorgeous husband, Jake. He had hidden his inner pain behind a façade of cynicism that had very nearly destroyed her sister's life and his own as well. But Ashleigh's enduring love had found a healing pathway to his soul.

Did she have what it took to do the same for Bryn? And more to the point—did she even want to try?

'I think you'll like my house,' Bryn said after another lengthy silence. 'I had it designed specially.'

As olive branches went it wasn't quite what she had been hoping for but she realised he was making an effort and she forced herself to accept it in the spirit in which it was given.

'I'm looking forward to seeing it,' she said.

Mia looked around her a few minutes later in awe. She had been expecting Bryn's beach hideaway to be luxurious but nothing had quite prepared her for the sheer brilliance of the design that gave him sweeping views over the Noosa River on one side and the beaches and national park on the other. The house was on three levels and was tucked in the bush land that fringed the area, offering a level of privacy that was unbelievable. There were no curtains at any of the main windows—they weren't necessary as the house was set higher than the rest of its neighbours and the thick surrounding bush was an effective screen.

'What do you think?' Bryn asked as soon as he'd shown her the entry level where the main lounge was situated as well as the kitchen and spacious dining area.

'It's…wonderful…' She turned to look at him. 'No wonder you love coming here. It's like a private paradise.'

'Come and I'll show you the rest of the house from the top floor down,' he said, leading the way to the open-plan stairs.

Mia followed him as he showed her the three large bedrooms on the top level. A wall of built-in wardrobes gave each room a feeling of space, as did the minimalist décor and pristine white bed linen on the beds. Each *en suite* had a large, free-standing bowl-like white basin on top of a simple vanity and a big walk-in shower, and the floor and walls were tiled with marble the colour of flecked sand.

He led her back down the stairs to the lower level, where an impressive gym was set up in a large room that led out through French doors to a lap pool in the private garden in which frangipani trees scented the balmy night air.

'Wow…' Mia breathed in wonder as she looked around. 'You sure know the way to an exercise junkie's heart.'

Bryn chuckled as she bent down to trail her fingers in the water of the pool to test its temperature. 'I was wondering how you maintained that stunning figure of yours. Now I know.'

Mia felt his compliment wash over her like the warm silk of the water around her fingers. She straightened from the pool and tried to hide her reaction but he caught one of her hands and brought her to a standstill right in front of him.

He stroked the backs of the knuckles of one hand over the heightened colour of her cheek in a movement so gentle her breath came to a stumbling halt right in the middle of her chest. Her stomach gave a little flutter, just like the wings of a trapped moth inside a tiny confined space.

She moistened her suddenly dry mouth at the dark intensity in his midnight-blue gaze as it locked with hers.

The perfumed air swirled around them, wrapping them in

a sensual mantle of summer warmth, the exotic atmosphere tipping the balance of distance Mia had desperately tried to maintain between them ever since their marriage was formalised that afternoon.

She felt sure he was going to kiss her. She could feel it along the exposed skin of her arms and legs, the tiny hairs on the back of her neck lifting in anticipation as his head came inexorably closer. Her eyelids fluttered closed as his mouth touched down on hers with breath-like softness, as if the moth from inside her stomach had somehow escaped and landed ever so gently on her lips.

Bryn lifted his head a mere fraction, his mouth still so close she could feel the movement of air from his breath over her acutely sensitive skin.

Two beats of silence passed before he lowered his mouth back to hers, the pressure increasing subtly and tantalisingly. Mia felt the full rush of her blood surging through her veins at the first stroke of his tongue over her lips. She parted her lips and he entered her mouth with gentle but firm insistence, searching for her tongue and mating with it possessively.

Mia felt the prickling of her breasts as he drew her closer into his embrace, her nipples tightening, while her legs and spine felt as if they had been instantly liquefied when one of his hard thighs slipped between hers. She leaned into his hold, her body craving more of his touch, her senses on fire where his hardness probed her softness. Desire exploded inside her, running like a hot stream that threatened to get out of control now it was finally unleashed. She tried to pull it back, tried to get her responses under some semblance of control, but it was impossible. His mouth was like a lighted taper to the spilled fuel of her need, sending hot, licking flames to every single part of her body. She could feel the fullness of her breasts aching for his touch and almost unconsciously began to press herself closer. His erection burned and pulsed against her and she heard his low groan of spiralling need as he deepened the kiss even further.

Without taking his mouth off hers he pressed her back against the wall of the house, one of his hands going to her breast, cupping it through the thin fabric of her top, his thumb rolling over the hardened point of her nipple. Mia felt her breath trip over something invisible as he lifted his head from her mouth, his dark eyes glittering as they held hers for a tiny pause.

Her stomach gave a complete somersault as he slid his hand beneath her top, the warm glide of his fingers over her bare flesh sending her senses into a tailspin. He pushed aside her lacy bra and brought his mouth down to her breast, his lips closing over her nipple and suckling gently until she felt as if he had pulled on an invisible string that was attached to her feminine core. She felt each delicious tug on her sensitised flesh, the tiny arrows of delight like spot fires being lit throughout her quivering body.

His lips left her breast to return to her mouth, this time with increasing urgency, as if he was not quite in control of his reaction to her. She felt his struggle to hold back, the increasing tension in his body where it pressed so temptingly against hers and the latent strength in his arms as he hauled her even closer.

Her hands were in the dark brown silk of his hair, her mouth kissing him back with all the passion of her nature. Her tongue flirted with his, danced with his and became boldly intimate with his, while her heart raced with breakneck speed and her body pulsed with escalating need.

She heard him give another low, deep groan as he wrenched his mouth away, looking down at her with eyes ablaze with unalleviated desire.

It was a moment or two before he spoke but when he did he did so with an ironic twist to his mouth. 'I can only assume from your unbridled reaction to me just now that none of your previous would-be lovers had a comprehensive gym and pool with which to impress you.'

She injected her tone with disdain. 'So you can kiss. Big deal. So can most primates, even chimpanzees and gorillas.'

He gave a soft chuckle that tugged on that invisible string again. 'That's not all I can do, baby. If you continue to respond to me like that—virgin or not—I'm not sure this is going to stay a paper marriage for very long.'

'You shouldn't have kissed me in the first place,' Mia said. 'It's not exactly as if we have an audience right now.'

'I know, it was a bit unfair but you were so tempting I couldn't resist one little kiss. You have such a beautiful mouth when it's not slinging insults my way.'

'I wouldn't sling insults your way if you would just keep your hands and mouth to yourself.'

'I seem to remember your hands and mouth doing their own little bit of wandering.'

'You're imagining it. I was trying to get away.'

He gave her another taunting smile. 'That was some struggle you were putting up.'

She gave him a withering look without answering.

'In case you're wondering, there is no housekeeper we have to act in front of here,' he said. 'The place is maintained by the neighbours. I pay them a fee to keep an eye on things when I'm away, but while we are here we will have absolute privacy.'

He held the French doors open for her and once they were indoors added, 'You can have whichever bedroom you like.'

'Which one is yours?'

'Are you asking because you want to avoid it or to share it?'

She gave him a glittering glare. 'What do you think?'

He held her defiant look for a little longer than was comfortable. Mia felt herself inwardly squirming under his steady surveillance and wondered if he could see the truth written on her face even though she did her level best to disguise it.

She wanted him.

For the first time in her life she had come face to face with a man who was temptation personified. Her flesh was still tingling from his touch and she knew if he took even one step towards her and took her in his arms again she would not have the strength of will to resist him.

'Go to bed, Mia,' he said after a short, throbbing silence. 'Otherwise I might be tempted to ravish you right here and now.'

'You wouldn't dare.'

His night-sky eyes grew even darker and his voice when he spoke was gravel-rough. 'Don't play with matches, sweetheart. I'm sorely tempted to finish what we started out by the pool and one look from you is all it will take to get the flames going again.'

Mia turned for the stairs, forcing herself to go at a dignified pace even though she felt like bolting.

'Goodnight, little virgin wife of mine,' Bryn said, his tone distinctly mocking.

She gritted her teeth and with one last blistering look over her shoulder, opened the first bedroom she came to and closed the door on his taunting smiling face.

# CHAPTER TEN

MIA headed straight for the *en suite*. Shutting the door, she stared at her wild appearance in the mirror, her hands clutching the edge of the vanity to steady her trembling legs.

She had to learn to control herself around him! What was she thinking, kissing him back like that? It was totally crazy. It was just asking for the sort of heartbreak she could well do without.

She turned around and, leaning back against the vanity, released a heavy sigh. Of course, resisting him would be a whole lot easier if he weren't so damned tempting. Those dark blue eyes positively smouldered with sensuality every time they locked with hers. And those lips! What woman could resist a kiss that felt as soft as a butterfly landing on an exotic bloom, or not respond when the same kiss turned into something deeply erotic with the determined thrust of his searching tongue?

She looked down at her breasts and suppressed a little shiver of reaction as she thought of his mouth around her nipple. He had been so very close to tipping her over the edge if only he knew it.

She gave a little scowl as she reached for the shower tap. Maybe he did know it.

The shower was just what she needed; it was cool and refreshing and washed away the dust and damp stickiness of long-distance travel.

It had been a long day and tiredness was creeping up on her, making her sway on her feet as she wrapped the soft, fluffy white towel—bigger than any towel she'd ever seen before—around herself like a sarong.

The bed beckoned her as soon as she left the *en suite*, its wide white-feather softness looking like a cloud of comfort in the middle of the floor.

She gave the room a quick, sweeping glance for her suitcase so she could retrieve her nightwear. She'd seen Bryn carry their luggage upstairs earlier but there was no sign of it in here.

She gave a little shrug of tired indifference and slipped the towel off, climbing in between the cool sheets and laying her head down on the soft-as-air feather pillow as she closed her eyes with a sigh of relief…

'So guess who's been sleeping in my bed?'

Mia's eyes sprang open at the deep, lazy drawl, the bright glare from the overhead light making her wince as she struggled upright, clutching the sheet to cover her nakedness.

'*Your* bed?' she gasped, her heart thudding in alarm as she registered that he was wearing nothing but a towel slung loosely around his waist.

Bryn gave her an indolent smile. 'And here I was, thinking it was going to take me the best part of the week to convince you to sleep with me.' He reached for the edge of his towel and dropped it to the floor.

Mia's eyes nearly popped out of her head. She suddenly realised she was staring and quickly flung the sheet over her head. 'For God's sake, cover yourself!' she croaked.

He gave a deep chuckle of laughter. 'Haven't you seen a naked man before?'

'Yes,' she said, her voice muffled from under the sheet.

'So what's the problem?'

'My nephew is five years old, that's what's the problem.'

'So he's got a bit of growing to do, but we all end up more or less the same.'

Mia wasn't so sure about that. She'd seen plenty of toned male bodies at her local gym, admittedly covered by close-fitting gym gear, but Bryn's was something else again—especially naked.

She felt a little tug on the sheet covering her and clutched at it in panic. 'What are you doing?' she shrieked when it slipped out of her desperate grasp.

Bryn's gaze burned as it ran over her and she hastily crossed her legs and covered her breasts with her hands. Her words of protest locked somewhere in her throat as he stepped towards her, her mouth going dry and her heart threatening to make its way out of her chest when he sat down next to her, his muscled, hair-roughened thigh touching her smooth one.

'You're in my bed, which I can only assume means you've changed your mind and now want to sleep with me,' he said.

'I—I didn't know it was your bed.'

He stroked a finger over the upper curves of her breasts where her hands couldn't quite conceal them. 'Don't be shy, Mia. I want to look at you. All of you.'

Mia could hardly breathe; his touch was so light but so very tempting. She could feel the stirrings of desire deep within her and there was nothing she could do to control them. Electricity fizzed along her flesh wherever he touched; even the air seemed to be charged with it. She could feel the crackling tension as his eyes roved her slim form, lingering on the length of her tightly crossed legs and what she was desperately trying to hide from him.

'Uncross your legs, Mia,' he commanded gently.

She shook her head, her lips tightly compressed, not trusting herself to speak.

'I want you, Mia, and I know you want me,' he said. 'I can see it in your eyes, I can feel it in your kisses and I can even smell it on your skin.'

She wished she could deny it but she could smell it herself. The delicate feminine fragrance of desire, the silky liquid that betrayed her vulnerability to him as nothing else could do. He had only to touch her where she most ached to be touched and he would feel it for himself. She could almost feel the thick, smooth glide of his finger moving inside her, stretching her in preparation for his possession.

'It's just hormones,' she said, somewhat breathlessly. 'You shouldn't be feeling flattered at all.'

She could tell he didn't believe her by the laughing glint in his eyes but he didn't press the issue. Instead, he patted her thigh and stood up, not even bothering to hide his erection.

'I'll leave you in peace. I was just teasing. I know you'll come to me when you're ready.'

'You'll be waiting a very long time,' she said with much less conviction than she'd intended.

'I can be patient,' he said, holding her defiant gaze. 'Besides, there are some things in life that are well worth the wait. It makes the prize all the more valuable if you've had to wait for it, don't you think?'

She gave him a sour look. 'If you want a prize, go and enter a meat-tray raffle. I'm not on offer.'

He picked up his towel and wrapped it around his waist

once more, a smile still playing around his mouth. 'Sweet dreams, Mia. I'll be in the next room if you want me.'

'I don't want you,' she said but she knew it was more for her own benefit than his.

He picked up the sheet off the floor and spread it over her, tucking her in like a child, stooping to place a soft kiss to her forehead. 'So you keep saying but we both know it isn't true.'

'I suppose someone with the ego the size of yours could only be expected to say something like that,' she bit out resentfully. 'Has there ever been a woman you haven't been able to lure into your bed?'

'Not so far.'

'Poor misguided fools,' she muttered. 'I wonder if there's a support group for them all. It should be called BDCO.'

'What does that stand for?'

'Bryn Dywer's Cast-Offs,' she said. 'Life-time membership free in exchange for a broken heart.'

His shoulders shook as he laughed. 'As far as I know I haven't broken any hearts irreparably,' he said as he reached for the door knob. 'Sleep tight. I'll see you in the morning.'

Mia let out a slow, prickly breath as the door closed behind him. If she wasn't very careful hers could well be the first heart he would damage beyond repair. If she was honest with herself, she was more than halfway to being in love with him as it was; it wouldn't take too many more of those scorching kisses of his to make her go beyond the point of no return.

Mia woke to brilliant sunshine and the chorus of birds, the distant roll of the ocean in the distance filling her with instant energy. She tossed the sheet aside and came up short when she saw her suitcase next to the built-in wardrobe. Bryn must have brought it in during the night or the early hours of the morning.

A feathery sensation passed over her at the thought of him seeing her sleeping in that big bed, perhaps uncovered and totally vulnerable. She'd been hot during the night and recalled throwing the sheet off at one point until the cooler air of the morning had made her reach for it again.

She gave herself a mental shake and quickly unpacked a bikini and a two-piece sports outfit and trainers from her case and dressed quickly, tying her hair in a high pony-tail.

The house was quiet as she came downstairs but she saw signs of Bryn having had a cup of tea in the kitchen. The kettle was still warm and his cup was rinsed and placed upside down on the draining board.

She heard the clang of weights below her in the gym downstairs and pictured him working out, no doubt lifting three times her body weight as if it were nothing. She decided against joining him. She'd seen enough of his body last night and didn't need reminding of how fabulously toned and muscled he was.

Besides, it was a beautiful day and she could hear the ocean calling. Hard exercise was what she needed to clear her mind from the disturbing images that kept creeping in. Images of her pinned intimately by Bryn's hard body, his hips moving in time with hers as they both climbed towards the summit of sensual release. She could imagine he would be an exciting and demanding lover; every time he'd touched her she'd felt the hot charge of sexual energy pass from his body to hers.

She let out a frustrated breath and set a brisk pace as she ran down the steps leading to the footpath to the beach.

There were a few surfers already out riding the point break on Main Beach and she jogged along until she came to the pathway leading to Noosa National Park. She followed the

coastal track looking out over Laguna Bay and then on to
Boiling Pot and Dolphin Point, the growing heat of the
morning making her turn just past Winch Cove to head into
the cooler shadows of the melaleuca and tea-tree forest.

The honey-sweet smell of the white-canopied bush filled
her nostrils as she jogged past gnarled banksias and spiky
pandanus. Bush turkeys scratched around the undergrowth
and overhead she heard the flap of large wings and looked up
to see a pair of glossy black cockatoos flying past.

Further along the track she passed a young couple who
were walking hand in hand, their easy-going, loving chatter
striking a note of regret in Mia's chest.

How wonderful it would be to be loved like that, she
thought. She wanted to be loved the way her sister Ashleigh
was loved by her husband, Jake, the way her parents had
loved each other for nearly thirty years.

But what she wanted was impossible; Bryn wasn't the thir-
ty-year-relationship type. Thirty days was too long for him.
He wasn't interested in continuing their association past the
point of his great-aunt's death. And that could be a matter of
just a few short months or possibly even weeks.

The track veered back to Laguna Bay and Mia ran on down
to Main Beach, and, leaving her shoes and outer gear on the
sand, headed for the waves in her red and white bikini.

She swam the length of the beach, which ran parallel to the
popular shopping and restaurant strip of Hastings Street. She
turned at the rocky outcrop at one end to go back the way
she'd come, the water warm but still refreshing. Every so
often a swelling wave would pick her up and let her down
again in a gentle rolling movement before it gathered force
on its way to the shore.

The sun burned down with intense summer heat and when

she waded back through the wash to the sand she could see the numbers on the beach had swelled. Young children were playing at the water's edge with buckets and spades, their parents close by, where several colourful umbrellas were already up in defence against the scorching rays of the sun.

She sat and looked out to sea, hoping for a moment to gather her thoughts before returning to Bryn's house. But even after sitting there soaking up the warmth of the sun for several minutes she had to finally acknowledge that her vigorous run and swim hadn't been able to do what she'd hoped they would do. It was impossible to avoid any longer the truth that was as persistent as the waves as they drummed against the shore.

She couldn't escape it any more; there was no running away from it even if she ran around the world and back twice over.

She was in love with Bryn Dwyer.

She wasn't sure how it had happened. She had thought him the most detestable man alive and yet somehow over the past few weeks he had become the very focus of her life. She couldn't imagine how her life was going to be without him in it once their marriage was brought to its inevitable end. How would she cope with hearing him on the radio every weekday or reading his acerbic comments in his weekly column? Perhaps once his great-aunt was no longer around he would even joke about his publicity stunt, making a fool of Mia in front of the whole of Sydney, telling his listeners he'd married a twenty-four-year-old virgin who couldn't act to save herself.

'I thought I might find you down here.' Bryn's deep voice suddenly sounded above her.

Mia looked up at him in surprise. 'I...I went for a run...'

His eyes swept over her reddened features. 'So I see.'

She turned back to the sea. The sight of him in nothing

but a pair of board shorts and trainers was far too unsettling. 'I've just had a swim and now I think I'll have a little sunbake for a while.'

'Have you had breakfast?'

'No.'

'Aren't you hungry?'

'No,' she lied.

'Have you had something to drink?'

'No…'

He stretched out the large beach towel he'd brought with him next to where she was sitting. 'Here, lie down on that and I'll go and get you some water.'

Mia turned onto her stomach so she could watch him as he walked back along the promenade to a café on Hastings Street. She saw several female heads turning as he went past, his tanned and muscular but lean frame obviously as attractive to others as it was to her. She gave a little sigh and rested her chin on her hands and closed her eyes.

He came back in a few minutes with a bottle of water and some fresh fruit salad and handed them both to her.

She met his eyes briefly. 'Thank you.'

He sat down on the edge of the towel and looked out to sea. 'How did you sleep?'

'Fine,' she said between mouthfuls of juicy mango and tangy pineapple. 'I like listening to the sound of the ocean. It puts me to sleep every time.'

Bryn wished he could say the same for himself. He'd spent a great deal of the night tossing and turning restlessly, his body still on fire. When he'd taken her bag into her room once she was asleep it had been all he could do not to join her in the bed and pull her into his arms. His desire for her was beyond anything he'd ever experienced before. It gnawed at him relentlessly, making his body ache to possess her. He could feel it now just sitting next to her on the sand, her trim, golden body so close he could smell the hint of vanilla on her skin in spite of the exercise she'd taken.

He turned to look at her and asked, 'What would you like to do today?'

'I don't know…sun-bake and stuff… What did you have in mind?'

'If I told you what I had in mind you might slap my face.'

Mia stared at the piece of kiwi fruit she'd just speared with her plastic fork, her skin prickling all over as she felt the weight of his studied gaze. 'Don't you ever think of anything else besides satisfying your bodily urges?'

He leaned on one elbow, his long, tanned legs stretched out beside hers, his expression teasing. 'Is that why you're an obsessive exerciser? To control your own bodily urges?'

She gave him a chilly little glance. 'I happen to believe in living healthily. The human heart is a muscle like any other. Daily exercise is essential to keep it in good working order.'

'There are other ways of exercising the heart,' he pointed out. 'I could show you if you like.'

'No, thank you.'

He laughed and, picking up a handful of fine sand, began to trickle it over her up-bent thigh.

'Stop that!' She slapped his hand away and began dusting off the grains from between her legs.

'Come in and rinse it off with me,' he suggested, springing to his feet and holding out a hand.

Mia scowled at him but her hand slipped into his regardless. He pulled her to her feet and, releasing her hand, issued her an irresistible challenge. 'I'll race you to the water.'

'You're on,' she said and took off at full speed for the ocean.

She had to skirt around a toddler and his mother at the water's edge, which cost her valuable seconds, but she made it to the first breaker and would have beaten him convincingly except he grabbed one of her ankles and tugged her backwards.

She came up spluttering and in revenge scooped a handful of water up and tossed it at his face. 'You cheated!'

He ducked her liquid missile and caught both of her hands in his, pulling her towards him. 'I warned you once before, sweetheart, I don't always play by the rules.'

A gentle wave at her back pushed her even closer to him and he steadied her with his hands on her waist, his eyes, even bluer than the water around them, locking on hers. She moistened her mouth as his head came down, her eyes closing on her soft sigh as his lips found hers. It was a deeply sensual kiss, made all the more alluring because they were skin on skin in the warm water. Mia had never felt so aware of her body before. She could feel the tightening of her breasts and the melting of her bones as he deepened the kiss. The waves rocked against them, leaving her in no doubt of Bryn's thickening erection pressed so tantalisingly against the naked flesh of her lower belly. She writhed against him, wanting more of his burning heat but lower, where a hollow ache pulsed for him to fill.

After a few breathless minutes Bryn lifted his mouth from hers and looked down at her with a mocking glint in his eyes. 'I can only assume that your rather convincing performance was for the benefit of the crowd on the beach.'

Mia was temporarily lost for words. She hadn't given the crowd a single thought. All she had thought about was how he made her feel and how much she wanted him.

'That's what you're paying me to do, isn't it?' she said at last, her tone sounding terse and embittered as she pulled herself from his hold and stalked back through the waist-deep water to the sand.

Bryn turned to watch her make her way through the foamy wash and frowned. 'Yes…' he said but the words were lost on the waves as they rushed to follow her to the shore. 'Yes, it is.'

## CHAPTER ELEVEN

MIA gathered up her things and waited on the promenade for Bryn, who had stopped to help a small child who had tumbled over close to the water's edge. She watched as he crouched down and gently set the toddler back on his feet, handing him his tiny plastic bucket and spade, his warm smile doing something all mushy and wobbly to Mia's insides.

The child's mother rushed up to thank him and after exchanging a few words he picked up his sports shoes off the sand and walked over to where Mia was waiting.

'Your boy-scout deed done for the day?' she queried with an arched brow.

He frowned at her tone. 'I happen to like kids. Is there a law against it?'

'I thought playboys avoided them like the plague.'

He sent her an inscrutable sideways glance as he bent to tie his trainers. 'But I'm not a playboy now, am I? I'm a married man.'

'Only temporarily,' she reminded him, 'and only on paper,'

'That paper is already starting to burn at the edges,' he said as he straightened to look at her. 'Could be it's a pile of ashes by morning.'

Mia didn't answer but she felt a sensation of something hot

and liquid flood her lower body at his arrogantly confident statement. She had never met a more sexually compelling man in her entire life and she knew it would take every single gram of her will-power to resist him.

She swung away and began to walk at a brisk pace but within two strides he was alongside her, his beach towel rolled up under one arm.

'Do you fancy a walk through the park or have you had enough exercise for the day?' he asked as they came to the Noosa Heads Surf Life-Saving Club building.

Mia would have loved a cool shower but the thought of going back to the house with him where they would be on their own was a lot more disturbing than a walk through the national park, where at least there would be others about.

'I'd love to,' she said. 'I cut my run short. I only ran as far as Winch Cove as I was getting so hot. I came back through the bush.'

'We can walk to Alexandria Bay for a swim if you like. There are usually less people there, as it's a bit further along the circuit.'

'That sounds good.'

'Wait here while I get us some water to carry,' he said as they came to a shop.

Mia waited as he purchased some bottled water and they were soon on their way, walking in silence under the shade of the eucalypts that fringed the walkway to the national park.

They were not far from Boiling Pot when Bryn took her arm to stall her. 'Look,' he said, pointing above their heads.

She looked up and saw a mother koala perched in the fork of a eucalypt, a tiny baby clutching at her back.

'Oh, wow!' she said excitedly. 'Aren't they adorable?'

Bryn smiled at her. 'This is a natural habitat for them. I occasionally see them in my garden but they generally avoid suburbia if there are dogs about.'

'It's so wonderful to see them out in the wild instead of behind bars at the zoo,' she said as they continued walking along the path.

'Zoos have their place,' he said. 'Think about all the breeding programmes that have been set up specifically to protect endangered species.'

'I know but it seems so sad that animals can't run free as they are meant to do. My sister Ellie is a bit of an animal-rights campaigner. She's told me horror stories of what some people do to animals for financial gain. I had no idea people could be so cruel. I wonder if their conscience ever bothers them at night.'

'It takes all types, I guess,' he agreed, suppressing an inward frown.

They walked on a bit further until they came to Dolphin Point. Mia joined some other tourists who were peering over the cliff to see if there were any dolphins about, but as far as she could tell there was no sign of any in amongst the rolling waves.

'Have you seen any there before?' she asked Bryn as they continued on.

'Sometimes—that's why it's called Dolphin Point. There are several whale-watching tours you can take on the Sunshine Coast, and you often can see dolphins on them as well as humpback whales.'

'I went on one of those the last time I came here,' she said with a wry grimace. 'I was seasick the whole time. I had to be taken to hospital to be rehydrated. Ellie was totally disgusted with me for spoiling the trip.'

'Well, I guess I'd better strike that off the entertainment list for this week.'

'Oh, I'm much better now,' she said. 'I've been out sailing with friends lots of times and haven't had any trouble.'

'You sound like you have a very busy social life.'

She sent him a reproachful little glance from beneath her brows. 'Yes, well, I used to.'

'Just because we are married doesn't mean you can't have friends.'

'But no male friends, right?'

He stopped walking, snagging her arm before she could go on without him. He turned her around to face him, his fingers sliding down to the slender bones of her wrist. 'Male friends are fine if they remain platonic, although I still find it hard to believe any man could look at you without thinking how it would feel to make love to you.'

Mia felt her skin lift as his dark eyes ran over her, all her senses going on full alert at the feel of his long fingers around her wrist, where she was sure he could feel her pulses already leaping.

'Not all men have an insatiable appetite for sex,' she said. 'And the ones I associate with would never dream of tainting our friendship with repeated attempts to get me into bed.'

He gave a little grunt of cynicism. 'That's only because they're probably gay or already involved with someone else. Anyone else would have to be dead from the waist down not to notice you and want to have you as soon as they could.'

Mia felt as if the hot summer air was alive with bristling tension as she held his gaze. His desire for her was like a living, breathing entity. She could feel it burning through her skin where his fingers encircled her wrist, and she knew if it hadn't been for the sound of other hikers coming towards them on the track he would have pulled her into his arms and kissed her senseless. And what was more—she wouldn't have stopped him.

He released her wrist and stepped aside to make room for the tourists, the frustration at being interrupted evident to her in the way his jaw was set, even though he offered the group a polite greeting in response to theirs.

He waited until the group was well ahead before he resumed walking, asking after a few more strides, 'Were you disappointed none of your family could make it to the wedding?'

Mia quickly averted her gaze to look at Granite Bay, a small, rocky beach below them. 'No, why should I be? It wasn't as if it were real. Who knows, our marriage could even be over before they get back? I could probably have got away with not telling them at all.'

He gave her another sideways glance, a small frown settling between his brows. 'When did you tell them?'

She met his eyes briefly before turning to concentrate on stepping over the tree roots on the sandy pathway. 'The day before the ceremony.'

'Hardly enough time for them to get back,' he observed. 'Why did you leave it until then?'

'I hated lying to them. I wasn't sure I'd be able to pull it off in front of them on the day. A last-minute telephone conversation was much easier to handle. I figured there was no way they could get back in time and see the truth for themselves. I can act in front of strangers, even some friends, but my family is another thing entirely.'

Bryn frowned as she walked ahead, her back stiff as she strode out to put as much distance as she could between them. His fairly limited experience of family life had made him insensitive to what she might have felt lying to her family and friends about their relationship. He'd assumed the money he was offering her would settle any of her misgivings, but it was clear she was having a hard time of it now.

His conscience gave him another sharp nudge. He had sought a quick-fix solution to his own problems without truly considering the impact on her. Yes, he'd achieved his goal of fulfilling his great-aunt's dream for him, also securing her considerable estate, but what about Mia's hopes and dreams? He'd crushed them with a few ill-chosen words, got her removed from the company, dropped by her agent and practically blackmailed her into a temporary marriage with him.

A marriage she couldn't wait to get out of.

He drew in a breath that felt like pain at the thought of their marriage ending soon. He'd become used to having her around to spar with him. He'd also become a little too used to having her soft mouth beneath his. But the terms he'd laid down were temporary. As soon as his great-aunt passed away Mia would be free to move on.

But what if their marriage was no longer temporary? What if their relationship was no longer just an act, but real and vibrant and passionately fulfilling for both of them?

She said she hated him but he knew in spite of it she was attracted to him. What would it take to get her to agree to a more permanent relationship with him?

He lengthened his stride and caught up with her. 'Do you remember when I said no one thought I'd ever go through with marriage?'

She turned to look at him. 'Yes…'

'The truth is, Mia, if you hadn't come along when you did I probably would never have married.'

Mia wasn't sure where this was leading. 'You have something against marriage?' she asked.

'Not entirely,' he said. 'I recognise that it occasionally works, but close to fifty per cent of marriages end in divorce, often acrimoniously. I wasn't sure I wanted to add to the stats.'

Her forehead creased in a frown as she pointed out, 'But you're going to add to them anyway now that you've married me temporarily.'

His dark gaze was trained on hers. 'If we divorce we don't have to do it acrimoniously.'

'*If?*' She gave him a startled look. 'What do you mean, if?'

'When you think about it there's at least a fifty per cent chance of things working out between us,' he said.

'One has to really admire your optimism but I'm afraid in this case it's totally inappropriate.'

'What? You don't think we could make a go of it? Arranged marriages are conducted all over the world where the couple neither like nor know each other initially and yet many of them go on to live very happy lives together.'

'Arranged marriages are an insult to women!' she said, beginning to stomp along the path once more. 'It's utterly barbaric to be forced into a marriage with a perfect stranger or someone decades older than you.'

'Marriages have been arranged for centuries,' he countered as he worked hard to keep pace. 'In fact, the notion of a couple falling in love and marrying is a very recent one. Before about two hundred years ago couples married for political reasons or for the sake of securing family property and asset-building or to strengthen community relationships. Of course, affection often occurred in ages past but it wasn't a given.'

'I always knew you were living in the Dark Ages. Where exactly did you get your doctorate in chauvinism?'

He smiled at her sarcasm. 'I'm just quoting history, Mia. Our marriage has just as much chance of being successful as any other; in fact, it may even have more chance.'

'I can't imagine how you came to that conclusion,' she said

as she pushed a broken melaleuca branch out of her way. 'I dislike you intensely and I can't see that changing unless you undergo some sort of immediate character reconstruction.'

'As I said previously—you might think differently after a few days alone with me.'

'If the last twenty-four hours is any indication I'm afraid you're in for a big disappointment if you're expecting me to subscribe to your fan club.'

'Look, Mia, I'm just asking you to try and get to know me as you would any other person. You're so prejudiced against me you can't see me for who I am.'

'Here we go again.' She rolled her eyes expressively as she turned back to face him, her hands on her hips. 'The replay of the I'm-nothing-like-my-public-persona speech. Give me a break.'

'Damn it, Mia,' his voice rose in frustration, 'why won't you just give us a chance?' His dark eyes held hers. 'Will you at least consider the possibility of our marriage becoming a little more permanent?'

'Define what you mean by a little more permanent. Are you talking months or years?'

'I'm talking about you sleeping with me.'

It was a moment or two before she could get her voice into gear. 'I see.'

'I want you, Mia. You know that. I've wanted you from the moment I met you.'

The silence of the bush surrounded them, closing in on them until Mia felt as she was being cut off from the rest of civilisation.

She was alone with him, alone with him and her unruly, traitorous desire for him, which was getting harder by the second to control.

'You only want me because I'm the first woman to have said no to you.'

'That's not true,' he said. 'It's much more than that.'

'You're surely not going to tell me you've suddenly discovered you're in love with me,' she said with a brittle look. 'That would be about as low as anyone could go.'

He took a moment to answer, his expression giving little away. 'I have some feelings for you, yes.'

'No doubt lust is at the top of the list.'

'It's up there, yes, but so too are admiration and respect. That's more than I've felt for anyone else in the past.'

'Wow, I feel really honoured,' she said mockingly. 'I bet you say that to all the girls when you set out to seduce them.'

'I'm not trying to seduce you for the heck of it, Mia,' he said. 'I really want a relationship with you.'

'A *temporary* relationship,' she put in. 'Where you get to wave the chequered flag when it's all over—when you get bored or find someone else a little more interesting.'

He didn't answer immediately and it made Mia wonder if he did in fact care something for her. She unconsciously held her breath as his eyes shifted away from hers to stare out to sea. He turned back to her after a moment and handed her one of the bottles of water he was carrying. 'I can't promise you forever, no one can.'

'What exactly are you offering?'

'A relationship for as long as it works for us.'

'So at the first rocky patch we encounter you'll be off to find your next candidate.'

'All I'm asking is for you to think about it, Mia. We're in this marriage for the time being and it makes sense to put in some kind of effort to see if it could work out between us.'

'I can't see how two people who hate each other can make a go of marriage, especially considering the way ours came about.'

'You don't really hate me. I admit you've done a great job of acting like you do but I see the way you look at me when you think I'm not watching. You're seriously attracted to me.'

Her eyes shifted away from his. 'You're imagining it.'

'Am I?'

'Of course.'

'Little liar,' he said, capturing her chin to force her to meet his eyes. 'You want me just as much as I want you. I can see it in those big grey eyes of yours.'

Mia could feel her heart begin to thud when he pulled her closer, his arms coming around her to hold her to his hard frame. His bare chest was hot and slick against hers as his mouth came down on hers, searing her with a kiss full of erotic promise. His tongue was hot and hard as it thrust through the shield of her lips, curling around hers and urging it into a sensual dance that was totally irresistible. A deep ache of longing pulsed low in her belly, the feel of his aroused length pressed up against her increasing her desire to a point where she completely forgot they were standing in the middle of a bush track where anyone could see them.

The sound of approaching footsteps finally broke them apart. Mia stood flushed and unsteady on her feet before him, her eyes lowering from the heat and fire still burning in his.

'We should press on,' Bryn said, stepping back from her. 'There are other people heading our way. We can finish this later.'

The promise in his words left her breathless with fevered anticipation as she tried to get her legs to follow where he was leading. All her reasons for resisting him were being obliterated by her need to feel his mouth on hers again. She craved to feel his hands on her body—all of her body—his caressing touch preparing her for the most thrilling intimacy of all. She could almost feel his hard, thick presence between her thighs as she tried to negotiate the uneven path on her increasingly unsteady legs. A pulse was still beating deep inside her, made all the more insistent when she fell into step behind him as the length of his long, muscled legs and firm buttocks kept reminding her of how very male he was and how he affected her in a way no man had ever done before.

They passed a few other hikers and just when she thought she would pass out from a combination of the heat of the sun and the burning desire he had activated, he indicated the path down to Alexandria Bay. 'Fancy a quick swim to cool off?'

She looked at the sparkling blue water of the bay and sighed with relief. 'I can think of nothing better.'

They made their way down the path to the beach, where the waves were crashing against the shore. They weren't the only people on the beach but it took Mia a moment to realise the other sun-seekers weren't wearing bathers.

'Uh-oh,' she said, quickly turning her back.

'What's wrong?' Bryn asked as he heeled himself out of his trainers.

'Those people…' She indicated with a quick flap of her hand behind her and whispered in an undertone, *'They're naked.'*

'I know.'

*'You know?'*

'Of course,' he said, stripping himself of his board shorts and tossing them to the sand at his feet. 'This is an officially recognised naturist beach.'

She forced her gaze upwards with an effort. 'I'm not taking my clothes off.'

'You don't have to if you don't want to.' He strode off

towards the surf while she was still standing there open-mouthed at the taut line of his back and buttocks.

She watched as he entered the turbulent water, cutting through it effortlessly as he swam out beyond the breakers, his broad, tanned back glistening in the sun.

She sucked in a ragged breath as the sun beat down on her, rivulets of perspiration trickling down between her breasts and thighs. The thought of dispensing with her shorts and top and even her skimpy bikini was suddenly very tempting. It wasn't as if she hadn't skinny-dipped before. Of course, skinny-dipping when you were with a group of girlfriends at a twelfth birthday party, at the dead of night in a small backyard pool when there wasn't a male in sight wasn't quite in the same league as this, but maybe she needed to show Bryn she wasn't the uptight little virginal prude he thought she was.

She stripped off her shorts and flung her T-shirt to the sand and with a deep breath reached behind her to untie her bikini top. She watched as it fell in a little heap on the sand and with another deep breath her hands went to her hips and tugged downwards…

# CHAPTER TWELVE

THE water was like chilled champagne against her hot, sticky skin, the turbulent waves breaking over her like thousands of tiny, effervescent bubbles. The wildness of it was exhilarating and so too was the thought that nothing separated her from the feel of the ocean's deep, rhythmic pulse on her body. Her bikini was hardly what anyone would have described as conservative, but bathing without the barrier of fabric was intensely sensual, especially knowing that Bryn was only a few metres away, and the same water that was moving against and over her body was touching him as well.

She caught sight of him diving under a wave before resurfacing to swim out a bit further, his strong, muscled body making light work of the powerful surf.

Mia was a confident and competent swimmer but she could already feel the heavy undertow dragging at her legs and decided against joining him. She body-surfed a few smaller waves before making her way back to her things on the sand, relieved to see the other people had moved further along the beach.

Once she was back in her bikini she sat watching the pounding surf, her thoughts drifting to her earlier conversation with Bryn. His shock announcement about their marriage continuing for an unspecified period of time had thrown her completely. He had made his motives very clear; he wanted her—but for how long? He hadn't put an exact time frame on it, probably because he couldn't see their relationship lasting longer than a week or two; a month if she was lucky. He would no doubt slake his lust for her and within weeks she would be left with nothing but the memories and heartbreak.

She frowned as she thought about his past, how losing his parents so young had made him wary of committing himself emotionally, as his great-aunt had indicated the day Mia had visited her.

Would it be possible to remove the armour from around his heart? Was she in fact the special woman Agnes Dwyer already believed her to be?

She suppressed a deep sigh of remorse over the deception she had been complicit in. She had always hated all forms of deceit, it went against everything she'd been taught. And certainly lying to an old lady seemed particularly immoral, but what if she could change that right now? All she had to do was agree to make their marriage a real one. The lies she'd told her parents and sisters would no longer be lies. What had begun as a lie would now be the truth. She loved him and, while he was uncertain about his feelings for her, perhaps in time she could teach him that loving someone wasn't always painful and unpredictable.

She watched as he came out of the water to join her, his tall naked body making her breath hitch in her throat. How could she have ever thought she would be able to resist him?

'Did you enjoy your swim?' he asked, showering her with droplets of sea water as he sat down next to her on the sand.

She kept her gaze averted and toyed with the sand near her toes. 'Yes, I did.'

He brushed one finger along the heightened colour of her cheek. 'You're blushing.'

'I'm not used to sitting next to naked men.'

He lay back on the sand and closed his eyes against the glare of the sun. 'You never know, you might get used to it in time.'

Mia sneaked a look at him, her belly doing a little flip-flop all over again. His abdominal muscles were sculptured to perfection; they were like tight rods of steel under the smooth tanned skin, the sprinkling of masculine dark hair that spread from his belly button over his pelvis and down his long strong legs making her skin crawl with the need to feel it rasping against her smoother softness.

He opened one eye and caught her staring at him but before she could turn away he caught her hand and brought it to his chest. She could feel the deep thud of his heart beneath her palm and her own heart started to race when he began to move her hand downwards.

'What are you doing?' she gasped and tried to jerk away.

He held her firm, his gaze locking with hers. 'I want you to feel what you do to me.'

She swallowed as her palm came over his growing hardness, the feel of him swelling beneath her tentative touch making her stomach flutter and her legs go weak. She heard him suck in a sharp breath as she began to explore him and another wave of deep longing rushed through her. His erection was like satin-covered steel, the pulsing heat in her hands making her feel powerful in a way she had never felt before. She looked down at him encased in her slim fingers, the latent power of his body totally under her command. She saw the tiny, pearly bead of moisture starting to pool at the head and her entire body shivered with a thousand tickling fingers of desire.

He let out another deep groan, removed her hand and brought it above her head as he turned her on her back so he could lean over her, his head blocking the sun as his lips found hers.

It was a deeply sensual kiss, unhurried, lazy almost, but no less enthralling. Mia could feel the delicious tension building in her body, the sun's warm rays on her legs and arms making her feel increasingly uninhibited as she responded to each slow-moving glide of his tongue against hers. She sighed with pleasure when he released her bikini top, his warm hand taking the weight of her breast, his thumb rolling over the already puckering nipple.

He lifted his mouth from hers to kiss his way down her neck to each breast, his lips and tongue inciting her desire for him to an almost unbearable level. He suckled and kissed each breast in turn, his teeth grazing her sensitised flesh, making her wriggle until she was beneath him properly, the pressure of his weight as his legs entrapped hers in a steely embrace sending her senses skyrocketing. His erection probed against the barrier of her bikini bottoms, the sensation of him being so intimately close but blocked by just a tiny scrap of fabric making her want him all the more.

His mouth left her breast and his eyes came back to hers, their dark blue depths smouldering with pent-up need. 'We can't do this here, sweetheart.'

Mia blinked up at him. 'W-we can't?'

His mouth twisted ruefully. 'This is a public beach and even though it's practically deserted I don't happen to have a condom on me right now.'

'Oh…'

He tipped up her chin and pressed another hot, lingering kiss to her lips. 'Let's go back to the house and begin our honeymoon properly.' He saw the tiny flicker of doubt come and go in her eyes and added softly, 'That's if you want to. The decision is yours, Mia. If you don't feel ready then that's fine.'

Mia held his gaze, finally realising now she'd never really had a chance in refusing him. She wanted him so much she

wasn't sure how she was going to make the journey back to
his house, her limbs felt so weak with her need of him. She
was surprised he couldn't see her love for him shining from
her eyes every time they came in contact with his.

'I want you to make love to me,' she said on a husky
whisper of sound.

His eyes were unwavering on hers. 'Are you sure?'

'Yes.'

He got to his feet and offered her a hand, pulling her up to
stand in front of him. He didn't say anything, just stood looking
down at her up-tilted face for what seemed a very long time.

Mia wondered if he was inwardly gloating about her ac-
quiescence but if he was there was no sign of it on his face.
After a moment he appeared to give himself a mental shake
and stepped away to pick up his board shorts, dusting the sand
off his body before he put them back on and then rolling up
the towel they'd been lying on.

She picked up her bikini top and once she was dressed
fell into step beside him as they returned to the path that led
the way back.

They walked in silence for most of the way. Mia was aware
of Bryn's hand reaching for hers now and again when the
width of the path allowed it, but apart from the occasional
comment about the view or wildlife he seemed to be preoc-
cupied with his own thoughts.

When the house finally came into view he suggested she
have a shower while he made them both some lunch.

She looked at him in uncertainty. 'But I thought you
wanted to…you know…'

'I do,' he said and pushed the door open for her. 'But
you've had nothing but a few mouthfuls of fruit and water all
day. I don't want you fainting on me.'

She was conscious of his gaze following her up the stairs and turned to look at him when she got to the landing.

'Mia?'

'Yes?'

He seemed about to say something then changed his mind. 'It doesn't matter. Go and have your shower. We can talk later.'

She gave him a tremulous smile and went into the bathroom.

When she came downstairs half an hour later Bryn had also showered and changed into shorts and a T-shirt. He looked up from the salad and cheese and cold-meat platter he was assembling as she came into the kitchen. 'Would you like a glass of wine?'

'Sure, why not?'

He handed her two glasses of chilled white wine. 'Take those out to the deck and I'll bring our lunch out.'

The deck was set amongst the trees and overlooked the pool and lower garden. Some rainbow lorikeets were jostling just a few feet away and Mia began hunting the upper limbs of the trees for any sign of koalas.

'Have you found any?' Bryn asked as he set the lunch platter down on the table.

'Not as yet,' she said, reaching for her wine. She took a tiny sip and let out a breath of delight. 'This is such a lovely setting. It feels as if the bush is an extension of the house.'

He smiled and took the seat opposite, lifting his glass to hers. 'What shall we drink to?'

'Dutch courage?' she suggested after a moment.

His expression softened as he held her gaze. 'Don't be nervous, Mia. I won't hurt you. I promise.'

She gave her bottom lip a little nibble and then, releasing it, confessed, 'I can't help it.'

He put down his glass and reached for her hand, his fingers strong but gentle as they entwined with hers. 'Trust me, Mia. I know what I'm doing.'

'I know this is stupid but I can't help thinking I'll disappoint you. You've had millions of lovers. What if I don't…you know…satisfy you?'

'Not quite millions,' he said, smiling at her little furrowed brow. 'How could you ever think that you won't satisfy me? You're so damned sexy I can barely keep my hands off you. I know you and I are going to be dynamite together. I can feel it every time you touch me. I was ready to explode on that beach with your soft little fingers crawling all over me.'

Mia felt a warm glow at his words. Never had a man made her feel more like a woman. He only had to look at her with those dark blue eyes and her flesh began to tingle all over. The thought of him possessing her thrilled her until she could barely sit still on the seat.

He took another sip of wine, his gaze thoughtful and steady on hers. 'I still find it hard to believe you haven't had a lover before now.'

She pushed at a bit of salad with her fork. 'When I was seventeen a close friend of mine contracted a sexually transmitted disease. It was so awful for her. To make matters worse the boy who gave it to her blamed her and started spreading rumours. In the end she had to change schools.' She gave a little sigh and added, 'I guess I've always been a little bit afraid of getting hurt since then.'

He reached for her hand, his long fingers interlinking with hers. 'I have always practised safe sex. I absolutely insist on it no matter what the circumstances. It's not fair on either partner to be landed with a disease or a pregnancy that wasn't planned, not that accidents don't happen, of course, but at least there are ways to deal with it these days.'

'If an accident did happen...' she stared down at the table in front of her rather than meet his eyes '...what would you expect me to do about it?'

He thought about it for a moment and in the end didn't answer her question but asked one of his own. 'What would you want to do?'

'I guess you can already tell I've had a pretty conservative upbringing,' she said. 'There are no doubt circumstances when a termination seems like the only option, but having an adopted sister has made me realise that even if a baby is unwanted by its natural parent or parents there are plenty of other people who do want it and would love it as dearly as their own.'

Bryn sat in silence, thinking about the gentle, loving wisdom behind her convictions.

'But don't worry,' she added with a little upwards glance before looking down again to rearrange the food on her plate, 'I'm on a low-dose Pill to regulate my cycle. There won't be any little accidents.'

'If there were I would not expect you to do anything you weren't comfortable doing,' he said. 'I would support you through whatever decision you felt was appropriate.'

She brought her gaze back up to his, surprised by his sincerity. 'Thank you.'

He sat watching her playing with her food, his own meal barely touched.

'You're not eating,' he said after a short, throbbing silence.

'I'm not all that hungry for some reason...'

'I am,' he said, his dark eyes glittering with desire. 'But not for food.'

He got to his feet and came around to where she was sitting, and, taking her hand, in his brought her to her feet. He bent his head and kissed her deeply, the rasp of his skin against the softness of hers making her tingle all over with fevered longing.

By the time they got to his bedroom Mia was breathless with anticipation, every nerve and pulse leaping under her skin in growing excitement. Tension crackled in the air as he closed the door and came towards her, his hands gently removing her sarong from around her chest. She felt the soft-as-air fabric glide down her body to land in a circle at her feet.

His eyes ran over her naked breasts before he cupped their light weight in his hands. She could hardly breathe with him so close, the pulse of his aroused body pressing against her.

He released her briefly to tug his T-shirt over his head, tossing it to one side as he stepped out of his shorts and briefs. She gave a tiny swallow as he came back to her, his fingers untying the strings that held her bikini bottoms in place.

Without a word he lifted her in his arms and carried her to the white expanse of the bed, laying her down before joining her, his weight balanced by his arms.

His mouth found hers, softly at first and then with increasing pressure, taking her on a sensual journey that totally captivated her. His mouth moved from hers to scorch a pathway to her breasts, the hot lave of his tongue turning her insides to liquid heat. He travelled lower, exploring the dip of her belly button before his warm breath feathered over the tiny landing strip of soft, dark blonde, closely cropped curls that shielded her femininity. With the gentlest touch possible he parted her delicate folds before tasting her with his mouth. The sensation of his tongue against her arched her back and made her whimper in intense pleasure, her hands clutching at his shoulders.

'Relax for me, baby,' he coached her softly. 'Let yourself go.'

'I can't…'

'Yes, you can,' he said. 'I want to pleasure you.'

'But I want you to…to…be inside me.'

He moved back up her body with slow but exquisite caresses, building her need of him to fever pitch. Each stroke of his hands along the flanks of her thighs, each hot, moist kiss to the indentation of her waist and each tender suckle on her breasts made her nearly mad with the need for more. Just when she thought she could stand it no longer he reached between her legs, gently easing her apart to insert one finger, waiting until she was comfortable before deepening his tender stroke, the silky dew of her desire making it easier and easier for her to accept him further.

'Oh, God…' she breathed, writhing beneath his touch.

'You feel so warm and wet,' he said, his voice low and deep, his breath like a caress on her skin. 'You're so ready for me.'

He leaned across her to the bedside drawer and took out a condom. She watched with bated breath as he applied it, coming back to position himself over her.

'Tell me to stop if it hurts.'

'I will…'

He moved against her, parting her to take him partially, waiting for her to accommodate him before going further.

'Are you OK?' he asked.

'Yes…'

He hesitated. 'Are you sure?'

'I'm sure…'

He moved slowly, holding back as her tight body wrapped itself around him. He felt her flinch and stalled again. 'Did that hurt?'

'No…not really.'

'God, Mia,' he groaned and began to withdraw. 'I wish I could do this but I can't bear to hurt you.'

Mia clutched at him to hold him in place. 'You're not hurting me; I like it. I like the feel of you. Please don't stop.' She saw his throat move up and down as he looked at her. 'Please, Bryn, I want this. I want you to make love to me.'

Bryn hesitated but she lifted her hips against him and he was lost as he surged against her, sheathing himself in the tight, moist cocoon of her body. He tried to move slowly but she wouldn't allow it, her hands digging into his buttocks to increase his pace. He fought to keep control but she was urging him on, her panting little cries of pleasure as he thrust deeper and deeper making his heart contract with totally unfamiliar feelings. He shifted position so she could feel him more intensely, caressing her with his fingers to take her to the summit with him so he could feel the contractions of her orgasm to finally push him over the edge. He could feel the pulse of her body as it built in arousal, her slim limbs wrapping around him, holding on tight for the rapidly approaching storm of sensation that threatened to burst at any moment.

Suddenly she was there, her high, keening cry of ecstasy washing over him as she convulsed against him, triggering his own release with an explosion of pleasure that lifted the hair on his scalp with its breathtaking force.

'Oh, wow…'she said on an expelled breath as her heart rate began to lower.

He dragged himself off her chest, where he'd collapsed, to smile down at her radiant face. 'Oh, wow?'

She returned his smile, two tiny dimples appearing either side of her mouth. 'Definitely oh, wow.'

'I didn't hurt you?'

'Not much.'

He frowned. 'I wanted to take things slowly. I didn't want to cause you any pain.'

'I'm fine, Bryn,' she reassured him. 'It was wonderful. You were wonderful. Thank you for being so gentle with me.'

He tucked a tendril of hair behind her ear, his eyes meshing with hers. 'I've never met anyone like you before. It felt different somehow.'

Hope fluttered inside Mia's chest at his unexpected confession. 'How?' she asked, hunting his face for a sign of what he was feeling.

'I've always experienced sex as a physical thing. I've always been able to keep emotions separate.'

'What are you trying to say?'

He released a sigh and pressed a soft kiss to her forehead, lifting his head to look down at her, a small frown bringing his brows almost together. 'I have no idea.'

She frowned as he lifted himself away. He was pulling away from her again. She could feel the barriers come up as if their intimacy had affected him more than he wanted to admit, to her certainly, but even, it seemed, to himself.

'Bryn?'

He turned back to look at her, his expression now stripped of all emotion. 'Sorry, Mia, I know this is the part where women like you expect a declaration of love, but I can't give it to you. I'd like to but I can't. It wouldn't be fair to you. I'm sorry.'

Mia felt as if someone had ripped open her chest and stomped heavily on her heart. 'I'm not looking for that from you,' she lied. 'I understand the terms of our relationship.'

He held her gaze for a lengthy moment. 'You deserve much better than me, Mia. You really do.'

She opened her mouth to respond but he turned and left the room, closing the door behind him.

She flopped back on the pillows in sinking despair. How would she ever find a way to his heart?

# CHAPTER THIRTEEN

IT WAS early evening before Mia saw him again. When she'd come downstairs he had already cleared the abandoned lunch things away and a brief note propped on the bench informed her he had gone back to the beach for a surf.

He came into the lounge just as she was leaving it, almost colliding with her in the doorway. He steadied her with his hands, looking down at her as if seeing her for the first time.

'Sorry,' she said. 'I didn't hear you come in.'

His gaze dipped to her mouth for a moment before returning to her grey eyes. His hands fell away from her shoulders and he moved further into the room, a hand making a rough pathway through his already disordered hair.

'Are you OK?' Mia asked.

He gave her a twisted smile as he turned to face her. 'I think I might have had too much sun.'

'Would you like me to get you some water?'

'No, I don't need water. I need my head read, that's what I need.'

She wasn't sure what to make of his mood. She stood in front of him uncertainly, beginning to worry her bottom lip with her teeth.

'Damn it, I wish you would stop doing that!' he said roughly.

She blinked at him in surprise. 'Stop doing what?'

'Everything.'

She frowned in confusion. 'Everything?'

He let out his breath in a stream. 'God, I must have been crazy that day. I should have known something like this would happen.' He sent his fingers through his sand-encrusted hair.

'What are you talking about?' she asked. 'Wh-what's happened?'

His eyes cut back to hers. 'Everything you do gets to me. Every look, every smile, and every word you say. It all gets to me.'

She lowered her eyes. 'I'm sorry…'

He stepped closer and forced her chin up to hold his gaze. 'I have spent most of the years of my life avoiding the complication of emotional entanglements and in one brief meeting with a feisty little fitness fanatic all my defences get knocked down.'

Mia stared at him speechlessly, her heart beginning to ram against her sternum. What was he saying? That he loved her after all? Hope began to flicker in her chest, the tiny, frantic, flapping wings of it making it hard for her to breathe properly.

'I promised myself I wouldn't touch you again after this afternoon,' he went on. 'It was wrong to touch you in the first place but I just couldn't seem to help myself. From the moment I met you I wanted you. I still want you but I can't give you what you deserve, what you've been brought up to expect, what is your right as a lovely young woman with a generous heart. You need someone with the capacity to love. I'm not that person.'

'How do you know you're not?' she asked.

'Mia, listen to me.' His hands tightened on her shoulders, the gravity of his expression unnerving her totally. 'I've never told this to anyone before.' He took a ragged breath and continued, 'Do you know what the last thing I said to my mother was the night she and my father were killed?'

She shook her head, tears starting to sprout in her eyes, her bottom lip trembling.

'They were going out to dinner together. My father was already in the car but my mother had turned back to give me one last cuddle. I told her I loved her.' His voice cracked over the words. 'I don't think I had ever said it before. I told her to tell my father I loved him too.'

'Oh, Bryn…' She choked back a sob.

'When the police came to our house where I was being looked after by a babysitter my whole world collapsed. If I hadn't called my mother back at that moment she and my father would still be alive. But I called her back and those few precious seconds it took to tell her I loved her cost her and my father their lives. I taught myself not to feel from that moment. It's like a switch was turned off inside me and I can no longer find where it is.'

'You just need to give yourself time… Your great-aunt's health is bringing it all back up for you. You're still grieving…you haven't dealt with the past and it's coming back to haunt you.'

'I don't want to deal with the past!' He threw the words at her as he released her almost savagely. 'It won't change a thing rehashing it all now.'

'But it won't go away just because you choose to ignore it. It will plague you all your life. You'll end up a lonely old man with nothing to show for your life. No fulfilling relationships, no children to love you.'

'I would hate any child of mine to go through what I did. It's just not worth the risk. Losing a parent is the most devastating thing that can happen to a child. Losing both of them in one fell swoop is beyond anything I can describe.'

'It might not happen. Just because you lost your parents in a tragic accident doesn't mean history will repeat itself.'

'Mia, you are the sweetest, most adorable person I've ever met,' he said, taking her by the shoulders again. 'If there was anyone I would be able to love, it is you. But I can't pretend to feel what is just not there.'

She let the tears fall unheeded, touched by his honesty in a way no one had ever touched her before. 'I love you enough for both of us… I thought I hated you at first but somehow it all changed, and I can't turn it off.'

He gave her one of his twisted smiles. 'We're an odd couple, aren't we? You have too much love to give and I don't have any.'

'You do but you can't recognise it,' she said. 'You won't allow yourself to become vulnerable but that's what life is all about. You hide your feelings behind a façade of biting cynicism, taking pot-shots at whoever comes across your path. Your public reputation is built on that but I know now it isn't really who you are as a person. Inside is a deeply sensitive, caring man who is just too afraid to love again in case it gets snatched away.'

'I can't give you what you want. I know I can't.'

'I haven't even told you what I want, so how can you say that?'

He let out a sigh and rested his chin on the top of her head. 'What do you want, Mia?'

She hugged him to her in a desperate effort to get close to him. 'I want you. Only you. For as long as you'll have me.'

He eased her away from him to look deep into her tear-washed eyes. 'You're prepared to risk being hurt by me?'

'I'm prepared to be vulnerable because that's what love is all about.'

'Even if I can never find that switch inside of me?'

She linked her arms around his neck and brought his mouth down to hers. 'Don't worry, I'll find it. You've just been looking in all the wrong places.'

Her lips were so soft and yielding he had no choice but to respond even though his common sense told him to let her go before he damaged her permanently. He sank into her warmth, his arms tightening around her, fighting for the control he had always taken for granted in the past. Something about Mia touched him where no one else had ever been. He couldn't put his finger on exactly what it was but he felt as if she lightened the load he had been carrying for so long.

He pushed her back towards the sofa, his hands going to her sarong, releasing it so he could suckle on her small but perfect breasts. Her little gasps of delight released a trickle of sensation deep inside him; she was so responsive to his touch, as if she had been waiting for him all this time.

He carried her to the bedroom, laying her down only long enough to get a condom. She writhed against him, wanting more and he gave it unreservedly. He dispensed with the rest of her clothes and sank into her with a single thrust that he should have checked but somehow couldn't. She welcomed him with silky moistness, the delicate fragrance of her need filling his nostrils. He drove a little harder, hoping she wasn't still tender from earlier but unable to pull back the pace. He could feel the pressure building around him, hers mingling with his in an erotic pulse that grew more frantic by the second. He struggled to hold back but she was with him all the way, arching her back to receive each deep surge of his body, her gasping cries like a haunting tune he had been searching for all his life but never found until this moment. She went soaring a few moments ahead of him, the tight clench of her feminine form leaving him no choice but to follow in a rush of feeling that threatened to overwhelm him. He felt the explosion of his life force within her, the emptying of himself beyond anything he had ever experienced before.

It was a long time before he could find the strength to speak and the only thing he could think of to say was, 'Oh, wow…'

Mia smiled up at him. 'Oh, wow?'

He kissed the tip of her nose. 'You are very definitely an "oh, wow" sort of lover.'

*Even though you don't love me*, Mia thought sadly.

Bryn brought her close, tucking her head against his chest, his fingers splaying through her hair, wondering if he could ever find the words to tell her what he had done to bring about their relationship. His immediate lust for her had overridden every other consideration; he had not stopped to weigh up the cost if she in the end proved to be someone very special.

And very special she was.

In a way he had never expected.

He had not thought it possible to trust life enough to care for someone unreservedly, but somehow Mia had invaded his emotional firewall, finding a way to his heart that no one had ever done before.

He had told her bluntly and rather clinically he could not offer her a declaration of love but what if what she'd said was true? That he was unable to recognise his true feelings for fear of life hurting him the way it had in the past?

He had definitely felt something from the very first moment he'd met her—her sparkling defiance had got his notice, but so too had her spirit and her big heart, not to mention her passion and zest for life. Every time she looked up at him with her beautiful, elfin face with those big grey eyes he felt that tiny fish-hook tug on him deep inside his chest. Was that love, the sort of love that could last a lifetime?

In spite of her dislike for him she had agreed to marry him for the sake of his great-aunt. She hadn't done it for the money; she had done it out of the kindness of her heart. She gave of herself so generously, laying herself bare for him even though he had offered her nothing in terms of emotional commitment.

He recalled all the bitter mornings-after he'd endured in the past; women who had wanted much more than he'd been prepared to give, one even stalking him relentlessly, making his life unbearable for a time.

Mia, on the other hand, was a young woman who was prepared to love him unconditionally. She'd agreed to his conditions and with grace and dignity accepted them.

He wished he could be truly honest with her but the thought of her finding out how he had engineered their marriage made him baulk. How on earth could he frame the words in any way that would make them less offensive to her? He had swept her career out of his way with a sleight of hand that was no less than despicable.

He was still thinking about how best to make it up to her when his mobile phone rang. He kept Mia close to him, his hand on the back of her silky head as he reached for it, the voice on the other end informing him of the one thing he had been dreading and yet preparing himself for over the last few months.

'What's wrong?' Mia asked as he put the phone down a few seconds later.

His voice was flat and emotionless as he informed her, 'My great-aunt slipped into a coma a short time ago. She's not expected to come out of it.'

Her face fell, sending yet another dagger to his heart. 'Oh, no…'

'We'll have to fly back in the morning,' he said, moving away before she could reach for him to offer comfort. It didn't seem right to be accepting her comfort when she had no idea of how he had acted. He felt tainted with it, hating himself, hating his vulnerability where she was concerned. Hating that life yet again was letting him down and there was nothing he could do to stop it.

'Bryn…I'm so sorry… Is there anything I can do?'

'No,' he said, a shutter seeming to come down over his features as he faced her. 'I'll re-book the flights on line. You go to bed. You look tired.'

'But I'm not tired,' Mia insisted. 'I want to be with you to help you through this.'

'I don't want company right now.' He turned to look out of the window. 'Please leave me to deal with this on my own.'

'I don't think you should be alone at a time like this,' she said softly. 'I want to support you and—'

'Didn't you hear what I said?' He swung around to glare at her. 'I said, I want to be alone.'

Mia stood her ground, even though her legs were quaking at the burning glitter in his eyes. 'You can't push me away. I want to be with you. I love you. This is what love is about, supporting and helping when things are tough.'

'Leave me alone, damn you!' He grabbed her by the arm and led her to the door, almost shoving her through. 'I don't need you. I don't need anyone.'

The door slammed in her face and her shoulders slumped in defeat. She heard the sound of a glass smashing against the wall and then nothing but silence. An empty, aching silence that tore at her heart for what he was going through.

Alone.

She went upstairs and, going to his room, quietly packed his bag before going to do her own. She sat on the edge of her bed and stared at her hands where his rings encircled her finger.

It would soon be over.

He didn't need her any more.

His great-aunt was close to death so the final curtain would soon be coming down on their act. In spite of what he'd said about continuing their relationship for a period of time she knew their temporary marriage was now coming to an end.

Bryn barely spoke to her on the way back to Sydney the next morning. He sat staring out of the window for the entire flight, even ignoring the air steward's offer of refreshments.

After they collected their baggage they drove in silence to the palliative-care unit. Mia glanced at him several times but his face was set in the same impenetrable mask, no hint of emotion showing.

Agnes was lying like a thin shadow on the bed, her chest rising and falling so slowly it looked as if she was hardly breathing at all.

The doctor spoke to Bryn in an office further down the hall while Mia sat by the bedside, holding the thin, papery hand and wishing with all her heart she could make things right for both of them.

When Bryn came back she gave up her seat for him so he could be near his great-aunt. He gave her the flicker of a grateful smile and sat down, reaching for the limp hand on the bed.

Mia stood behind him, gently massaging his shoulders as he leaned forward in the chair, his voice low and deep as he spoke to his great-aunt. 'I'm here, Aunt Aggie. Mia and I are here.'

The day passed slowly, the clock on the wall measuring time as if heavy weights were attached to its hands, each minute crawling by, each hour turning over like a month instead of sixty minutes.

\* \* \*

There was no change in Agnes's condition over the next five days. Bryn spent as much time at the hospital as he could, sitting by his great-aunt's bedside until it was time to broadcast his radio show. While he was on air Mia sat by the bedside, stroking the thin hand of his great-aunt, listening to the radio playing softly in the background, amazed at how normal and unaffected Bryn seemed. The show must go on, she thought as she watched the shallow rise and fall of his dying relative's chest. No one would ever know what he was dealing with in his private life. His lively banter with the people he interviewed and the upbeat music he played gave no clue to the grief he was privately preparing himself for. He spoke of their honeymoon as if it had been the most wonderful experience of his life and yet she knew it was all an act, for he had no such feelings for her. At least he had been totally honest with her. So many men wouldn't have been. How many times had previous boyfriends declared their undying affection for her, only to walk away without a backward glance when she refused to sleep with them?

No, at least Bryn had been honest from the word go. He had told her he needed her to act the role of his fiancée and wife for his great-aunt's benefit as well as his ratings. He hadn't pretended anything he didn't feel and, even though it was heartbreakingly disappointing, in a way she was grateful he had been so up-front about it. If only she had more time to let her love for him heal the hurt he'd carried for so long, maybe then he would open up to the possibility of a permanent future together.

'How is she?' Bryn asked softly when he came in later that evening.

Mia made room beside the bed for him. 'The doctor was

in a while ago,' she said, swallowing back the emotion. 'It's not looking good, Bryn. He doesn't think it will be long now.'

He placed his hand against the nape of her neck, his warm palm easing the stiffness that had gathered there from sitting so long. 'Why don't you go home and get some sleep? You've been here for hours.'

'I'm fine…I just didn't want her to be alone…'

'I'm here now,' he said. 'I'll call Henry to take you home.'

'No, please, let me stay,' she said, looking up at him. 'Please?'

His hand came around from her nape to gently cradle her cheek, his thumb stroking the creamy softness as he looked into her shining with moisture eyes. 'You really do love me, don't you?'

She gave him a wobbly smile. 'Yes…I do.'

There was a long, intense pause as he held her gaze.

'Mia,' he said, stopping to clear his throat. 'There's something I need to tell you—'

There was a sudden beeping from the monitor attached to Agnes's chest, signalling her heart was failing.

Two nurses and a doctor came rushing in but there was nothing they could do.

Agnes Gabriella Dwyer died at seven twenty-three that evening with both Bryn and Mia by her bedside. It was a peaceful passing and Mia was glad the old woman had not died alone. She found it impossible not to cry but did so as quietly as she could, knowing it would be hard on Bryn, who was clearly fighting to maintain control. She saw the up and down movement of his throat and the tight clench of his hands when he finally moved away from the bed to discuss arrangements with the staff over his great-aunt's personal belongings.

It was late by the time they left to go back to his house and

Mia could see the lines of exhaustion around his eyes as he opened the car door for her.

'I can drive if you're too tired,' she offered.

He gave her another on-off smile touched with sadness. 'No, I'm fine. It's a short drive anyway.'

He waited until they were parked in the garage before he spoke again. He switched off the engine and turned in his seat to face her. 'Thank you for what you did this week.'

'I didn't do anything…'

He captured a strand of her hair and tucked it behind her ear, the gesture so tender she felt more tears springing to her eyes.

'Yes, you did,' he said, his voice sounding as if it had been dragged across something rough. 'You supported me through a tough time. I can't imagine how I would have coped without you.'

'I'm so sorry about your great-aunt…' she said, stroking the hand that had come up to cup her cheek.

'She died happily and peacefully because of you. I couldn't have achieved that for her without your help.'

'I'm glad you asked me to help.'

He looked at her for a long time without speaking. Mia could hear the faint ticking of the dashboard clock and the squeak of leather as he shifted marginally in his seat.

The pad of his thumb moved over her bottom lip, his eyes growing darker as they meshed with hers. 'I want you, Mia.'

'I want you too,' she said softly.

He unfolded himself from his seat and came around to her side, helping her out on legs that felt weak and unsteady. He slipped an arm around her shoulders and walked with her into the house, shutting the door behind him and giving her a look burning with such sensual promise she felt as if she was melting on the spot.

'Come here,' he commanded.

She stepped into his arms, her mouth connecting with his in a fiery kiss that spoke of deep mutual longings. He broke the kiss to carry her upstairs, looking down at her with smouldering heat as he placed her on the bed. She watched as he removed his clothes, her pulse leaping at the sight of how very aroused he already was. She began to fumble with her own clothing but wasn't getting very far until he came down over her and helped.

His hands moved over her breasts, his mouth anointing them with hot, wet kisses and suckles that curled her toes and arched her back. He went lower and lower until she felt the flicker of his tongue against her dewy feminine heat, the sensations rippling through her at this most intimate of all caresses. The pleasure he evoked was mind-blowing and totally unstoppable. It hit her like a huge wave crashing against the shore, lifting her, rolling her over and over before tossing her down once more to float in a sea of euphoria.

He moved back up and, leaning across her, rummaged for a condom, putting it on before slipping between her parted thighs. He entered her in a single deep thrust that sent her back against the pillows with a gasp of delight as he filled her completely. He set a hectic, breathless pace and she got carried along with it, relishing the feel of his pulsing need. She felt him briefly tense before his final plunge, and then his deep groan of satisfaction as he emptied himself, the aftershocks of his release triggering little shivers of pleasure all over her skin.

She held him to her, listening as his breathing gradually came back to normal, his chest rising and falling against hers as she stroked his back with her fingers. How would she live without this when he called an end to their relationship?

So many times over the last few days she'd caught him

looking at her when he thought she wasn't aware of it, frowning slightly, as if he couldn't make up his mind about her. Even as they'd sat beside his great-aunt's bed he had seemed on the brink of saying something important. What had he been about to say to her? she wondered. Had he been mentally preparing his announcement that their temporary marriage was coming to a close?

But then, as she considered another possibility, she felt a tickling sensation inside her chest, as if a tiny feather residing there had been lifted by a gentle breeze of hope.

What if he had been trying to tell her he loved her?

She took a small breath, her fingers stilling on his back. 'Bryn…'

'Mmm…'

'You were going to say something just before…before your great aunt passed away.' She eased him off her so she could look into his eyes. 'What was it you were going to tell me?'

He held her gaze without speaking for what seemed an age before he got off the bed and reached for his trousers, turning his back as he got dressed.

'Bryn?' She sat up, her stomach hollowing as she felt his barriers come up. 'You said it was something important.'

'It wasn't.' His tone was curt as he turned to face her, his face an expressionless mask. 'I have some phone calls to make in regards to the funeral arrangements.'

She glanced at the clock and frowned. 'At this time of night?'

He didn't answer but left the room, closing the door with a sharp click behind him.

Mia lay back on the pillows with a sigh. Was this how it was going to be between them, her love trying desperately to reach out to him, while he kept pushing it away?

# CHAPTER FOURTEEN

THE funeral was a private one and Mia thought how well Bryn coped with it, considering the pain she knew he was feeling. For the days leading up to the memorial service she had been aware of him keeping his distance, reminding her of an injured animal that didn't want anyone else to see its true vulnerability as it dealt with its wounds in private. The only place he let his guard slip was in bed at night. She treasured those times when he rocked and shuddered in her arms, his body finally relaxing as he spilled himself, his iron-clad control slipping as he took her with him to paradise.

She woke one morning a week after the funeral to find him watching her, his dark blue eyes steady and thoughtful on hers.

'Hi…' she said, lifting a fingertip to his lips, tracing them lovingly.

He captured her hand and kissed her fingertip, making her flesh tingle anew at the passion she had felt last night in his arms. He had taken her on a sensual journey that had known no limits. Her body still throbbed tenderly where he had driven so hard, as if he had wanted to demonstrate his desire for her in the most primitive way possible. He hadn't even bothered with using a condom, his passion so out of control as he had taken her from behind, causing a catastrophic explosion of ecstasy that had left her totally boneless.

'What are you thinking?' she asked after a long, pulsing silence.

He gave a rueful grimace. 'I wonder how many men are being asked exactly that question all over the world right now.'

She tried to smile but something about his expression unnerved her, making her lips twist unevenly instead. 'I know, but I guess women like to know what's going on in men's minds. You always seem to hide it so well.'

A small frown brought his brows even closer. His fingers picked up a strand of her hair and coiled it absently, his dark gaze for once not quite connecting with hers. 'There are things we need to discuss, Mia, now that my great-aunt has gone.'

Mia felt her chest tighten painfully. This was it, she thought with a sinking heart.

Their temporary marriage was over.

She lowered her gaze, staring fixedly at his chest. 'I understand…'

He released her and got out of the bed, reaching for a bathrobe and wrapping around himself before turning to address her in a tone that was distant and detached. 'I have a meeting with my producer and the team this morning so I have to leave soon, but I'd like to have dinner with you tonight so we can talk about where we're going from here.'

She swallowed the thickness of dread in her throat and forced a stiff smile to her lips. 'Where would you like to go to dinner? Do you want me to book somewhere in particular?'

'No, I'll do it. Just be ready by seven-thirty,' he said. 'If I'm going to be late I'll get Henry to pick you up.'

'Whatever.'

His unreadable dark eyes met hers briefly. 'We have to talk,

Mia, you know that. Your family will be returning soon and I wouldn't want them to get the wrong idea about us.'

'I know…'

He left the room and the house soon after but it was a long time before she could bring herself to get out of the bed, where the scent of his desire for her wrapped her in a shroud of something that felt like comfort, which she knew would very probably have to last her for the rest of her life.

It was purely by chance Mia ran into Shelley from the café as she was coming back from having her hair done in the city. She'd been filling in time, trying to distract herself from the evening ahead, which she knew would spell the end of her relationship with Bryn.

'Mia…' Shelley gave her an uncomfortable look as they jostled in the doorway of a boutique in the Strand Arcade. 'I was just thinking about you.'

'You were?' Mia frowned at her former workmate's expression.

'How are things with your dream husband?' Shelley asked after a tight little pause. 'Still madly in love?'

'Why wouldn't I be?' she asked guardedly.

Shelley took her by the arm and led her out of the hearing of the other shoppers, waiting until they were in a quiet corner near the stairs to the upper floors. 'Mia, I hate to be the one to tell you this but someone needs to before you get hurt any further.' She took a deep breath and said, 'Your marriage to Bryn Dwyer is a total sham.'

Mia fought to conceal her reaction and asked in a calm, unaffected tone, 'What makes you say that?'

Shelley glanced right and left to make sure no one was listening and lowered her tone even further. 'I overheard a conversation in the café this morning. Bryn was there with your agent, Roberta Askinthorpe. They were looking very cosy.'

Mia felt as if someone had thumped her in the chest. 'Oh really?'

'I hovered about, pretending to be clearing the table behind, and I heard something that I wish I didn't have to tell you but I think you should know.'

Mia fought against the wave of nausea that had risen in her throat. 'Wh-what did you hear?'

'Bryn Dwyer had you dropped from Peach Pie Productions. Theodore Frankston was against it but Bryn insisted. He also had you removed from your agent's books because he wanted you to have no choice but to act as his wife in order to secure his great-aunt's estate. Apparently her will was written in such a way that unless she thoroughly approved of his choice of wife the fortune—and I mean fortune in capital letters— would be given to the man who killed his parents.'

Mia stared at her in shock, the blood draining from her face. 'But no one knows about his parents…'

'I sort of guessed that, it was the first I'd heard of it too, but the way Roberta and Bryn were speaking about it made me realise it must be the truth. Apparently Bryn's great-aunt felt he should forgive the man responsible for the death of his parents. It was her way of ensuring he did something about his life and the way it was heading.

'I'm sorry I had to tell you this,' Shelley went on awkwardly. 'I just thought you should know.' She let out a little sigh of empathy. 'Look, I know you love him—there's hardly a woman in Sydney who doesn't—but you can't let him do this to you. He married you for money, Mia. Now his great-aunt is dead he'll get rid of you. Your marriage will be over. He doesn't love you. I thought he did, everyone thought he did, but as actors go he surely takes the Oscar. He used you to get what he wanted. He used you despicably and very cruelly.'

'Thank you for telling me.' Somehow Mia found her strangled voice.

Shelley gave her an agonised look. 'I wish I hadn't been there to hear it with my own ears. God, Mia, what will you do?'

She straightened her shoulders, her grey eyes firing up with determination. 'I'm going to do what I'm best at. I'm going to act.'

Shelley frowned. 'Act?'

'You just watch me, Shelley,' Mia said. 'Bryn Dwyer is not going to get away with thinking he can walk all over my career.'

'What about your heart?'

'That too.'

Shelley gave her a doubtful look. 'If you need me at any time, just let me know. He's a bastard, Mia, a total bastard who has no heart.'

'I know,' Mia said through gritted teeth. 'But I'm not letting him have the satisfaction of trampling over mine. If it takes every bit of acting ability I possess I am going to teach him the lesson he should have learned a long time ago.'

'What are you going to do?'

She met her friend's troubled gaze. 'I'm going to get in first, that's what I'm going to do.'

'You mean, pull the plug on your marriage before he gets the chance?'

Mia smiled even though it hurt unbearably. 'I may not be up to scratch on acting the *femme fatale* role according to Bryn Dwyer's opinion, but the one role I can do convincingly is the I-never-loved-you-in-the-first-place one.'

'But you really do love him, don't you?'

'I'm an actor, Shelley,' Mia reminded her. 'And I'm telling

you if I can't pull this off then I'm going to give up and go back to college and find some other career.'

'Such as?'

Mia frowned as she thought about it. 'I don't know... maybe working in a café wouldn't be so bad after all.'

Shelley reached out and gave her a quick hug. 'Don't even think about it. You were born to be on stage—you just haven't found the right one yet.'

Mia had no choice but to tell Gina about the true state of her marriage, for as soon as her former flatmate answered the door Gina could see for herself the emotional despair on her face.

'I can't believe it!' Gina said once Mia had told her everything. 'I thought he was in love with you.'

'He's in love with himself, not me,' Mia said, wiping at her eyes.

'But what if Shelley didn't hear correctly? I mean, a café is hardly a quiet place. There are usually several conversations going on at once and cups and plates rattling in the background,' Gina said. 'Surely you owe Bryn a chance to explain his motivations for marrying you?'

'We're having dinner this evening,' Mia informed her. 'He said this morning before he left that he wanted to discuss our future. That could only mean one thing.'

Gina's face fell. 'Oh…'

'I'm not going to give him the satisfaction of waving the chequered flag in my face. I'm going to ask for a divorce.'

'Your room is still empty,' Gina said. 'You can come back here any time.'

'Thanks, Gina. I'm going back to pack my bags now. I'll bring them here as soon as I'm done. I just want to tell Bryn Dwyer what I think of him and get it over with.'

'Look what happened the last time you said that,' Gina said wryly. 'It doesn't always pay to go looking for revenge. You're the one who will get hurt.'

Mia scrubbed at her eyes determinedly. 'I'm not going to let him see how much he hurt me. You just wait and see, Gina. This is going to be the performance of my life.'

# CHAPTER FIFTEEN

Mia had not long finished packing her things at Bryn's house when she received a phone call from Ellie, who was now safely relaxing with a group of friends on the Greek island of Santorini.

'I can't thank you enough for what you did for me,' Ellie said. 'It was such a harrowing time. I really thought I was going to lose it there for a while. The money you sent helped release fifteen people. You should be very proud of yourself.'

'Yes, well, that's what sisters are for,' she said with a touch of wryness, 'to make sacrifices. You've done it for me lots of times.'

'So how's the gorgeous husband?'

'He's…' Mia hesitated, wondering if she should ruin her sister's well-earned holiday with the news of her impending divorce. 'I'm having dinner with him tonight. I can hardly wait.'

'I'm so happy for you, Mia, you so deserve to be happy. You're always so good at helping others. It's time you got to be treated like a princess. Love you, sis. I'll be home in a couple of weeks and thanks again for not telling the folks about the drama I was in. I knew I could count on you. You're the best.'

'I love you too, Ellie. Don't go saving any whales or forests on your way home. Just come home and be with me, right?'

'It's a deal,' Ellie said.

A short time later another call came through, this time from Mia's previous agent, informing her of a role she thought Mia might be interested in auditioning for.

'But I thought you were too busy to represent me,' Mia said with unmistakable bitterness.

'Yes, well, it's more of a permanent role so it doesn't quite fall into our regular guidelines for representation. I just thought, since you were at a loose end, you might like this. You would be perfect for it.'

'What is it?'

'It's a job working with sick children in hospital. It sounds like a lot of fun and the money is good. All you have to do is entertain them for a couple of hours each day by reading to them and doing the odd magic trick. I know how good you are with kids so I thought you'd jump at it. There's an audition tomorrow at four pm at the church hall in Boronia Avenue, not far from here.'

'OK, I'll be there, but I would still like to know why you—'

'Great, I'll put in a good word for you. I'll text you all the details. Good luck.'

'Roberta—' Mia began but the agent interrupted her again, making up some excuse that she had an important call coming in.

'Sorry, Mia. Gotta go. Let me know how you get on. Bye.'

Mia stared at the phone in her hand, her brow furrowing slightly.

It rang a few minutes later and she was not at all surprised to hear Bryn's voice informing her that Henry would be collecting her for their dinner engagement that evening.

'Sorry about that, Mia,' he said. 'But I've got some legal work to see to over my great-aunt's estate. It will save time if

Henry brings you straight to the restaurant. I've booked it for seven-thirty and I should be there soon after if all goes well.'

'Why don't we eat here instead?' she suggested, wondering if what she had to say would be fit for the ears of other diners.

'No, I gave Marita a couple of days off, as one of her kids is sick. Don't worry, I'll be there as soon as I can. How was your day by the way?'

'Wonderful,' she lied. 'I had my hair done and went shopping; I even bought a dress for tonight.'

'You sound like you're looking forward to seeing me,' he said at her light and cheery tone.

'Of course I am,' she said. 'I have so much to tell you. I can hardly wait.'

There was a tiny pause before he asked, 'What have you got to tell me?'

'It's a surprise,' she said. 'I'll see you tonight.'

'Mia…'

The sound of the doorbell gave her a perfect excuse to end the call. 'Oops, got to go. It sounds like there's someone at the door.'

'It's a present for you,' he said. 'I hope you like it.'

'How sweet,' she said, grinding her teeth. 'I'll see you later. Bye.'

She opened the door to find a florist delivery-service man with a huge bunch of tall red roses and a slim box wrapped in pink tissue with a white bow around it. 'Mrs Mia Dwyer?'

'Yes, that's me,' she said, mentally tacking on: *but not for much longer*.

'These are for you.' He handed them over and smiled. 'Hey, I've never met a really famous person before. Can I have your autograph?'

She blinked at him. '*My* autograph?'

'Yeah, my two kids loved you in that ad you did with the puppy and the toilet rolls. They'll be tickled pink to hear I've met you in person.'

She put the roses down and rummaged for something to sign her name on and, asking for his children's names, scribbled a greeting and drew a big smiley face beside each one. 'Here you are.' She handed it to him with a smile.

'My wife listens to your husband's programme,' he said. 'She reckons it's the most romantic thing how you two got together.'

'Yes...yes, it was.'

'Well, I'd better be going. Nice meeting you.'

'And you,' she said.

She waited until he'd driven away before picking up the roses and the box and carried them inside. She unpinned the card and, taking it from the tiny envelope, opened it to read the message. It said: 'I hope you like these. See you tonight, Bryn.'

She frowned as she put it to one side and opened the tissue-wrapped box, where inside was an exquisite string of pearls resting on a bed of plush blue velvet.

Anger bubbled up inside her. No doubt this was his parting gift, a stupid bunch of roses and expensive pearls to soften the blow of him calling an end to their marriage.

She went to the kitchen and, taking a pair of scissors out of the utensil drawer, came back to where she'd left the roses and one by one snipped off each perfect, fragrant bud, leaving the tall stalks standing looking forlorn and headless.

She then picked up the string of pearls and snipped her way along it until they rolled like marbles all over the tiled foyer. She gave a satisfied little sigh as the last one rolled underneath the hall stand.

It would probably take him months to retrieve them all.

\* \* \*

Mia ferried her bags over to Gina's and, leaving her car there on the final trip, caught a taxi back to Bryn's house to dress for the evening. She was ready and waiting when Henry arrived, and, quickly closing the door behind her, followed him out to the car.

'You look very beautiful this evening, Mrs Dywer,' he said as he helped her settle inside the car. 'Mr Dwyer is going to be knocked sideways when he sees you, I'm sure.'

She gave him a sugar-sweet smile. 'That's the plan. I can't have him thinking he married a woman with no taste or style, now, can I?'

'You are the perfect wife for him, if you don't mind me saying,' he said once they were on their way. 'Mr Dwyer has had a hard time of it but since you came into his life I've noticed some real changes. He would never have coped so well with his great-aunt's death without your help. You're good for him.'

'Thank you, Henry,' she said softly, desperately trying to control the urge to cry.

The restaurant was on the harbour in Rushcutters Bay and although it was crowded the table Bryn had booked for them was tucked away in a quiet corner.

She was sitting at the table with a glass of champagne in front of her, mentally rehearsing her performance, when Bryn arrived. She watched him exchange a few words with the *maître d'* before looking in her direction, his dark blue eyes meshing with hers.

She watched as every head turned as he wove his way through the restaurant to where she was sitting, bending his head to place a soft kiss to her forehead before he took the seat opposite. She held her breath as his gaze dipped to her unadorned neck.

'Did you get my gift?' he asked.

'Yes, thank you. They were…beautiful.'

'You're not wearing the pearls.'

'I had trouble with the clasp,' she said. 'I thought I might lose them if I didn't do it up properly.'

He seemed satisfied with her answer and smiled as the waiter approached with the menu and wine list.

'How did your meeting go?' she asked once the waiter had taken Bryn's request for a bottle of cabernet sauvignon.

'It was fine,' he answered. 'I had some papers to sign, that's all.'

'How about your meeting with your producer this morning? Was that productive?'

He waited until the waiter had poured their wine before answering. 'Yes…it was.'

Mia watched as he toyed with his glass, staring into its blood-red contents as if wondering how they came to be there.

'I had a phone call from my ex-agent today,' she said into the silence.

'Oh?' He took a sip of wine.

'Yes; apparently she's found some work for me. Isn't that nice?'

His eyes fell away from hers as he leaned back in his chair for the waiter to place some hot bread rolls on the table.

'And here I was, thinking she thought I was hopeless,' she went on once the waiter had gone. 'I lost so much confidence when she and Theodore dropped me but it seems she thinks I have some measure of talent after all.'

'There's never been any question of your having talent,' Bryn said, meeting her eyes. 'I should never have written the review in the first place. God knows I've regretted it ever since.'

'No, you shouldn't,' she said. 'But then there are a lot of things you shouldn't have done, aren't there, Bryn?'

He held her gaze for a tense moment, his throat moving up and down slightly.

'Mia, the reason we are here now is because I have a confession to make. I should have told you in the first place but I had no idea I would end up feeling this way. I didn't see it coming. I should have but I didn't. I guess I didn't want to.'

Mia waited for him to continue, her fingers tightening around her untouched glass of red wine, her anger building so steadily she hardly took in what he was saying. She just wanted to say her piece and get away before he had the chance to hurt her further.

'I don't think it's fair to continue our relationship on the terms I laid down,' he said, 'I think it's time I told you the truth about how I engineered our marriage.'

It was just the cue she'd been waiting for. 'You mean about how you insisted Theo drop me from the play?'

He frowned. 'So you know about that?'

'Yes, and I also know how you told Roberta to stop finding me work so you could force me to act your little role for you,' she continued. 'It had nothing to do with your ratings, did it, Bryn? It had more to do with you wanting to secure a fortune for yourself. It was clever, I admit, and if I were the gullible, innocent fool you seem to think I am I would have fallen for it.'

He stared at her speechlessly as she went on, 'You see, Bryn, I knew what you were up to. I decided to teach *you* a lesson. You thought I couldn't act to save myself but in the end I completely fooled you and everyone else as well with my convincing performance.'

His eyes narrowed slightly. 'What do you mean?'

She gave him a cat-that-swallowed-the-canary smile. 'I'm not really in love with you, Bryn. And I wasn't a virgin either. How was that for a performance? Brilliant, don't you think? You fell for it hook, line and sinker. God, how I was laughing at you the whole time! You thought I couldn't act but boy, did I show you.'

His features became rigid and white-tipped with anger, his eyes like dark blue diamonds as they clashed with hers. 'You bitch. You lying little bitch. And here I was, feeling guilty for using you.'

She gave him a cold look of disdain. 'You didn't use me, Bryn. I used you. I got the leg-up to fame I needed. People are stopping me for my autograph now. How cool is that? And all because of you. I guess I should be thanking you for giving my career the boost it needed, but do you know what, I think I'll make a toast to you instead?' She got to her feet and raised her glass of red wine. 'Here's to the end of our temporary marriage.' She gave him an imperious smile. 'Cheers, Bryn. Thanks for the memories—I'm going to be dining out on those for years,' she said and tipped the contents of her glass into his lap.

As exits went it was one of her best. She wove her way through the tables with a smile of victory plastered to her face, raising her hand to him in a tiny fingertip wave as a taxi pulled into the kerb outside the restaurant.

Her last sight of him was the absolute look of incredulity on his face as he got to his feet, the red wine over his groin looking as if someone had stabbed him.

The taxi driver looked at her in the rear-view mirror. 'Hey, don't I know you? I think I saw you in the paper the other day. You're famous, right?'

Mia gave him a tight little smile. 'Yes, I am. But guess what? It's not all it's cracked up to be.' And she promptly burst into tears.

# CHAPTER SIXTEEN

'Wow, an audition at last!' Gina crowed with delight the following afternoon. 'This is just what you need to take your mind off you-know-who. What's this one for?'

Mia put the final touches to her pixie costume, marvelling yet again at the pointy silicone ears which looked so real. 'Roberta organised it for me.'

'But I thought she wasn't representing you any more.'

'Yes, well, maybe she had a twinge of conscience, because she rang and told me she had an audition lined up for me. She told me I was perfect for the role.'

Gina peered at Mia's ears. *A pixie?*

'Not just any old pixie,' Mia said. 'If I get the job I'm going to be officially known at the Pain Pixie.'

'The Pain Pixie?' Gina wrinkled her nose. 'That sounds a bit weird.'

'No, it's a fabulous idea,' Mia said. 'The Pain Pixie visits sick kids in hospital, reading to them and entertaining them to take their minds off their pain. I've even got a pot of pixie dust, see?' She sprinkled some in the air. 'And a wand.' She waved it about for a moment, privately wishing it could bring about the miracle she wanted in her own life.

'You're right, that does sound fabulous,' Gina said. 'What time is your audition?'

She glanced at her watch. 'I'm going now. Wish me luck.'

Mia knocked on the door of the church hall half an hour later and was greeted by a woman who asked her to stand on the stage and read from a well-known children's book.

She did as she was told, reading in a clear, animated voice.

'Thank you, that's great,' the woman said before Mia had even finished the page. 'You're perfect for the role. You can start this afternoon. I'll give you the schedule with all the contact times. You will be paid a wage plus travel expenses.'

Mia stepped down from the stage and took the sheet the woman handed her. 'Is that all you want me to do?' she asked. 'I mean, I can do accents and tell jokes and that sort of stuff.'

'No, you're fine. You've got the job. You came with very high recommendations.'

As auditions went it was certainly the easiest Mia had ever experienced, she thought as she made her way back to Gina's.

'How did it go?' Gina asked.

'I got the job,' she said with a little frown.

'What's wrong? You don't seem all that thrilled. Isn't it what you were expecting?'

'I don't know...' she said. 'I'm just getting a funny feeling about this.'

'What do you mean? Don't you like the sound of the work?'

'No,' she said. 'It's a dream job. I get paid to make kids happy. I can't think of anything I'd like better, but still...'

'You're still thinking about him, aren't you?' Gina said softly.

'I'm trying not to...'

'I heard him on the radio,' Gina said.

Mia felt herself tensing. 'Was he his usual cutting self?'

'Actually, no, he wasn't.'

'What did he say?'

'Nothing much, he just played a whole lot of soppy romantic songs instead of that usual stuff he plays.'

Mia gave a little snort. 'He's just trying to make his listeners feel sorry for him. No doubt it will lift his ratings to an all-time high.'

'You could well be right because his ratings have toppled Maxwell Murdoch's from the rival channel for the first time in years,' Gina said. 'But it's funny in a way because I read in the paper that Bryn is not renewing his contract at the station.'

Mia's lip curled cynically. 'That's because he's so filthy rich now he's got his hands on his great-aunt's estate.'

'Not according to his column in this morning's paper,' Gina said. 'He said he'd given the whole proceeds of his great-aunt's estate to a well-known children's charity. It was finalised with his lawyers yesterday.'

Mia stared at her flatmate for several heart-stopping seconds. 'Do you still have the paper?'

'It's here somewhere…' Gina began to search for it, finally unearthing it from beneath the sofa cushions. 'Here.' She pressed it out flat for Mia to read.

Mia read the column, her heart beginning to thud unevenly in her chest.

'What's wrong?' Gina asked. 'You look like you're about to faint.'

'No…no, I'm fine…' She forced a smile to her stiff lips. 'I'm just nervous about my first session at the hospital.'

Mia turned up at the hospital as arranged and was led to the children's ward, where she spent an enjoyable hour or two reading and playing with the young patients. She couldn't believe how rewarding it was to see each child's face light up when she came in. It was the most rewarding role she had ever played and she didn't want it to ever end.

If only someone could sprinkle some pixie dust over her and take her own pain away, she thought as she made her way to the next child's bedside.

'Are you really a pixie?' a little boy with wide, dark brown eyes asked.

'Of course I am,' Mia insisted. 'See my pot of magic dust? This is what I sprinkle around to take pain away. It has special magic powers.'

He gave her a sceptical look. 'Does it really work?'

'How's your pain been while I've been here?' she asked.

He smiled at her, showing his missing front teeth. 'I haven't even thought about it.'

'See?' She gave him a grin. 'That's what I'm here for.'

She went next to a little girl who'd had extensive chemotherapy for acute myeloid leukaemia. The sight of the frail seven-year-old with no hair struck at Mia's heart and she sat down by the bed and started talking to her. She found out the little girl's name was Ellie, the very same as her sister's.

'It's short for Eleanor,' the little girl informed her. 'But I still have trouble spelling it so I much prefer Ellie.'

'I can't say I blame you,' Mia said. 'I have an adopted sister whose name is Eleanora. That's even harder to spell. We've always called her Ellie.'

'I don't have any sisters,' the little Ellie said. 'I have a brother but he's only two.'

'This must be tough for you in here,' Mia said. 'I've heard your parents live in the country on a farm. It must be hard not having regular visitors.'

'It's nice that you're here,' the little girl said. 'Is it true you have magic powers?'

Mia felt like the biggest fraud in history but something about the little girl's dark blue eyes reminded her of Bryn and she found herself confessing, 'I have the ability to take pain away with the wave of my magic wand. That's why I'm called the Pain Pixie.' She pulled out her wand and waved it in the air. 'But I have to let you in on a little secret. It only works if the patient really wants to get rid of the pain.'

'I'm not in pain right now but I feel sad that my parents can't always be here with me,' Ellie said. 'Do you think your magic wand can help with that?'

Mia felt as if her heart was being clamped by an industrial-strength vice. 'I can be here as often as you need me to be here,' she said, fighting back tears. 'I can read to you, watch DVDs with you or sit and talk to you as long as you want.'

'Really?' The little girl's eyes lit up like bright little diamonds.

Mia smiled and, reaching out, squeezed the little girl's hand ever so gently. 'That's what the Pain Pixie's job is all about. I'll be here for you whenever you need me and if I'm off with another patient you have only to tell the nurse on duty so I can get back here as soon as possible.'

'I feel better already,' little Ellie said. 'I'm so happy you've come to visit me. I don't miss my mummy so much now.'

Mia bent forward and pressed a soft kiss to the little girl's forehead. 'You know something, Ellie? I'm a whole lot older than you but I still sometimes miss my mum. You're a very brave girl.'

'I'm not really very brave,' Ellie confessed. 'I cried heaps last night.'

It was on the tip of Mia's tongue to confess the same but somehow she stopped herself in time.

A few minutes later a nurse came over to her to inform her of a patient in a private room who particularly needed her attention.

'I'm afraid this is a very tragic case,' the nurse said in grave tones. 'I'm not sure you'll be able to do much to help the poor darling boy but it's worth a try.'

'What happened to him?' Mia asked in an undertone.

'Heart trouble,' the nurse answered, shaking her head sadly.

'Is it a congenital condition?' Mia asked, thinking of the heart murmur her father had had since birth.

'He's had it since he was a little boy, I believe,' the nurse said and indicated the door of the private room. 'But evidently the problem has become more serious of late. Go on in, he's expecting you.'

Mia gave the door a little knock and opened it to find Bryn sitting on the edge of the single bed. She stared at him for several moments, her mouth opening and closing in shock.

She took a step backwards but he sprang off the bed and captured her before she could get away, closing the door so no one could listen in. 'No, don't go, Mia. I want to talk to you.'

'Let me go, you…you…' She was so furious she couldn't think of a bad enough word to flay him with. 'I should have known you'd be behind this! How *could* you? I really love this job and now I find, like everything else to do with you, it's all a stupid act!'

'I had to see you,' he said. 'I need to tell you how much I love you. And this job is genuine. It's yours as long as you want it.'

She stared at him with wide eyes, her heart beginning to hammer unevenly. 'You're…you're sure?'

'Yes, Mia, I'm sure. The job's yours.'

She moistened her mouth, her eyes still focused on his. 'I—I mean about the…the I-love-you bit…'

He smiled as he drew her closer. 'I fell in love with you the very first day I met you but I was too stupid to see it. I guess I didn't want to admit it. I hated feeling so vulnerable. But believe me, Mia. I love you. I can't imagine life without you. When I went home after our dinner I was so angry at what you'd said it took me a while to realise the clues you'd left behind that made me realise how you really felt.'

'You mean the roses and the pearls?'

His eyes glinted with amusement. 'Agnes is probably turning over in her grave at what you did to her precious pearls.'

*'Oh, my God!'* She put her hand up to her throat. 'They belonged to your great-aunt?'

'She left them for you in her will. They're worth a small fortune, or at least they will be when I finally find them all and have them restrung.'

She gave him a shamefaced look. 'I was so angry. I thought you were giving them to me as a consolation prize to mark the end of our temporary marriage.'

'Can you ever forgive me for what I did?' he asked. 'I was wrong to have you dropped from the company, and as for getting Roberta to stop representing you…well, all I can say is I'm deeply ashamed of myself. I didn't stop to think of how you would be affected. I just wanted you so badly I was prepared to put aside every other consideration so I could have you. As for my great-aunt's estate, I never wanted it for myself but I just couldn't bear the thought of giving it to the man who had killed my parents. My great-aunt was right, though; it is time I learnt to let go of the past and forgive the poor man. He didn't do it intentionally and has paid for that one error of judgement all of his life.'

'It's all right,' she said. 'I don't think I was right for that play either. To tell you the truth I haven't been all that happy with any of the roles I've had in the past. All of my life I've been searching for something to do that really makes a difference and today I found it.' She looked up at him with hope shining in her eyes. 'Do you really mean this job is for real?'

'Of course it is,' he said. 'I'd been thinking about it for ages. I once spent a week in hospital not long after my parents died. I had my tonsils out. I was so lonely and afraid, I have never forgotten it. I swore one day I would try and do something to help kids who were sick.'

She smiled up at him. 'So you became a principle sponsor for a major children's charity even though you pretend you're not capable of love.'

'You have taught me how to love, Mia,' he said, 'and not only that, you taught me how to recognise it. If you hadn't come along and tossed that coffee in my lap I might have very well ended up alone and lonely for the rest of my life. No one has ever affected me the way you do. I looked into those big grey eyes of yours and I was totally lost. It was a frightening experience for someone like me who has clung to what is predictable and controllable all his life. When you told me you loved me I was so overcome, I felt so guilty for what I had done. I couldn't imagine you ever forgiving me.'

'Of course I forgive you—I love you. I think I fell in love with you the first day too. But I had my own reasons for marrying you which had nothing to do with how I felt about you.'

'You did?'

She gave him a sheepish look. 'I would never have agreed to take things so far but Ellie was in trouble in South America. She needed money in a hurry and your marriage proposal was the ideal way to solve a problem I just couldn't solve on my own. It was only as we were officially married that I started to realise that I had got myself in a little deeper than I'd initially intended.'

'So will you agree to stay married to me for real? No acting this time?'

She gave him an impish smile, two tiny dimples appearing in her cheeks. 'I wasn't acting in the first place.'

'You know something, sweetheart?' he said as he brought his mouth down to hers. 'Nor was I.'

# THE GREEK'S VIRGIN

BY
TRISH MOREY

**Trish Morey** is an Australian who's also spent time living and working in New Zealand and England. Now she's settled with her husband and four young daughters in a special part of South Australia, surrounded by orchards and bushland, and visited by the occasional koala and kangaroo. With a life-long love of reading, she penned her first book at age eleven, after which life, career and a growing family kept her busy, until once again she could indulge her desire to create characters and stories – this time in romance. Having her work published is a dream come true. Visit Trish at her website, www.trishmorey. com.

One of the best things about being part of the romance-writing community is that you make such fantastic friends you can call on in a crisis anywhere around the world for brainstorm, plot-storming or just general laughs, inspiration and support. Here's special thanks to just a few of my favourite-romance writing friends, many published, some yet to be (but who sure as eggs will be one day!), who never fail to help a fellow writer out in a crisis –

The Wipits – Yvonne Lindsay and Bronwyn Jameson.
The Pyrate and Ferret Galz – Anne Gracie,
Kelly Hunter and Holly Cook.
SA Galz – Kathy Smart, Anne Oliver, Sharon
Francesca and Linda Brown
and the entire Wet Noodle Posse
(http://wetnoodleposse.com)
Without you all, this book would have been written eventually, but it wouldn't have been half as much fun.
Thanks, everyone!

# PROLOGUE

*Sydney, Australia*

*BLISS!* Life could never get better than this.

Saskia Prentice allowed him to ease her naked body down amongst the soft pillows, her young heart swelling, her lips still humming and swollen from his latest kiss, every cell in her body tingling, plumped and primed in anticipation.

Moonlight stroked against the window, rippling through the silk curtains, turning his skin to satin and illuminating the room in a warm, lunar glow, as if even the heavens approved. And offering just enough light to look up into the dark depths of his eyes as he positioned himself over her. She melted, her body softening even more, as she looked into them.

*The eyes of the man she loved.*

A moment of crystal-clear clarity pierced the pleasure fog surrounding her as his legs nestled into a welcome place between her own. Not quite eighteen, and already she'd found her soul mate, the one special man on this earth truly destined for her. There was no mistake. He was the one. And they would have years of loving together, years of feeling just like this.

How lucky could one woman get?

Then she stopped thinking and gave herself totally to the

feeling of him pressing against her, wanting to feel him make her his own, wanting to welcome him inside her, compelling him to press harder to unite them and to end this desperate, urgent need…

Their eyes connected briefly as her body began to accept his, as their burning bodies began to meld.

'I love you,' she whispered, putting in words what her heart already knew, her eyelids fluttering closed as she arched against him, urging him to break through that final stinging barrier, urging him to completion.

A second later the bed bucked and all pressure was gone. *He* was gone.

*And cold air swept cruelly over the places he'd been.*

She opened her eyes, blinking in shock, searching for him. But already he was across the room and dragging on his jeans, throwing on a shirt. And his face was as bleak as the stormiest night, his eyes filled with the darkest savagery.

'Put something on. I'll order you a taxi.'

His voice was coarse and gravelly, and nothing like she'd ever heard before. She looked up at him in horror, feeling suddenly exposed and vulnerable and inadequate all at the same time.

'Alex? What's wrong?'

*'Tsou,'* he spat roughly, tossing his head back as if he was disgusted with himself. His eyes glinted in the moonlight, hard and cold as granite, as he threw her clothes at her on the bed. 'This was a mistake.'

She curled herself behind them as best she could, shame and humiliation flaming her exposed flesh. Was her innocence so much of a turn-off?

'Did I do something wrong? I'm sorry—'

'Get dressed!' he ordered, his words uncompromising, his voice unrecognisable. *The voice of a stranger.*

'But…' Tears pricked at her eyes as she forced back the lump in her throat and fought her way into her clothes. 'But why?'

In the half-light his face was all dark shadows and tight ridges, his muscled body moving with a tenseness tainted with something that simmered like hatred.

'Just get out!' he roared. 'I don't do virgins!'

# CHAPTER ONE

*London—Eight years later*

*SUCCESS!* Saskia Prentice breathed in that sweet smell as she approached the boardroom doors, the high of achievement fizzing in her veins.

In less than five minutes it would be official—she'd become editor-in-chief of the business magazine *AlphaBiz*.

*And she'd worked so hard for this!*

Twelve months of intense and sometimes bitterly fought competition with fellow journalist Carmen Rivers was proof of that. Carmen had made no secret of the fact that she'd do *anything* to ensure she got the job—and, given her rival's reputation, she probably had. But still it had been Saskia who'd consistently filed the best stories from around the globe, producing the most difficult-to-extract business profiles. Just two days ago the chairman had intimated that she'd won, that the job would be hers come today's board meeting.

She'd been waiting on tenterhooks all day, until at last the summons had come. Finally the job would be hers. And finally she'd have the means to rescue her father from his grungy retirement bedsit and get him a place in a decent care facility in the country. She had it all planned—a small cottage for herself close by with a back garden for him to potter around in on the weekends. The generous sign-on bonus, together with the substantially larger pay packet that went with the job, would make all that possible and more.

One hand on the door latch, the other checking her crazy curls were well slicked down and locked into the tight bun at the nape of her neck, she took one last glorious breath, stringing out the extra buzz of adrenaline at the imminent realisation of her dreams. This was her big chance to make the Prentice name really worth something in business circles once again. And this was her opportunity to give her father back something of the pride that had been so ruthlessly stolen from him.

She let go her breath, tapped lightly on the rich timber doors and let herself in.

Muted sunlight streamed in through the large window, momentarily blinding her. She blinked, surprised, as her eyes adjusted to see not the entire board, as she'd been expecting, but just the chairman, sitting near the head of the table, the sunlight framing his silhouette, transforming him to just a blur of dark against the bright light, his expression indiscernible. In spite of the temperature-controlled air, she shivered.

'Ah, Miss Prentice...*Saskia*,' his voice a low rumble, as he gestured her to sit opposite. 'Thank you so much for coming.'

She responded automatically as she blinked into the light, a disturbing feeling of unease creeping along her spine.

*Something was wrong.*

Sir Rodney Krieg was a bear of a man, with a booming voice, and yet today he sounded almost gentle. Sir Rodney *never* sounded gentle. And where was the board? Why weren't they all present for the announcement?

The chairman huffed out a long sigh that almost sounded defeated. 'You know that when we organised this meeting we were expecting to be able to formalise our plans to appoint you as the new editor-in-chief?'

She nodded, a sudden tightness in her throat rendering her speechless, feeling his words tugging at the threads of her earlier euphoria.

'Well, I'm afraid there's been a slight change of plans.'

'I don't understand.' She squeezed the words out, battling the crushing chill of disappointment suddenly clamping around her heart, yet still refusing to give up on her dreams just yet. Maybe it was just a delay?

*Unless they'd given the job to Carmen after all...*

'Has the board decided to go with Carmen instead?'

He shook his head, and for one tiny moment she felt relief.

'Or at least,' Sir Rodney continued, 'not yet.'

And her hopes died anew.

But she wasn't about to go down without a fight. She wouldn't give up on everything she'd worked for that easily. Dry-mouthed, she forced herself to respond, anger building inside. 'What do you mean, "not yet"? What happened? Only two days ago you said—'

He held up one hand to silence her. 'It's irregular, I admit, but Carmen has been having a word in the ear of some of the board members, doing some lobbying on her own behalf...'

Saskia froze. So Carmen had got wind of the board's decision and decided to head it off at the pass? It might be an uncharitable thought, but if Carmen was desperate enough for this position, she didn't want to think about the type of *word* she'd been having in the board members' ears.

'...and to cut a long story short,' Sir Rodney continued, 'the board has decided that a decision as to who is going to head the editorial team shouldn't be rushed.'

'It was hardly rushed,' she protested. 'The board has been deliberating on this for the last twelve months.'

'Nevertheless, the board feels that perhaps Carmen has a point. You've been engaged on different projects during that time. Maybe she hasn't had the opportunity to show her full potential after all.'

Saskia might almost have sneered if she hadn't been more concerned at the mental image of her small cottage in the country misting, the fabric of her dreams unravelling faster than she could tie off the ends. What would she tell her father? With only one, maybe two years of time before his increasing frailty rendered him bedridden, he'd been so looking forward to the move out of the city. She couldn't afford any delays to her plans, let alone risk losing this chance altogether.

'So what happens now?' she asked, her spirits at an all-time low. She'd worked so hard for this opportunity and it had just about been in her grasp. To have it pulled from her reach now, when it had been so close, was more than unfair. 'How long will the board take to make a final decision?'

'Ah. That all depends on you—and Carmen, of course.'

She raised an eyebrow. 'What do you mean?'

Sir Rodney actually managed to look enthusiastic. 'You see, the board has decided that the best way to compare your talents is with a head-to-head contest. You'll each be given a subject we've chosen—in this case, extremely successful businessmen who've chosen to live for whatever reason almost completely out of the public eye. Their public appearances are so rare we know hardly anything about the men themselves, while we see their businesses grow in stature every day. So we want you and Carmen to bring in the goods—what makes them tick? What drives them? The one who brings in the best profile within the month gets their story on the cover of our annual special edition, along with the news of their promotion.'

'But Sir Rodney, I've been consistently turning in great profiles all year—'

'Then one more shouldn't present any problem! I'm sorry, Saskia, but this has come from the board. They want you two to slug it out for the position, and that's what you're going to have to do to get it.'

'I see,' she snipped, hoping her subject wasn't too far flung. With this promotion she'd been counting on an end to her incessant traveling, so she could keep an eye on her father's condition. But she took heart from the time frame. This job couldn't take longer than a month. She'd make sure she did it in less. And then the promotion would be hers. Because she *would* deliver the best profile. There was no question of that! This was no more than a short delay to her plans.

'So who have I been assigned?'

Sir Rodney pushed his glasses on as he lifted up a manila folder lying nearby and flicked open the cover, scanning the information contained within.

'One very interesting character, it appears. You've scored a fellow Sydney-sider who now has extensive interests all over the world. Another one of Australia's Greek success stories, apparently.'

Cold needles of dread crawled up her spine. A Greek Australian from Sydney?

Oh, no way. It couldn't be…

There had to be dozens that fitted that description…

There wasn't a chance in the world…

'A fellow by the name of Alexander Koutoufides. Have you heard of him?'

Every organ and muscle inside Saskia seemed to clamp

down tight, squeezing the air from her lungs and the very blood from her veins. *Had she heard of him?* Part of her wanted to laugh hysterically even as the vacuum in her stomach began to fill with the bitter juices of the past.

He was the man she'd so stupidly imagined herself in love with, the same man who had so savagely thrust her from his bed—right before he'd turned around and coldly destroyed her father's business!

Oh, yes—she'd heard of Alexander Koutoufides!

And there was no way in the world that she was going to profile him. Hell, there was no way she was ever meeting that man again, let alone hanging around long enough to play twenty questions.

Sir Rodney hadn't waited for her response, clearly expecting her to answer in the positive. She forced herself to put aside her shock and focus on his words.

'…seems he made a big splash in business circles until about eight years ago, when he suddenly dropped right out of business circles and became almost a recluse, nonetheless quietly expanding his business interests into the northern hemisphere while refusing all requests for interviews…'

She raised one hand, beseeching him to stop. She didn't need to hear any more. 'I'm sorry, Sir Rodney. I really don't think me doing a profile on Alexander Koutoufides is a very good idea.'

He paused, leaning forward in his chair so slowly that it creaked. 'I'm not actually *asking* whether you think this is a good idea. I'm giving you your assignment!'

'No,' she said. 'Not Alex Koutoufides. It's not going to happen.'

He surveyed her, disbelief unbridled in his eyes, before he slapped the folder back down onto the table. 'But, Saskia, why on earth would you dip out of this opportunity when the promotion is at stake?'

'Because I've met Alexander Koutoufides. We…' She licked her lips while she searched for the right words. 'You might say we have history.'

His eyes widened, glinting with delight as he straightened in his chair. 'Excellent!' he announced, his voice back to booming proportions. 'Why didn't you tell me? That should give you a real head start. I hear our Mr Koutoufides is very wary of the press—although, given his celebrity sister and her latest escapades with a certain twenty-something Formula One driver, that's hardly surprising.'

Saskia blinked as the meaning behind his words registered. 'Marla Quartermain is Alex Koutoufides's sister?' She'd seen the articles—they'd been impossible to miss after *AlphaBiz's* sister magazine, *Snap!*, had run a cover spread on the scandal that had blown the affair both sky-high and worldwide. She vaguely remembered he had an older sister, but they'd never met, and not once had she connected the glamorous jet-setter with Alex. 'He sure kept that under wraps.'

'Exactly the way he wanted it, no doubt. It helped that she took her first husband's name—some joker she married aged sixteen, only to divorce him less than a year later. The first of a long string of failed marriages and sad affairs.' He sighed as he rolled his fountain pen between his fingers. 'But this time she's obviously gone too far—Alex must have decided it was time to take control. He was spotted by one of our photographers whisking her out the back entrance of a Sydney hotel. At first he was assumed to be some new love interest, but a little digging turned up the family connection—something infinitely more interesting to all concerned.'

Saskia's mind digested the new information. *AlphaBiz's*

sister magazine had been none too complimentary about the aging party girl, charging her with all manner of celebrity crime. Any brother would want to protect his sister from that kind of exposure.

'Given what *Snap!* published about Marla,' she reasoned, putting voice to her concerns, 'Alex is hardly going to be receptive to a request for a profile from this organisation—even if the two magazines are poles apart.'

Sir Rodney held out his hands in a wide shrug. 'That's where your previous relationship will give you the inside running, wouldn't you say?'

'Not a chance,' she stated, shaking her head defiantly. 'Alex Koutoufides…' She paused, choosing her words carefully—Sir Rodney didn't need to know the whole sordid story. 'Well, more than twenty years ago our fathers were in business together in Sydney, but my father struck a deal that saw him whisk Alex's father's business out from under his feet. Alex never forgave him. Eight years ago Alex destroyed my father's business as payback. He's ruthless and thoroughly without morals, and I dare say he hasn't improved with age. I hate the man with a passion. And I won't profile him.'

'You must be kidding, surely? You have right there the seeds of a brilliant profile!' The chairman peered at her as if he couldn't believe what he was hearing. 'I've never seen you back away from anything or anyone. What are you so afraid of?'

'I'm not afraid! I simply have no desire to ever see that man again.'

'Then consider it your chance to get back at him for what he did!' He slammed his hand on the table. 'Find the dirt on Alexander Koutoufides. He must be hiding something other than that sister of his. Find out what it is.'

She turned on him in a flash. '*AlphaBiz* doesn't do dirt—not in my profiles! Not that it matters, because I won't do it anyway.'

'You'd give up your chance at this promotion?'

'Why does it have to be him? Surely there's someone else I can profile?'

Sir Rodney harrumphed and drew back in his chair. 'I dare say the board won't be impressed, but I suppose if you feel that strongly about it we could possibly come to some arrangement. Perhaps we could swap your assignment for Carmen's?'

So she'd get Carmen's subject and Carmen would profile Alex instead? Saskia choked back her instant irrational objection. Maybe the chairman had a point. Why *not* set Carmen onto Alex? They probably deserved each other. Carmen would be only too eager once she discovered how good-looking he was—the perfect specimen on which to employ her famed horizontal interview techniques. And, let's face it, once she got him there Alex would have no reason to hurl Carmen from his bed—leastways not for the same reason *she'd* been so viciously ejected all those years ago!

Oh, yes, maybe they did deserve each other. She could just see it now... Pictures splashed across her mind's eye, shockingly vivid, staggeringly carnal, frame by slow, pulsating frame...

Carmen with Alex. Carmen on top of Alex, crawling all over him, over his chest, her mouth on his nipples, her hair tickling the firm flesh of his chest. And Alex, flipping her over, finding that tender place between her thighs...

Bile rose sharp and bitter in her throat.

Carmen didn't know the first thing about Alex! Whereas she herself *did* have a head start. She knew what the man was like, and she had a compelling reason, so he might just agree to do it.

Perhaps Sir Rodney was right—maybe this *was* her opportunity to get even with the man who'd destroyed her father's life

and humiliated her into the deal? And maybe this was her chance
to take Alex Koutoufides down a peg or two in the process.

'Sir Rodney,' she ventured calmly, in a voice that sounded
strangely distant, as if separated from logic and reason.
'Maybe I was too hasty…'

He leaned his bulk across the desk in anticipation. 'Then
you'll do it? You'll profile Alex Koutoufides?'

She lifted her eyes to meet his and swallowed, still half
wondering what the hell she was letting herself in for and why.

*For my father,* she answered herself in the hammer of her
heartbeat.

*For revenge…*

'I'll do it,' she said before she could change her mind again.
'When do I leave?'

# CHAPTER TWO

ALEX KOUTOUFIDES was playing hard to get. Word on the streets in Sydney suggested he'd gone to ground, hoping to sit out the interest in his sister's latest affair. There was probably some logic in that, Saskia acknowledged as she edged quietly along the shadowy strip of sand lining the tiny and exclusive Sydney Harbour cove. Before too long another celebrity scandal was bound to knock Marla Quartermain's latest indiscretion off the front pages. Not that that would let Alex off the hook as far as Saskia was concerned.

But, with no sightings of him since the incident at the hotel, and no record of him leaving the country, Saskia had no option but to follow up on a hunch. Which was precisely why she was here, hugging the vegetation that lined the beach, contemplating the multi-storey beach house alongside.

*The same beach house Alex had brought her to eight years before.*

Saskia tried to ignore the steel bands tightening around her gut as she scrutinised the outline of the house in the fading sunlight, searching for any signs of life behind the curtain-lined glass walls. She wouldn't let herself think back to that night or she'd never be able to focus on her job. It was just a house, and Alex was just a man—not that it even looked as if he was here.

The garages facing the road high above had all been locked down, and there'd been no answer to her several rings of the gate bell. And she'd found not one reference to the property being owned by Alex or any of his known companies in any of her searches. Maybe it had never even been his.

Yet the strange prickle at the base of her neck told her otherwise, and despite the bad taste in her mouth at the prospect of meeting Alex Koutoufides again the thrill of the chase still set adrenaline pumping around her veins. It might be a long shot, but she'd won her fair share of industry accolades for stories that had resulted from her following up on just such hunches.

Alex obviously didn't want to be found. And if nobody knew about the beach house, then maybe this was the perfect place for him to lie low?

Her eyes scanned the height and breadth of the building, an architectural triumph in timber and glass, its stepped construction clinging to the slope behind as if it was part of it, and its generous balconies extending the living space seawards on every level. And from what she remembered the house was just as magnificent on the inside.

She jumped, swallowing down on a breath as a light came on inside. Because she knew that room. She'd been there, had lain naked across the endless bed while the welcoming sea breeze had stirred the curtains and the sea had played outside on the shoreline below. Even now she could recall the magic promise of that night. And even now she could feel the raw shock of Alex's cruel dismissal…

She squeezed her eyes shut, trying to banish those unwelcome memories. No way would she let herself relive the hurt he'd inflicted so savagely. She'd buried the mistake that had been her infatuation with Alex long ago. She was over it! Besides, right now she had more important things to think about. The house wasn't as empty as it looked. *Somebody* was in residence and she needed to get closer.

She flipped the collar of her dark jacket up, and checked to ensure her crazy hair was safely tucked under her cap—she was taking no chances that her honey-gold curls would give her away in the moonlight—before she looked back behind her, checking she was alone. But this was a private beach, almost impossible to get to, the steep path from the road barely more than a goat track. The shoreline was deserted behind her, the sounds of the wind moving through the leaves and a distant ferry her only companions.

Until the sound of a door sliding open pulled her attention back to the house. There was movement, the curtains pulled back, and she shrugged back into her cover of foliage as a lone figure wearing nothing but a low-slung pair of faded jeans stepped onto the balcony. Breath snagged in her throat. The light might be fading fast, but it couldn't disguise the identity of the owner of the powerful stride that carried him almost arrogantly to the balustrade. Nor could it hide the width of those broad shoulders, or the sculpted perfection of that bare torso as it tapered down to meet his jeans.

She lifted her gaze to his face, knowing she'd already had all the confirmation she needed before she even registered his features. But there was no mistake. She could just make out the stubble shadowing his jaw, his hair damp, as if he'd just showered, glossy and strong, framing his dark features and the chiselled lines of his face.

And inside her hatred simmered alongside satisfaction. She'd found her quarry. She'd found Alex Koutoufides in the flesh!

He shifted position against the railing and shadow and light rippled down his torso, stirring memories and comparisons. *In the flesh, indeed.* He didn't look so different from the way she remembered. His face might be leaner and harder, his chin more determined, as if he didn't make a habit of smiling, but he'd filled out across his shoulders, power under-lined in each swell of muscle. Her eyes took all of him in, scanning him for changes, drawn to his chest and dark nipples, then further down, to where a whirl of dark hairs disappeared downwards into the soft denim that hugged close and low over his lean hips.

Those same hips had lain between hers. Those same shoul-ders had angled broadly above her as he'd positioned himself, preparing to take her...

She shifted, all dry throat and hammering blood, agitated with her body's instinctive feminine reaction and angry with herself for believing she could ever forget what had happened here so many years ago. She would never forget—*mustn't* let herself forget—not after the way he'd used her and abused her and stripped her father's company bare!

Saskia lifted her digital camera and fired off a couple of low-light photographs—just for confirmation. Sir Rodney would be delighted she'd tracked him down so quickly. How ironic that the place Alex had brought her to all those years ago, the place where he'd smashed her youthful dreams of love eternal to smithereens, had now put her in the driver's seat. It brought a smile to her lips as she stashed her camera back in her bag; there was a certain symmetry about it that appealed.

She'd get Alex to co-operate on this profile to give her the best chance to win that promotion, provide her with financial security and the means to take care of her father, or he'd pay for it with the publication of a few salient facts she was certain he would not want to be revealed to the world. Of course, the choice would be his, she thought with a smile. Unlike him, nobody could accuse *her* of being ruthless.

Right now he gazed out to sea like a master surveying his domain, one hand nursing a tumbler, the other angled wide along the brass-railed glass balustrade. Shrouded in shadow, she watched from below. Now all she had to do was watch for a chance to scramble up the hill and wait it out in her car. If he made so much as a move she'd know about it.

He turned his head her way and she shifted instinctively, aiming to get deeper under cover. But she stumbled on something solid behind her—a piece of driftwood. She managed to clamp down on a cry of surprise but momentarily lost her footing, grabbing onto a branch and rattling her cover of leaves while the driftwood skipped away down the thin strip of firm sand, rolling into the sea with a soft plop.

It was good to get some fresh air. The sea breeze on his face felt refreshing. The darkening ripples of the harbour were starting to sparkle as lights went on around the shore. The last few days staying here, with Marla constantly complaining about being cooped up, were really starting to get to him. But what choice did he have? The paparazzi were still swarming all over the Sydney office, waiting for him to put in an appearance, and there was no way he was risking letting them anywhere near Marla—not when they'd done such a great hatchet job on her already. He couldn't even rely on the beach house remaining secret, not now he knew all his records and property transactions were currently being raked over by every two-bit reporter in town, trying to track down where they'd disappeared to. As it was, someone had been leaning on the doorbell just an hour ago. A coincidence? Unlikely.

But they'd be out of here soon. All he was waiting for was the phone call to confirm they'd secured a place for Marla in a place near Lake Tahoe. Once inside the private clinic that doubled as a resort, Marla would be both safe from the press and entertained twenty-four hours a day. Tennis, massage or cosmetic surgery—the choice would be hers. By the time she came out the press would have lost interest. And maybe this time she'd manage to clean up her act for good.

He swirled his glass of soda unenthusiastically. What he'd really like right now was a slug of Laphroaig. The robust single malt would be the perfect accompaniment to the tang of sea air. But he'd made a deal with Marla and the house had been stripped of alcohol—he wouldn't drink if she couldn't. But hopefully tomorrow she'd be on her way. All that remained was to get her through the airport without being noticed.

His eyes scanned the surrounding beach. At least they were safe enough here.

The glass was tipped halfway to his lips when he heard it— the sudden rustle of undergrowth, the splash of something hitting the water. Instantly his eyes returned to the area below the balcony. An intruder? Or simply a possum skittering through the trees, sending debris seawards?

'Alex?' Marla called from inside the house. 'Where are you? What will I need—?'

'Stay there!' he barked over his shoulder. 'I'll be right in.'

He scanned the shoreline one last time before pushing away from the railing and turning for the door, sliding it home with a decided *thud*.

The breath she'd been holding rushed from her lungs. A close call. If the woman inside hadn't called out he'd have been bound to see her, lurking below his balcony. And skulking in the bushes was hardly the professional image she needed to convey if she was to convince him that she wanted a serious interview. She swung her bag over her shoulder and pulled her cap down low and tight. She'd acted on her hunch and she'd found Alex. Now it was time to climb back to the top and, if he wouldn't answer the door, wait him out. He had to come out eventually.

As for the woman? She clamped down on twinge of resentment—because it couldn't be jealousy—not a chance. Besides which, logic insisted it was most likely his sister he was protecting. Although the way he was dressed—or undressed…

She breathed out an irritated sigh. It didn't matter, anyway. It wasn't as if Saskia would have been the only woman Alex had brought here over the years. Whoever the woman was, she was welcome to him.

Carefully she picked her way along the shore. It was darker now, and the overgrown entry to the path was all but invisible in the low light. She was still searching for it when she heard the faint squeak of sand behind her.

There was no time to look around. A steel-like grip bit down on one arm and pulled, hard. She grunted in shock and tried to wrench free, but her feet tangled in her panic and she stumbled, the weight of her assailant behind her forcing her crashing down to the beach.

Breath whooshed out of her as she landed, her face cheek-deep in the sand, grains clinging to her lips and lashes, while behind her one arm was twisted high and tight. Pain bit deep in her shoulder.

'Who are you and what the hell do you want?'

His voice ripped through her like a chainsaw, and fear bloomed like a storm cloud inside her. Was it any relief that she knew her attacker? Hardly. Not when she knew the sort of low acts he was capable of. And not when he was hardly likely to be any more welcoming when he found out who she was.

She winced, her back arching and her head lifting from the sand as her arm was forced higher. 'You're hurting me,' she wheezed.

*What the—?*

Instantly he let go and eased his weight from her, horrified that he'd brought a woman down—but then he'd had no idea there was a female lurking under the bulky black jacket and cap, and whoever she was, she still had no right to be here. He crouched over her in the sand, not touching her, satisfied he didn't need to use any more force. She was going nowhere fast.

'What are you doing here? This is a private beach.'

She stretched her elbow, as if testing it, before planting it on the sand and using it to spin herself around into a sitting position.

Her jaw thrust up to meet him, and for a moment she was all pouting lips on a mouth that looked as if it wanted to spit hellfire and brimstone. He frowned, trying to make out more of the shadowed features of her face. She angled herself out from behind his cover and let moonlight hit her face, while at the same time she pulled the cap from her hair, letting her honey-gold curls tumble free. And finally those pouting lips turned up in a smile that came nowhere near her eyes.

'Why, I came to see *you*, Alex.'

And it hit him with all the force of a body-blow.

*'Theos!'* The word exploded from him like a shotgun blast, forcing him back up onto his feet. 'What the hell are *you* doing here?'

'I came to interview you,' she replied calmly, rising to stand in front of him and dust the sand from herself. 'But first I had to find you. Looks like I did.'

Before she'd finished speaking he'd already made a lunge for her shoulder bag and was rifling through the contents.

'Hey!' she protested, fighting him for control of the bag. 'What do you think you're doing?'

But he'd already found her mobile phone and camera and he ignored her, letting her snatch back the bag as a consolation prize. By the time she'd realised he had exactly what he'd been looking for, he already had the camera turned on.

Fury set his blood to a simmer as he scrolled through, finding the pictures of himself she'd taken from under the balcony. *'Vlaka!'* he swore under his breath, cursing himself for relaxing his guard for even just a moment. Just as he'd suspected—this was no innocent visitor! And now that *one* of the vultures had found them, at any moment the entire paparazzi contingent would descend upon them. Marla wasn't safe here any more. None of them were.

He flipped open the cover, popped out the memory card and flicked it low and long over the sea. He watched its trajectory over the water, only satisfied when it landed metres out into the bay.

'You can't do that!'

'I just did.'

He turned back to her, taking his time to really look her over this time—this ghost from the past come to haunt him. Little Saskia Prentice, all grown up. Sure, there were still those same long curls framing that heart-shaped face, the same too-wide mouth and milky complexion surrounding the greenest eyes he'd ever seen—but, from what he could see of the curves under that open zipper jacket, it looked as if the transition from teenager to woman had been good to her. Only the spark of innocence in those eyes was missing. Cold, hard cynicism ran deep in those liquid green depths.

For a moment he wondered—just how much had that been down to him? But he discarded that thought in a blink. No, her job would have knocked that out of her regardless. Nobody could stay an innocent for long in her line of work.

*A line of work he abhorred.*

'You're a reporter,' he said, pocketing both her phone and her camera in the shirt he'd hastily flung on before leaving the house. He hoped she wouldn't take his words as a compliment. They weren't meant to be. 'I suppose it's hardly surprising someone like you would end up working for the gutter press.'

'I'm a *journalist*,' she emphasised, her eyes now colder, her chest expanding on an angry breath. 'For a business magazine. And now that you've finished tampering with my goods, perhaps you'd care to hand them back?'

'And give you another chance at stealing one of your seedy shots or summoning up your cronies?' He knew exactly what kind of business magazine peddled the shots of the rich and the celebrated. He'd had his fair share of them. He'd seen how they operated—following their prey like vultures, wanting to make a fast buck by exposing someone else's private life. They were parasites, every last one of them.

'How am I supposed to do that? You've dispensed with the memory card, remember?'

'And a reporter would never carry a spare? I don't think so. Leave me your business card and I'll have your goods delivered to you.'

'That's my property! I'm not leaving without it.'

'And right now you're on *my* property, and I don't recall giving you permission to enter it—let alone take photographs you no doubt intend selling to the highest bidder. I'm sick of you parasites following Marla's every move, waiting for any chance to pull her down.'

'I wouldn't do that! Like I said, I work for—'

'Good,' he interrupted, not believing a word. 'Then getting rid of those photos won't present a problem. Now, who told you I was here?'

She looked at him, her hands on her hips, every part of her body taut and ready to snap.

'Nobody told me.'

'Then how did you find me?'

Her lips turned into something resembling a sneer, her eyes sparking resentment. 'Oh, I just thought I'd drop by on the off chance—*for old times' sake*. Surely you haven't forgotten that night? We had *such* fun together.'

Breath hissed through his teeth.

Forgotten that night? Not a chance. Though he'd tried to scrub his mind free of it time and time again, tried to put it behind him, his memory of that night was like a stain, indelibly printed on his psyche. It had been a mistake—an ugly mistake. And now Saskia herself was back, a three dimensional reminder of the mistakes of the past. What a fool he'd been to bring her to this house! And what a hell of a time to discover just how big a mistake it had been.

But, whatever she wanted from him, she was leaving. She was barking up the wrong tree entirely if she thought that what had happened all those years ago gave her an entrée into his private life now.

'I want you gone—now.'

'All I want is one interview.'

'You're wasting your time. My sister isn't giving interviews.'

'I don't want to talk to your sister. It's *you* my magazine is interested in.'

'Sure,' he said, shepherding her back towards the start of the steep path. 'Now, get going before I have to call the police and have you thrown out.'

She shrugged off his arm and stood her ground. 'I'm not going anywhere. Not without a profile on you.'

'And this is how you thought you'd get it? By lurking in the bushes and playing paparazzi?'

'I had to find out if you were here. You wouldn't answer the door.'

'Maybe because I didn't want to talk to anyone.'

'You have to agree to this interview.'

'Forget it. If you really had anything to do with the business world, you'd know I never give interviews or allow profiles.'

'This time you will. I work for *AlphaBiz* magazine—'

'Hang on.' He stilled in the moonlight. 'That's part of the Snapmedia conglomerate, isn't it? That bunch of dirt-raking parasites? I *knew* you were trouble.'

'I'm with *AlphaBiz*! It's a *business* magazine.'

'Closely aligned to *Snap!* magazine. Part of the same gutter press. And don't try and pretend you're anything special. I've seen the family tree.'

'You have to listen—'

'I don't have to listen to anything. Whereas *you* have to go. Right now.' He took a step closer, making it clear he wanted her to turn and leave. 'Goodbye, Miss Prentice. Be sure to watch your footing on the way up.'

She stood her ground, wishing she were taller, wishing she didn't feel so overwhelmed by his size and proximity, wishing his very heat didn't blur her senses and make her lose focus.

'You really don't want me to go, you know.'

'That's where you're wrong.'

'But if you don't agree to a profile I'll still have to turn one in. And I'll be forced to write it my way. Surely you don't want that?'

He scoffed. 'I have no doubt you'd work that way

anyway, whether or not I agree to this fantasy profile you insist you're here for.'

'I'll say how you assaulted me.'

'Go right ahead. You were trespassing—not to mention dressed like a burglar.'

She dragged in a breath, desperate for oxygen, searching for the courage to be able to force the words out. '*Then* I'll tell the world about the sick way you handle your business deals. You can say goodbye to being a recluse with the amount of media scrutiny you're going to get.'

He moved closer, looking down at her with the look of death he knew curdled the blood of any employee who stepped out of line. But she didn't back away. Instead her green eyes flashed up at him as if *she* was the one issuing a challenge. 'Just what the hell are you talking about?'

'I'll turn you from Mister Squeaky-Clean into a business pariah. Just as well you like living life as a recluse. Because you won't be able to show your face in public by the time I'm through with you.'

'You're bluffing!' he stated, even while a sick feeling foamed in his stomach, a festering of the unease he'd felt ever since he'd realised there was someone down below the balcony watching the house.

'You think so? Then watch me walk away. Because personally I can't *wait* to splash the sad truth of how you go about a takeover and exactly how you like to celebrate your victory by totally humiliating the opposition by seducing and then rejecting their innocent daughters.'

# CHAPTER THREE

FURY turned his eyes dark and potent. His top lip curled with hatred as Saskia waited for his response. 'So much for having nothing in common with the gutter press. Looks like you can rake muck with the worst of them.'

'I'm not talking about raking muck,' she stated as calmly as she could, belying the fact that her heart was going at a million miles an hour. 'I'm talking about telling the truth, telling it how it was and what you did to me the very day before you destroyed my father's life by smashing his company to pieces.'

His face came down low, his brows twisted, his skin pulled tight over his features—features that spoke of barely reined-in rage. He leaned so close she could feel his breath on her face, feel his heat setting her own blood on fire.

'And what exactly *did* I do to you?'

'You took advantage of me!'

'So you're planning to pretend I raped you?'

'No! I never said that. Although no doubt you'd like to pretend we never had sexual relations at all.'

'We went to bed together, and you were, I seem to recall, more than willing!'

'As were you! Or so I thought.'

He drew back for a moment, his eyes narrowing.

'Is *that* why you're so angry with me? Because I *didn't* actually finish off what I started?'

She blinked, gulping back on a sudden spike of truth.

'Is that to be your threatening headline, then?' he taunted. *'Man refuses to take woman's virginity.* Are you trying to damn me or make me out to be some kind of saint?'

'Whether or not you stopped has nothing to do with it. You got me into bed, remember?'

'No,' he said, brushing her objections aside. 'I don't know how many men would have stopped when it was so willingly offered to them on a plate! You were all but *begging* for it.'

'That's not the point!' she protested, her stomach churning at the crude way he portrayed what had happened that night. Was that what he believed? Was that how he remembered it? It hadn't been like that. Not for her at least.

Suddenly things were too personal, too painful, his words slicing fresh wounds so that she had to battle twice as hard to overcome both the hurt of the old and the pain of the new. And so what that they hadn't actually had sex? It had been damned close, and his rejection had left her feeling violated. He'd used her for whatever sick purpose he'd had in mind, and then he'd hung her out to dry.

'Then what *is* your *precious* point?' Alex demanded.

'If it hadn't been for the takeover,' she managed, her words spilling out in a rush, 'you would never have had me in your bed. It wasn't enough for you to crush my father and his business. You had to humiliate the entire family in the process!'

His eyes flared and burned like a planet in its death throes, and she knew she was right. But there was no victory in his silent confirmation. Instead, the memory of that night ripped sharp and jagged through her senses as if it were yesterday.

She was back in that bed, her feelings as exposed as her flesh. Bewildered, confused and frightened of the man he'd suddenly become. Her feelings slashed to the core as she realised the fool he'd made of her. *The fool she'd made of herself.* She gulped in air, trying to think, to keep control, to suppress the pain of a night that should never have happened.

'You would never publish that.' His words were whispered and intense. 'You have no idea what you'd be opening yourself up to.'

She could hear the steady wire of warning running through his lowered voice, linking his words together like a threat.

'Try me!' she challenged. If he was threatening her he must be afraid—afraid of what she could reveal about him, afraid of what it could do to his business. 'The whole world is going to learn what kind of man you really are. And won't that do your precious sister a whole lot of good? Seeing you dragged through the press just like her! Goodbye, Alex. Sleep tight.'

She turned and he cursed, low and hard under his breath. Damn her! Just when he'd had Marla almost clear. Just when he was trying to keep her away from that gutter press, that same gutter press was about to turn on him. And there was only one way to stop it happening.

He snaked out a hand, imprisoning her arm before she'd taken two paces. 'Wait.'

She looked down at his hand, then over her shoulder at him, her eyes flashing like green crystals, cold and deadly. 'I don't like you touching me.'

He let her go, not wanting to touch her himself but drawn to her at the same time. 'What's to say that even if I agree to this interview you won't publish that rubbish anyway?'

'My word says so.'

'And why on earth would I trust you?'

'Do you really think I want people to know what you did to me back then? Oh, yes, I'll use it if I have to. But you give me this profile and I won't have to reveal to the entire world how much of a bastard you are and how much of a fool I was.'

'Then I'll give you your interview.'

She blinked, slowly, and his eyes were drawn to the arc of her long lashes, sweeping down over her eyes. But not before he'd caught a glint of something inside—success? Or fear?

But when she opened them up whatever he'd glimpsed was gone.

'Fine,' she said, almost as if she was sorry. 'When is a good time to make the arrangements? I'll stay in the background as much as possible, but you will need to allow for some one-on-one question time.'

'Hold on. I said I'd agree to an interview. Nothing more.'

'But—'

'And you've got ten minutes for it. Starting now.'

'No! That's not how I work. I can't be expected to do an entire profile in ten minutes.'

'So how long does a profile take?'

'At least a week. Sometimes more. It depends how co-operative the subject is. I need to see how you work. I need access to your offices.'

'A week? No deal. I won't even be in the country.'

Her eyes hardened into a renewed ice age. 'Then we have nothing more to discuss. It's a profile, or you can look out for what I write in the paper. And I warn you, it will be very, very good. Although perhaps not so good for you.'

The wake from a long-gone ferry slapped lazily up the shore, cicadas buzzed in the dark foliage, and all the while her eyes held his, daring him, challenging him to make the wrong decision.

Why the hell had she had to come back into his life right now? And with a score to settle. She was the last thing he needed.

The mobile in his back pocket beeped three times, and without moving his eyes he reached behind and put it to his ear, knowing instinctively that it was his number one fix-it man, Jake.

'Yes?'

He listened for a few moments, still watching her, satisfied to hear that by this time tomorrow Marla would be safely on her way to the States. Then what he heard made him do a double-take. 'What do you mean, "a diversion"?'

'The airport's still crawling with reporters,' Jake Wetherill argued. 'We can chopper Marla up to Brisbane and exit from there, but there's no guarantee that will be any clearer. But if we could pull something to get the focus onto you—hopefully Marla can slip through unnoticed.'

Alex's eyes narrowed on Saskia. 'A diversion?' he repeated, thinking wild thoughts. It might just work. And it might just help his cause in the process… 'You've got it,' he snapped into the phone, closing it down and slipping it back into his pocket.

Saskia eyed him warily as he allowed himself a thin smile. 'What was that all about?'

'You'd better come with me,' he said, taking her by the wrist. 'You don't have much time to get ready.'

'What do you mean? Get ready for what?'

'I mean you'll get your profile after all.'

She dug her heels into the sand, clearly not trusting him. *Clever girl.*

'What's the catch? What was all that about "a diversion"?'

'There is no catch,' he responded, pulling harder and forcing her feet into a jerky run to keep up with him. 'I'm just making you a deal. You'll get your profile, and in return you'll do something for me.'

'What "something"?'

He stopped, and swung his body towards hers so fast that she almost slapped bodily into him. He looked down and saw eyes that were wide and mistrustful, lips slightly parted, as if he'd caught her unawares and she was trying to catch her breath.

'Did anyone ever tell you that you ask too many questions?'

'I'm a journalist,' she argued, her gaze glued to his unbuttoned shirt, surveying his chest before backing up as if it might bite her. Her eyes drifted up to his face, widening when she saw the way he'd been watching her, waiting for their eyes to connect. 'It's my job.'

'And all I'm doing is giving you the opportunity to do it,' he announced.

'What do you want *me* to do?'

Alex looked down at her, at the moonlight playing on her curls and her body within humming distance of his senses, and for just one crazy moment he felt like sliding a hand around that slender neck and tipping those lips up towards his.

He must be mad to even think it.

Another time, another place—*another woman*—and that question could almost have been an invitation. But not with Saskia. If there was one thing he'd learned from his mistakes over the years it was not to make them again. Saskia had been one hell of a mistake, and he wasn't about to revisit it.

He raised his eyes skyward to break the contact, to break whatever it was she was doing with those damned green eyes of hers, and started pulling her towards the house. 'We leave tomorrow for the States—do you have your passport handy?'

'At my hotel. But the States? Why?'

'Does it matter where you get your profile?'

'No, but…'

'Then I'll send for your things. You're coming with me. You want a week; you've got one. All I'm asking is that you help me let Marla slip through the airport without being noticed.'

'That "diversion" you were talking about, I take it?'

'Got it in one.'

'So what am I expected to do?'

'Just accompany me through the airport. The press are still looking for Marla. I want them to find me strolling casually through the airport and holding hands—with you.'

He let the last two words sink in.

'You and me?' Her eyes flashed cold fire at the same time as her head started to shake from side to side. 'You want them to think there's something going on between us—that, what?—that I'm your *love interest* or something?'

He allowed himself a smile. She'd ejected those two words like missiles, and he knew he'd found the perfect person for the job. Whatever happened tomorrow, whatever he had to do to convince the press that they were a couple, there was no way she'd want to hold him to it afterwards.

'You must be mad!'

'On the contrary. It's the perfect plan. You get to accompany me and get your precious profile, and Marla escapes the country without a peep.'

'It'll never work. I couldn't… I mean, there's no way I could…'

'There's no way you could what, Saskia?' He slid his hand up her arm over her jacket, skimming over her shoulder, curling around her neck, watching her eyelids flutter in reaction as his fingers smoothed over her skin.

'Pretend you care for me? I think we both know that's not true. I think, if you think back, you might recall just how easy it was to care about me.'

Her eyes snapped open, but the rapid jerk of her neck didn't come close to dislodging his hand. 'That was years ago! There's no way I can pretend to like you now—not after what you did to my family. Not now I know what you're capable of. *Not when I hate you with every bone in my body.*'

'And yet you're here,' he soothed, his fingers gently stroking her skin, marvelling at its satin-smooth texture, feeling the rapid pulse of her heartbeat through his skin. 'Don't you find that odd? If you really hated me, why would you take this job?'

'I had no choice! Not if I want any chance at a career and a future. I certainly didn't volunteer to be here.'

'So you had no choice? And that's the only reason you're here?'

Something fleeting skated across her eyes, but still she didn't pull away. Instead she let her gaze focus, its power intensifying as she glared at him. 'No, it's not the only reason,' she hissed, her delivery gift-wrapped in venom. 'Once I knew I was coming I relished the opportunity to do anything I could to pull you down.'

So she really *did* hate him? So much the better. 'Sorry to disappoint you,' he clipped. 'So we have a deal, then—my profile in exchange for your co-operation on this?'

She nodded. Eventually.

'Good. Then, as soon as Marla is safe and your profile is done, you can take yourself back to wherever you came from and file your story.'

'Agreed,' she said.

'Just one condition,' he added.

'And that is?'

'You don't talk to Marla. Tonight or any time. You don't talk to her, and you don't take photos. Got that?'

Her green eyes flared into life again. 'I told you, I'm not here to interview Marla. My business is with you.'

His own regarded her coolly. 'Make sure it is,' he said after a moment, pulling her with him up the steps leading from the shore to the gate that led from the beach to the house. 'Or you won't know what hit you.'

Regardless of what Alex wanted, Marla was there to meet them as soon as they entered the house. 'So there *was* someone out there?' she said, her face a picture of curiosity, but Alex gestured her to stay back with a firm sweep of his free arm.

'It seems we have an uninvited visitor for the night.' Alex tightened his grip on Saskia's arm, his fingers biting into her flesh as if he was worried she was going to make a dash for his sister now she was so close. 'But I want you to keep right away from her. I'm putting her in the guest wing and she's not moving from it.'

'Who is she?'

'Just some reporter.' He spat the word out as if it tasted of bile. 'Nobody you need worry about—'

'I'm a *journalist*,' Saskia interrupted, sick of being talked about in the third person and conscious of how Marla had recoiled at the word he'd used. 'I came here to ask for a profile on Alex. I work for *AlphaBiz* magazine, and my name is—'

'Not important!' Alex interrupted, turning on her savagely, the look in his eyes enough to stop her in her tracks. 'And no matter what she says,' he directed at Marla, 'we're not taking any chances. Don't talk to her. And, whatever you do, don't answer any questions.'

Marla looked at her warily, as if Saskia might bite. Without the sultry make-up she was used to seeing the woman photographed in, Marla looked pale and vulnerable, her eyes wide and innocent, almost naïve.

'So why is she here?'

Alex was already leading her past Marla and towards a flight of stairs. 'She's going to help us get through the airport tomorrow in return for this profile she claims she wants. While we lead the way, Jake will look after you.'

'I don't want Jake,' his sister cried out. 'I hate him. I don't need a babysitter!'

'You'll do what I say!' Alex called back over his shoulder.

'If you expect me to help you both it might pay to stop insulting me,' Saskia hissed, as he frogmarched her up to a mezzanine level facing the sea, letting go of her only once she was safely deposited in a large sitting room.

He closed the door behind them while she rubbed her arm where he'd held her. She took in the rich décor, in coffee and cream colours with soft golden highlights, and guessed the closed curtains must be hiding spectacular views of the harbour. Through an open door she could make out a bedroom, the large bed and enormous pillows reminding her of another bed in this house, another time… She jerked her eyes away, heat filling her cheeks.

He hadn't brought her here to continue where he'd left off. *Besides which, there wasn't a snowball's chance in hell she'd let him.*

'I don't want you leaving these rooms. I'll send up something for you to eat.'

'So I'm to be your prisoner here, in this—' she swung her arms out wide '—gilded cage?'

His eyes were hooded and dark, his delivery deadpan.

'You'll find you have everything you need. There's an *en suite* bathroom off the bedroom. You'll have no need to leave.'

'I need my luggage. And I have a rental car to return. I can't do either of those if I'm stuck here.'

'Give me your keys. I'll have everything taken care of.'

'I don't want someone else poking around in my things! I want to get them.'

'You're not going anywhere. Not until tomorrow. Until then you're going to do everything I say.'

'Do you get off on bossing around women, telling them what they can and cannot do? Even your own sister isn't allowed to decide who she speaks to or who she travels with.'

'Leave my sister out of this!'

'I wouldn't take that kind of treatment if I had a brother. I'm surprised she puts up with it. I'd tell you well and truly where to get off.'

A pointed hand spun close to her face. 'And I said it's none of your concern! You know nothing about it and you will stay out of it. Have you got that?'

She regarded the hand levelly. 'What I've got is that it wouldn't matter if she *did* complain about your interference. You probably wouldn't listen anyway.'

'For someone who claims not to be interested in my sister, you sure seem to be pretty focused on her right now.'

'Don't you think it's a bit hard when you're making me stay in the same damned house as her? It's not as if she's invisible!'

He spun around. 'You're here for one purpose, and one purpose only—to ensure that Marla gets through the airport without the paparazzi getting wind of it. Do that and you get all the time you want to do this profile you claim you need. Otherwise, no deal. Have you got that?'

'Oh, loud and clear,' she replied. 'But don't you forget—

one wrong move on your part and I'll write an exposé that's going to set your business back years.'

His eyes sparked white-hot and his face took on a rigidity that could challenge concrete. For a moment she felt the heated resentment pulsate across the distance from him in rolling waves. And then something else crossed his eyes and he smiled, all tight lips and sardonic pleasure. 'I'm so glad we understand one another. Your things will be delivered later. Until then, goodnight.'

Sydney's international terminal was buzzing when the black stretch limousine pulled up outside the departures gates. Saskia took a deep breath as she waited for the chauffeur to come around and open the door, trying to prepare herself for her role as Alex's love interest. *Love interest?* Ha! After the way he'd treated her last night she'd have more success playing his hate interest. But with any luck nobody would notice them, and she'd get away with little more than having to hold his hand as they walked through the terminal—though even the thought of touching him was abhorrent to her.

Then she stole a glance at the man at her side and swore a silent *No chance* in her brain. If it wasn't enough of a sign-board to get the longest stretch limo in Sydney, nobody could miss a man of Alex's stature and bearing. And if his dark looks, the Hugo Boss jacket, the fine wool sweater and dark trousers weren't enough, he wore power like a magnet, and it drew people's attention from all directions. And wasn't this whole exercise about being noticed? She was wishing for the impossible.

Alex alighted first and turned back, extending one hand towards her, sunglasses obscuring his eyes. 'Ready?' She'd thought she was, but having him waiting for her, holding his hand out to her in invitation, made her hesitate and catch her breath again as she reminded herself exactly why she was playing along with him.

*Just for show,* she told herself. *Just for my profile and then I'm gone.*

Saskia reached up a hand, doing her best to ignore the warm tingling rush to her skin as he folded his long fingers around hers, the pressure gentle and firm as he led her from the car. A late summer breeze caught at her curls and the silk chiffon layers of her dress as he drew her close alongside, and with only one free hand it was her hair that came off second best. Even in an atmosphere rich with traffic fumes bouncing around the sun-warmed concourse, it was his scent of which she was most aware, his cologne that teased her nostrils, his masculine warmth that curled its way inside her and did unwanted things to her heart-lung function.

She looked around nervously, trying to take her mind off the man at her side while the chauffeur unloaded their luggage onto a trolley. It seemed to be taking an inordinately long time. But that was no doubt for the press's benefit—to given anyone in the airport time to realise exactly who had just descended upon them. Already heads were turning their way, a palpable buzz of conjecture vying with the constant roar of vehicles. She looked back down the approach lane, knowing that a dozen cars back sat Marla, a brunette bob hiding her trademark bleached silver blonde mane, and a burgundy leisure suit dressing down a body usually more scantily clad. Jake was at her side, both of them waiting for Alex and Saskia to draw any unwanted attention from the press and allow them a clear run through check-in to the relative anonymity of the first-class lounge.

'Do you realise just how beautiful you look today?'

His words snapped her head around and up with a jolt, but neither his dark-shaded eyes nor the firm set of his chin added to the effect of the words. Part of the act, she realised, damping down her erratically beating heart. Besides which, she didn't give a damn what he thought. But then his free hand smoothed the hair she'd been unable to rescue from the wind, curving it behind one ear and lingering there, all gentle touch and potent masculinity at the same time, making a mockery of all her efforts at controlling her crazy heart-rate.

She mustn't let him affect her this way! Once upon a long time ago she had, and it had been the biggest mistake of her life. And yet still, in spite of all she'd experienced and all she knew, he had a knack of getting under her skin.

He'd driven her to frustration this morning, making her change twice before despairing of the serviceable suits and blouses she had in her luggage and ordering in a boutique's worth of outfits and shoes for her to choose from. And even then he hadn't trusted her. He'd selected the dress she was wearing—a confection of fitted artistry and floating length, the muted petal print feminine without being girlish. He'd called in hairstylists, who'd transformed her unruly curls into sleek waves. He'd made her into a woman he'd be prepared to be photographed alongside, and she had to admit she liked the effect. She felt good—better than good—she actually felt beautiful. It didn't help that his words mirrored her own thoughts. It helped even less that his touch magnified what she felt tenfold.

She moved to shrink away from his reach, but he stilled her by placing one hand on her shoulder. 'Easy,' he murmured, his mouth so close that his warm breath fanned her face, sending tiny tremors radiating through her. 'We want this to look convincing.' And then he slid his sunglasses from his face, laughing softly, as if sharing some intimacy, looking down at her as if she was the only thing on earth that mattered to him. A panicked feeling of *déjà-vu* clawed at her fragile insides.

She knew those eyes. She knew what they could do and how they could turn on the heat and the desire and the want. She also knew exactly how easily those eyes could turn savage and cold in an instant, slashing through her soul with ruthless efficiency.

*I can't do this.*

As if on cue his eyes turned hard and resolute, and instantly she knew she'd unconsciously given voice to her thoughts. 'You *have* to do this,' he ordered, snapping her out of her fears as he steered her towards where their luggage was being wheeled into the terminal. 'We have a bargain.'

She blinked, her mind clearing now that it was passengers and luggage and queues that filled her vision rather than his eyes. He was right. She *could* do this. She had to, because she had no choice. But this time she'd make sure she had nothing to fear.

Because knowledge was power. This time it would be different, because she knew exactly what kind of man Alex Koutoufides was. She knew how he could turn on the charm, and she knew how he could so quickly spin that setting to deep freeze.

So there was no way she'd let him get the better of her.

They hadn't taken half a dozen steps inside the terminal when it started—a swelling hubbub of interest and more swivelled heads. Even though first-class check-in was fast and efficient, the attendant the soul of discretion as he checked their bags, by the time they'd received seat allocations and turned towards the departure lounges they'd attracted every eye in the terminal along with a clutch of photographers, both amateur and professional, who had suddenly appeared out of the woodwork.

'Here come the vultures,' Alex said, taking her arm and ignoring the calls starting to come from the photographers to attract his attention. 'Let's go.'

He didn't wait for her agreement, just forged a path through security as the gathering throng formed an honour guard around them.

'How's Marla?' someone called.

'Where is she?' yelled another, thrusting a tiny microphone into his face.

Alex brushed it away, tossing a pointed, 'I was hoping you could tell me,' at them. 'You seem to know everything else about her,' he finished, while he continued to part the sea of reporters and intrigued bystanders in his path as if they weren't there.

Saskia kept up, swept along as much by Alex's powerful aura as his arm around her shoulders. The noise of the incessant questions, the flash of cameras and the closeness of the press was claustrophobic. No wonder he'd wanted to protect Marla from this sort of circus.

Over the sea of heads and raised cameras the promise of the first-class lounge access appeared, and then disappeared behind them as Alex forged on, irrationally forgoing privacy for a public lounge setting at a cosy bar nearby.

What the hell was he thinking? she thought as he pulled her down alongside him, wrapping a possessive arm around her shoulders.

'So who's the lady friend?' one intrepid reporter asked, obviously tiring of getting no answers about Marla and determined to get at least some copy to file and make today's expedition worthwhile. 'It's not often we get to see Australia's most eligible bachelor, let alone with a woman in tow.'

Like a barometer, his comment was indicative of a change

in the mood of the audience and instantly attention switched from Marla to Saskia. Any story was apparently better than none. Alex smiled at her as he turned from the waitress who'd taken his order for the best French champagne.

'No comment,' he said.

The reporters took the bait, focusing now on Saskia, hitting her with a barrage of questions, each indiscernible from the next. Saskia recoiled from the push of people and microphones, everything and everyone in her face, her eyes blinking at the never-ending flash of cameras, her heart thumping like a cornered rabbit, powering an urge to jump up and flee.

Alex held up one hand to quieten the mob while he took her hand in the other. 'Saskia is a good friend, nothing more.'

But the look he shot her for the benefit of the cameras was pure sin, hot with desire and so heavy with lust that even Saskia caught her breath as his eyes triggered an instantaneous feminine rush of hormones inside her. Under her wisp of a bra her breasts tingled, her nipples firmed and peaked, and electricity crackled from their aching tips all the way down to her core. She dredged up a smile in response as she clamped down on muscles suddenly making their unwelcome presence felt, battling to rein in her inner hormones. It was merely part of the act, she reminded herself stiffly, as the cameras went mad amidst more calls for details.

She smiled enigmatically for the cameras. At least she'd soon be out of here—her mission accomplished. Marla and Jake should have made it through to the first-class lounge by now, and thankfully her part in this charade would soon be over, with the press convinced she was some kind of girlfriend and totally unaware that by the time they reported it the big news affair would already be over.

'Maybe we should tell them after all, sweetheart?'

His words pulled her around, aghast. *Sweetheart?* Tell them *what?* Cold chills worked down her back and she knew she couldn't run now if she tried—her spine had turned to jelly, her legs would cave at the first step.

'Alex?' she whispered, looking for him to reassure her that this game was nearly over, even though her gut instinct told her that Alex was hardly the kind of man to suddenly turn from dragon into knight in shining armour.

'I know, I know,' he countered, still holding his other palm up as he nestled closer to her, his leg brushing against hers from hip to knee. Heated. Arousing.

*Irritating.*

'I know we meant to keep it just between ourselves for a little while longer.'

'Keep what between yourselves, Mr Koutoufides?' Reporters jostled for the best position, sensing a major announcement. 'So the lady's more than just a good friend?'

Saskia felt a roiling wave of panic course through her. What the hell was he playing at? She'd kept her end of the deal. Hadn't she done enough? She forced a smile to her face, leaned into his shoulder, and hissed, 'This isn't what we planned!'

He tugged her closer into the crook of his shoulder and pressed his lips to her hair. 'I know that, darling. But why wait?' He paused while champagne was poured, and ordered another half-dozen bottles so that everyone could join them in a toast.

'Gentlemen,' he announced, pulling Saskia to her feet alongside him. 'I'd like you to be the first to know. The beautiful Miss Prentice has just agreed to become my wife.'

# CHAPTER FOUR

THE atmosphere around them descended into pandemonium as cheers from watching travellers vied with even more questions. The pack were pushing and shoving around them, angling for the best photo opportunity, but Saskia was almost oblivious to the noise. White-hot fury blocked out almost everything and everyone—everyone, that was, apart from the smug tycoon standing alongside her.

'Alex!' she said. 'What the—?'

He didn't wait for her to finish. Whatever she'd been going to say, his mouth crushed the words flat. Shock registered in her eyes, in the way she held herself rigid, and in the exclamation he captured in his mouth. He pulled her hard against him to mould her closer, slanting his mouth over hers. It made a good fit even better. Her lips were lush and moist, her taste sweet and strangely welcoming, given her history of antagonism. She might not like to think she was involved in this kiss, but her body sure was, a body clad in little more than fabric less substantial than tissue paper. And underneath that sweet floral print lurked flesh so dangerously womanly he almost wished he was somewhere a whole lot more private.

He growled his appreciation and felt a tremor reverberate

through her in response, melting her curves into even closer contact with him.

His mobile phone sent out a single beep and his lips curved into a smile over hers. Marla and Jake were safe. Which meant he could stop kissing her now, he registered, even as his fingers splayed wide through her hair, keeping her tightly anchored as his mouth continued to take pleasure in hers. The plan had gone well. He'd kept the reporters entertained, no doubt drawing in any reporters hanging back to see what all the commotion was about, and now they had both a story and pictures to keep them happy. It was a win-win situation for everyone—including himself. He hadn't expected to have found diversionary tactics quite so enjoyable. But now he'd done enough.

Besides which, if he didn't stop kissing her soon, he wouldn't be fit to be seen in public.

Reluctantly he wound down the kiss, taking his time, savouring the fresh taste of woman, lush and ripe, in his mouth. He cradled her head in his arms as he ended it, wary that she still might want to tear him to pieces. But for now at least her fight was gone, her lips plump and pink, her cheeks flushed and her breathing fast and furious. She looked up at him with those large green eyes and he saw confusion competing with anger. Any minute now that anger was going to boil over, and he'd have a hard time containing it, but right now she looked stunned, thoroughly kissed and very, very beddable.

*Theos!*

One look at her and the reaction he'd sought to contain resumed, unabated. He spun her in front of him and wrapped his arms around her slim waist, feeling her slight gasp of shock as he drew her against his firmness as together they faced the press.

'Thank you,' he said, over questions about where they'd met and whether they'd set a date. 'But now you'll have to excuse us. We have a plane to catch. Feel free to stay and enjoy the champagne.'

Somehow Saskia made it to the escalators up to the first class lounge, her anger rising faster than the metal stairs beneath her feet. And once the sliding glass doors behind them had slid shut she wasn't staying silent any more.

'*That* wasn't part of the deal!'

He smiled down at her, even though he was standing one step behind, his arms spread wide on the risers. If he'd wanted to make her feel trapped his body language couldn't have been any clearer. 'The deal was for you to pretend to be my love interest. I'd say we were pretty convincing on that score, wouldn't you?'

She felt herself colouring under the cold perusal of his eyes—eyes that had looked at her with such savage heat just a few minutes ago, eyes that had all but incinerated her clothes from her. And the heat hadn't been restricted to his eyes. Once his mouth had meshed with hers, once his lips had bent hers to their will, temperatures had been rising everywhere. Compelling heat. Tempting heat. Heat that had stroked her senses and massaged her sensibilities. Heat that had curled into her secret places until they ached with longing.

Only when he'd pulled her in front of him and she'd felt the unmistakable evidence of his arousal pressing hard against her, the shocking equivalent of her own body's reaction, had that heat turned sour, curdling the juices of her stomach.

*Sickening heat.*

What the hell was he trying to prove?

'Those pictures are going to be splashed all over the papers by tomorrow.'

'I know,' he said, as if he was delighted by the prospect. 'The gutter press is nothing if not efficient.'

'Do you really think I want people to see me pictured— *like that*—with you?'

'Right now, I don't care what you want. It was the means to an end, nothing more.'

'So did you *have* to tell them we were engaged? What the hell was *that* all about?'

'I had to keep their interest,' he conceded. 'I didn't want them drifting off before Marla was safe.'

'Well, you sure kept their interest,' she snapped as they stepped off the escalator into the lounge proper, waiting until they'd been welcomed into the inner confines and been shown to a private room before continuing her tirade. 'But there'll be another story soon. It's going to be the shortest engagement in history.'

'Maybe not,' he answered with a smile, gesturing her to sit in one of the deep club chairs or small sofas surrounding a central coffee table.

She gazed around, momentarily losing her train of thought. 'Where's Marla? Didn't you say Marla was safe? I thought they would be here already.'

His eyes narrowed and his whole face seemed to tighten. 'Do you really think I'm letting you anywhere near Marla? It was enough of a risk having you both in the same house last night.'

'But I told you—'

'No,' he said flatly. 'Marla's safe. And you're not getting anywhere near her. We changed the arrangements last night. Jake is taking her on another airline. Right now they're half a terminal away.'

'I told you, I'm not interested in Marla!'

'Then we're all happy. What would you like to drink?'

She threw herself back into the chair. 'You mean you haven't had enough *celebratory champagne*? I think you should explain what you meant before.'

He curved a lazy eyebrow as he gave his order to the waitress. 'Before...?'

'When you said this engagement might not be the shortest engagement in history. What did you mean?'

He shrugged, as if it was of no consequence at all. 'Simply that it might suit us both to keep this "arrangement" going for a little longer—at least while you get your profile done.'

'You're kidding! You must be mad! This is hardly an "arrangement". You made an announcement. You lied to the press.'

'And tomorrow it will be fact. The world will believe we're to be married.'

'No,' she said, shaking her head. 'No way.'

'You'll find a way,' he said, raising his swiftly delivered glass of Scotch to her. 'Or you won't get your precious profile. It's as simple as that.'

'We already *have* an agreement! I've held up my end of the bargain.'

'I'm just extending some of the terms, that's all.'

'You're reneging on the agreement, that's what you're doing.'

'It makes sense for both of us. Although we'll be staying at Lake Tahoe while we're in the States, I do have a fundraiser to attend in New York in a couple of days. You'll no doubt want to be there, to get something for your profile, and if you *are* there, given this publicity, people are naturally going to ask about our engagement. It will be far less embarrassing to both of us if we maintain the image that we're engaged at least while we're to be seen together.'

'You mean maintain the deceit!' It was unthinkable. There was no way she could act like Alex's lover. It had been hard enough today. And what guarantee would she have that he wouldn't pull another stunt like that? 'I won't do it. I've done what I agreed to do. It's time to hold up your end of the bargain.'

He shrugged. 'That's too bad. Because if you won't do it, you won't be getting your profile.'

Blood pumped so hot and fast through her veins that she could feel it in her temples. 'Damn you! I should have known never to trust you. Knowing what you did to my father, the ruthless way you took over his business and crushed him, I should have realised you'd do anything to twist things your own sick way.'

His expression soured. His glass hit the table, slopping amber liquid over the sides, but he didn't seem to notice. His eyes were fixed on hers, his face filled with fury.

'And your father was such a paragon of business virtue? Don't give me that. He deserved everything he got. He *deserved* to be crushed!'

She stood up, her heart thumping in her chest, her blood pounding, outraged for her father who'd been destroyed by a ruthless takeover, outraged for her father who was now so ill and defenceless.

'How dare you? It's not enough to ruin the man's life and future. Now you have to stick the boot in with insults. Well, I've had enough of you twisting things your way. You can keep your profile, along with your phoney engagement. I'm telling the story I want to tell. You won't have to look for it—it will be everywhere—and it won't be pretty.'

'And what story is this?'

He sat back, his limbs sprawled over the furniture as if he owned it. The resentment was still there, but it was contained. And there was something new she didn't like—a smugness that irritated her bone-deep.

She looked around, aware that she might be making a scene, thankful that even if the noise of their argument escaped from this room the lounge outside was almost deserted, apart from a few travellers sprinkled around, either plugged into earphones, laptops or mobile phones. Then she looked back at Alex. 'I'm going to tell the world what you did—the way you crushed my father, the way you made a fool out of me.'

He only smiled in response, angering her still more, sending her hands clenching into fists, her nails pressing deep into her flesh as she reached boiling point. Her hands itched to let fly. Oh, to wipe that self-satisfied smile right off his face…

'This is a business magazine?' he said at last. 'Your *AlphaBiz*?'

She kicked up her chin. 'That's what I've been trying to tell you.'

'Do you really think the squalid history of your affair with the man you just became engaged to is going to be the stuff for business pages?' He waited a second, watching her, waiting for his words to sink in before he continued. 'On the other hand, maybe you could try to sell it at *Snap!* magazine. I hear they're always in the market for sordid tales. Perhaps they could use it instead of the pages they've got earmarked for Marla or some other poor victim?'

'But we're not really eng…'

Cold, chilling waves washed over her as the cruel implications of what he'd done to her today sank home. She had no story. Nobody would believe her now. Not once they'd seen the pictures of Alex kissing her spread all over the media. Why would someone who'd suffered such a shocking experience line up to marry the perpetrator? She'd be a laughing stock—if it was ever printed at all.

He'd painted her into a corner.

She'd been prepared to walk away from the profile, to walk away from her chances of promotion and a better level of care for her father—but only if she could have Alex Koutoufides's head on a platter. But now she had no chance of retribution if she took that course.

Revenge would have almost been worth the cost of losing everything. But now, if she walked away from this profile, she wouldn't get a thing. No revenge. No settling of old scores for what he'd done to her father. No satisfaction.

*And she'd be giving away all chance of getting that promotion and getting the kind of care her father needed.*

'You engineered that whole engagement fiasco!'

He barely raised an eyebrow. 'Of course I did. Did you expect to be able to hold the threat of telling what happened in the past over me the entire time?'

She swallowed, trying desperately to think and knowing instinctively that bluff was her only hope right now.

'It doesn't change anything. I'll still show everyone what a calculating animal you are. I'll tell them the truth—that you engineered this engagement to cover Marla's tracks.'

'Who do you think,' Alex persisted, 'is going to believe you? Nobody will take you seriously. Nobody.'

'But what you did to me! I was only seventeen.'

'And yet, if it was such a terrible experience, why would you turn around and be prepared to marry the man who subjected you to this awful experience?'

'You bastard! This engagement is a farce.'

'But the world won't know that.'

'I'll tell them! I'll make them believe me.'

'And risk making yourself look even more of a victim? Everyone will assume we've had a lovers' tiff, and that for whatever reason you're feeling aggrieved and want to get your own back. I admit it will be embarrassing, but it will hardly ruin my career. Yours, on the other hand…'

He raised an eyebrow and casually crossed his legs, brushing off an invisible fleck of nothing. When still she didn't move he said, 'You look like you could do with that drink now. Why don't you sit down?'

'I hate you,' she whispered, her teeth clenched. But she recognised that she had no choice, knew that bluffing was pointless and that if she wanted to use this opportunity to get back at Alex Koutoufides she was going to have to come up with a new way. Because he had her.

She sat down, as he'd suggested, but that didn't mean she was through with telling him how she felt.

'I hate the way you treat people—using them for whatever sick purpose you have, bending them to what you need them to be. I hate the way you destroy people and their dreams without a second glance. I hate the way you think you own the world.'

Without expression he regarded the remaining contents of his glass before tossing it back in one economical slug. 'I think I preferred it when I was kissing you.'

She tried to ignore the swift, sudden zipper of sensation that wrenched up her spine. 'And what's that supposed to mean?'

'It's the only time you haven't been arguing with me.'

For a moment she was frozen into inaction. Of course the kiss hadn't meant anything to him—what the hell had she thought he was going to say anyway?

'In that case,' she snipped, 'remember it fondly. Because silence like that sure as hell won't be happening again.'

Saskia came to and jerked upright, her vague dreams of warmth and comfort dissolving as the black limousine slowed to a crawl and edged onto a driveway. She looked around her as the car idled, its driver waiting for electronic gates to open. Through them she could see tall straight pine trees, spearing into the clear blue sky, and a large stone residence rising behind.

'What is this place? Are we at Lake Tahoe already?'

'So you're finally awake?' he said behind her. 'You have no further need of my shoulder?'

She looked around in horror—was he joking? But the look on her face told her he wasn't. His position, so close, with his arm extended along the back of the seat behind her, told her that the comfortable support she'd felt for her head had been none other than the crook of his shoulder, and that the warmth she'd been dreaming about and relishing had been none other than the body warmth of the man she abhorred more than anyone in the world.

She must have fallen asleep some time on the two hundred miles of Interstate from San Francisco—although it was barely the middle of the day here, and the flight itself had been relaxing. Or would have been relaxing, she admitted, if it hadn't been for the dark cloud of Alex sitting alongside her, ignoring her for the most part, regarding her through guarded eyes for the rest.

And when they'd entered this car they'd sat as far as possible away from each other. Somewhere along the Interstate that had all changed.

'I fell asleep,' she said, immediately feeling a fool as she realised how unnecessary it had been to say that. And just as instantaneously she changed her mind. It had been necessary. He had to be made to know there was no chance she would have used him for support if she'd been conscious.

She looked out of the window to cover her discomfiture—nothing to do with forcing her eyes from his unshaven skin, the dark stubble adding another texture, another dimension to the chiselled character of his face.

'I realise that,' he said, as the car proceeded down the long driveway. 'Do you usually talk in your sleep?'

Her head snapped right back. She was afraid of the unknown, but damned sure she wasn't going to let him know it. 'So what did I say? How much I hate you?'

He shrugged a little, one corner of his mouth rising as he pulled his arm down from the back of the seat and adjusted his shirt. 'No, I don't recall that.'

'Maybe I was just getting to the good bit,' she snapped, refusing to be cowed.

'Maybe,' he said, as if he didn't believe her. 'Ah, here we are.'

The car came to a stop outside the impressive building. Stone, timber and glass combined to form a two-storey masterpiece. 'This will be your home for the next week.'

'I'm staying here?'

'More or less. I'm putting you in the guesthouse on the lake's edge. I thought you'd appreciate the privacy. It's self-contained, with its own study.'

The fact he'd given any consideration to what she might appreciate surprised her. Likewise his knowledge of the place. She'd assumed he'd rented the house as some kind of bolthole. 'This place is yours?'

'It's one of my properties, yes.'

She looked up at the imposing façade of the house. 'You sure don't do modest well, do you?'

'I've earned everything I have.'

'That's one way of looking at it, I guess.'

'That's the *only* way of looking at it.'

She swung her head back round to look at him, letting ice infuse her words so that he could in no way mistake her meaning. 'If it makes you feel better.'

His eyelids stalled halfway over his eyes. 'I'll let Gerard

drive you around. You can settle in, and I'll come and give you a guided tour of where you can and cannot go on the property in, say, two hours from now?'

She almost laughed. So much for his consideration of her needs. She wasn't being offered privacy; she was being locked down in her own quarters. 'You trust me by myself all that time? I must have come up in the world.'

Behind him the door swung open, as if the driver had instinctively known it was time. Cool high country air swept into the car, the fresh smell of woods and lake flushing out the strained atmosphere.

'Two hours,' he said, stepping out.

'I can hardly wait,' she answered, too low for him to hear as the car pulled away from the main house and continued down the driveway through the trees. As they turned a bend, her breath caught in her throat as the brilliant blue of Lake Tahoe, framed by still snow-capped mountains, extended for miles in all directions.

And there, nestled between trees on a small plot of land edged by boulders, sat what had to be the guesthouse. Like a miniature version of the main house, it featured natural stone, timber and glass set to take in the views that extended for the entire three hundred and sixty degrees around.

Without a word Gerard brought her luggage inside as she explored the cottage, and withdrew just as discreetly, stopping only to ask if she required anything more. If he was unused to installing women in the guesthouse, he certainly didn't show it. Although Alex's lady-friends were much more likely to be received in the main house, she decided. It was only untrustworthy visitors such as she obviously was who would have to be locked away in the far corner of the property.

Though what a corner to be stuck in, she thought, as she

completed her exploration of the two-bedroom, two-bathroom cottage, complete with study and, she acknowledged, as her eyes fell thankfully on the communication facilities, a telephone and even internet capability. Perfect to get this profile done as quickly as possible and let her get out of here. And perfect for the calls she should make to home.

Alex had been right about one thing—she did appreciate the privacy. Even if his motives for stashing her here were entirely selfish.

An hour later, showered and changed into fresh clothes, and ready with a portfolio of her best profiles she wanted to show Alex when he arrived, she hung up the phone after her first call, tears in her eyes. Her father had barely been able to talk—the result of a viral infection, his visiting nurse had told her. Although thankfully she believed he was on the mend.

But damn his cold, damp flat! No way should he have to put up with that any longer—she was going to pull out all the stops to see that she made this promotion, and that her father got the care he so badly needed. If only he hadn't been so stubborn about not moving with her into her own tiny flat and cramping her style years ago—maybe she could have prevented all this.

She swiped back her tears and collected her thoughts, preparing herself for her next call, expecting it to be only marginally easier than her first. She heard the extension being picked up an entire country and an ocean away.

'Sir Rodney—'

'Saskia!' His voice was gruff and urgent. 'You're in all the papers! The Board want to know what the Dickens is going on. I told them you didn't get along with Alexander Koutoufides, like you told me, trying to get you a bit of sympathy here. But now all of a sudden you've not only managed to track him down, you've obviously got him eating out of your hand. What are you playing at?'

'Sir Rodney, listen to me. It's not what you think—'

'It's utter madness, that's what I think. I was expecting a profile. Instead we'll be lucky to end up with a wedding invitation. After all the protests you put up about taking on the assignment, you're not doing yourself any favours with the board for this promotion, you understand.'

'Please listen. Alex Koutoufides and I are *not* engaged.'

'What on earth were you thinking? I thought you *wanted* this promotion. What's that? What did you say?'

'I said we're not really engaged. It's all a sham.'

'But the papers all said…'

'You know newspapers,' Saskia replied, irony heavy in her voice. 'Never believe everything you read.'

'Then what's going on?'

'It's a long story,' she said. *And much too painful to relate right now.* 'But I just want you to know that I'm working on the profile and you'll have it on your desk as soon as possible, as agreed.'

'Just as well. Because you know what's at stake if you don't. Carmen's already managed the impossible, and has convinced Drago Maiolo to allow her to do his profile, so you've got a race on your hands if you really do want this job.'

Saskia tried to absorb the news about Carmen's progress philosophically. Carmen's assignment was bound to be less problematic, without the complications of a history angle to work through. Still, she'd hoped for more of an advantage in getting Alex's co-operation—co-operation that now seemed suspiciously weighted his way.

'I do want that job,' she said.

'Then I'm sure I don't have to tell you how important this assignment is to both of you,' the chairman continued. 'Only one of you can get this promotion. I want you to put everything you can into it—anything that might give you an edge over Carmen. Maybe you can use this strange arrangement of yours to your advantage. Do you think this so-called engagement might give you a different perspective? Something you might be able to exploit?'

'No,' she stated emphatically. 'The engagement won't cut it because there *is* no engagement. It won't be referred to in the article. And as far as I'm concerned the sooner it's forgotten, the better.'

'Then what about the Marla angle? Is there anything there worth pursuing, do you think? What is their relationship? What's it like to be a corporate hotshot with an aging wild-child sister? Is he afraid her bad press will impact on his business? The board want you to find out. There's *something* there, given that he kept the relationship quiet for so long.'

She sighed. 'I'm not sure about that line of attack, Sir Rodney. I've met Marla, and she still seems fragile from that awful *Snap!* feature. And I don't even know where she is at the moment. Alex has done everything he can to keep me away from her.'

'Well, you know the situation there. But you really have to pull out all stops with this one. Carmen's after this job, and it looks like she's off and running. If you can capture both Marla and Alex in your profile, you might just get the edge.'

Saskia gritted her teeth and looked up at the ceiling while she considered her response. Damn this sink-or-swim selection process! Sinking wasn't an option any more. Not now she wouldn't be able to take Alex down with her. She needed to swim if she was to secure this promotion—and fast.

But damn it all that she'd drawn the short straw and been assigned Alex Koutoufides! Especially now, if the board was looking to interfere with the way she worked.

She drew in a breath, not liking what she was hearing. 'Are you telling me that's what the board wants in this profile—the Marla angle played up? Because I'm telling you Alex isn't keen—he's put up barriers the whole time.'

'Who's doing this profile?' Sir Rodney demanded. 'You or Alex Koutoufides? If you expect to become editor-in-chief, don't think you're going to get away from making the tough choices and doing the tough asks.'

It wasn't the way she was used to working, and she wasn't about to start now. Not that she was going to discuss that with Sir Rodney when he was already annoyed with her over this whole engagement fiasco. But somehow she was going to have to find a way, find an angle, to make this profile the best she possibly could without compromising her own integrity and still giving her the edge over Carmen.

'I understand,' she said. 'And don't worry. I'll do it. I'll get you the best profile you and the board have ever seen.'

'I'm counting on it!' he grunted, before hanging up.

She put the phone down, her mind still reeling from the last few days' developments, her senses still torn with concern over her father's sudden deterioration, and yet still too sluggish from changing too many time zones too quickly to know how to deal with it all.

If only there was some straightforward way out of this mess!

But she was kidding herself if she thought there was an easy way out. Alex's ridiculous engagement sham had killed her escape route dead. Now there was no way out but to go forward. He'd made sure she had no choice but to do the profile. And now, with Sir Rodney's words about Carmen's progress, she would have to make it better than ever. But there was no way she was going to stoop to using Marla as bait. This profile was about Alex Koutoufides, it had always been about Alex. And that was what she was going to get.

Saskia heard a noise behind her. She turned and saw the man who'd been occupying her thoughts standing in the doorway to the office, his face like thunder, his stance battle-ready. Her stomach plummeted. How long had he been standing there?

And how much had he heard?

## CHAPTER FIVE

'YOU lying bitch!' He watched her take one guilty step towards him.

'Alex—'

'You liar,' he said, cutting her protest off, the blood in his veins surging and simmering into a crazy red foam that coloured his vision and crashed in his ears. 'All that garbage about wanting to interview me. All that rubbish about not being interested in Marla. Lies! All of it *lies*!'

'Alex, listen to me—' She took another step, but stopped dead when he started surging towards her.

'I knew it,' he jeered, coming to a stop right in front of her, so close that she had to crane her neck to look up at him. 'I knew you couldn't go on too long without showing what you were really made of. In spite of all your cries of innocence I knew what you were really after.'

'But it's not like that, I promise—'

'Is it any wonder I didn't want you talking to Marla?' he demanded, his index finger pointing damnably into her shoulder. 'You've obviously got the entire article scoped with—who was that?—your boss?'

'This profile is about you. Not Marla.'

'That wasn't your boss?'

She took a step back, then another, backing herself against the timber desk, swaying away from him as he followed her every move.

'It doesn't matter if it was, you have to understand—'

'Oh, don't worry.' He shook his head, the smile on his lips nowhere near reaching his eyes. 'I understand. I understand perfectly. You'll get this profile you agreed to. You're not sure how you'll get access to her, but you'll play the Marla angle up and you'll hand in the best profile ever. Isn't that what you promised?'

'Well, yes. But—'

'But nothing! You've lied from the start. You knew I'd never agree to let you interview Marla. So you thought that if you pretended to be interested in profiling *me* you'd get close enough to get the dirt on Marla. And you might have succeeded. It was a new angle. Nobody had tried getting to Marla via me before. And in spite of all my doubts, in spite of everything that warned me you were lying, I let you into my own home. I let you get close to Marla. And in spite of my trusting you, you let me down.'

'You never trusted me! Right from the start you've treated me like a cheat and a liar.'

He planted an arm either side of her on the desk, enjoying her desperation at her inability to shrink away from him any further.

'And is it any wonder?'

'What? Stop trying to take the higher moral ground, and stop pretending you let me into your home out of the goodness of your heart. You *never* trusted me. You only invited me into your house because you were too scared of what I was going to tell the world if you slammed the door in my face and afraid of what would happen to your business if you didn't!'

Her eyes were sparking green flame, her cheeks flushed, her

chest rising and falling rapidly, but all that mattered right now were those lips. Either fully animated and going at a hundred miles an hour, or lush and pink and warm when they finally stopped. *And he knew exactly how they felt when they did.*

'You're right,' he said.

She blinked. 'What?'

He scanned her face, watching her indignation turn to surprise, her eyes widening, her lips parting slightly, hesitant, uncertain...*waiting*.

He breathed in deep, inhaling the scent of her—a heady mix of one woman's clean individual smell enhanced with some fragrant lotion and all heightened by potent anger, *heightened by passion*—and he felt his own senses respond. He knew that scent. She'd drifted asleep in the car, her head lolling to the side, and he'd moved closer and thrown around his arm to support her. Only to have her nestle into his chest, fitting him as if she was made for it. So soft and trusting. So accepting. So different from how she was normally.

They'd stayed that way for at least an hour, her curves wedged tight and warm against him, her head tucked into the crook of his arm. And when she'd murmured something in her sleep, something indiscernible, he'd turned his face down to hers, thinking at first that she was stirring, and had felt her warm breath brush against his face, her lips so close, her scent so inviting, her body so warm and supple... But she'd still been asleep, her breath a warm promise against his skin, and as for those lips...

Right now he lifted one hand, unable to resist any longer, touching the pads of his fingers to the twin layers of their sculpted perfection.

'I said, you're right. I didn't want you to go public on what you knew.'

Her eyes dipped in one long blink, remaining still while he traced his fingers over the line of her lips, only the telltale flickering of the pulse in her throat betraying her nervousness.

'I didn't want you to go public on what happened between us.'

Her eyes opened and she swallowed, her lips moving under his fingers as the action in her muscles kicked up her chin. 'And now you've seen to it that I can't.' Her voice came across as rough and husky. *Sex with an edge*, he determined with some satisfaction.

He allowed himself a smile as he let his fingers drift lower, following the line of her jaw down to her throat, tracing the back of his hand down over the scoop neck of her knitted top. She shuddered under his touch, but she didn't pull away and neither did she lower her eyes.

'So I have,' he agreed, aware that his own voice had dropped an octave. 'So where does that leave us now?'

Her eyes were wide, the colour of emeralds sparkling back at him.

'It leaves me stuck here with you—trying for a different story entirely.'

'So maybe…' he ventured softly, '…maybe I should help you out with one.'

His eyes were dark seduction, his lips an invitation to desire. And when they touched hers barely, hardly at all, with just the lightest of touches, a switch flicked on inside her that sent her internal thermostat whirling and turned heated anger into a long, slow burn. She shuddered as his lips moved over hers, surprisingly tender, gently coaxing, achingly sweet, and her own lips could not help but accept his invitation.

So different from that kiss in the airport. That had been squeezed from her, stolen, wrenched from her like some trophy.

This kiss was like a dance set to the music of her beating heart, the rhythm slow and magical, mesmerising, evocative.

She felt one hand slide behind her neck, supporting her head as he deepened the kiss, his warm breath blending with his taste, his lips, his tongue seeking entry, gently probing, coupling with hers.

And it was, if the crust of the previous years had cracked and fallen away. It was like coming home. Because she recognised his taste, she recognised his touch. She let her hands do what they wanted, let them skim over his back, reacquainting themselves with familiar territory while his hands did the same, his touch so well-remembered, so cherished, so long missed. She didn't protest when he hoisted her up the short distance onto the desk. She made no sound other than to gasp when he cupped one breast with his hand and rolled one straining nipple between his fingers. She welcomed the way he found his way under her top so that she could feel his hand on her breast without barrier, his skin on hers. Compelling. Undeniable. Electric.

Was it minutes she felt him at her breasts? Or only seconds? Time expanded, each second filled with sensations too many to catalogue, too delicious to bother.

And then his hand was on her leg, shrugging away her skirt, sliding ever upwards, searing a path along skin to the place that wanted him, needed him, ached for him.

And when, like a replay of how his kiss had started, light and gentle and barely there, he touched her, she wanted to cry out with the bittersweet joy of it all. How many times had she dreamed this dream? Finding Alex the way he'd been, so caring and thoughtful and loving?

How many times had she longed for a repeat of just this special touch?

And now her dream had become reality.

This was the Alex she'd known. This was the way he'd made her feel. This was the Alex she loved.

*No!*

Her eyes snapped open.

Not loved.

*Had* loved.

This was the Alex who'd betrayed her.

This was the Alex she hated!

And yet she was letting him do this to her! His mouth was on her throat, hot open-mouthed kisses burning her skin, his hand pushing aside her panties, seeking entry…

She pushed hard at his shoulders. 'Alex. No.'

'Oh, yes,' he murmured, barely taking his mouth from her flesh.

She pressed her legs together, trying to stop him. 'No! Stop this.'

He levered his head away far enough to look her in the eyes, but he didn't remove his hand, continuing to gently stroke her in spite of the pressure of her thighs around him, continuing to find the sensitive nub of her femininity, issuing a challenge that he made it hard to overcome.

'Give me one good reason why I should.'

'Because I *hate* you.'

He allowed himself a smile. 'I figured as much. I could tell that by the way you groan every time I do this.' The pad of his thumb circled her, sending sensations shuddering through her, the barrier of her silk underwear no protection. She raised her eyes to the ceiling and dragged in a breath that was too full of the taste of him to fight. '*Now* tell me you want me to stop,' he dared.

'I—want—you—to…' The next word was nothing but a blur.

'I'm not convinced,' he replied with a low laugh, his fingers testing the lace edging of her panties, creeping beneath, undermining her resolve in the most potent way imaginable.

But she couldn't let him. Not now. Not ever. And breathlessly she battled to bring back all the reasons why.

'No,' she breathed, desperate. 'You have to stop.'

'Really? And why would that be?'

'You mean you've forgotten?' she taunted, with a shove at his shoulders, clutching onto the one thing she remembered so vividly from those days gone by. 'Because you "don't *do* virgins"!'

Alex drew back, allowing her enough room to escape from the desk and his confines to straighten her skirt and top, those words of hers jarring in his memory.

He'd told her that, he remembered. Was she still so resentful that he hadn't finished off what he'd started back then that she'd throw his words back in his face like that?

'So is this your idea of payback? Replaying a scene from years ago so it's you that has the upper hand this time?'

Saskia looked blankly at him, her empty stare frustrating him.

'Oh, come on. There has to be some reason why you'd pull a stunt like that. I mean, you're what? Twenty-five or twenty-six. It's not as if you could still be a virgin.'

She turned her face away. Too fast. But not before he'd seen the honest truth slice across her eyes, the hurt…

'Oh, my God,' he said, surprise fuelling an irrational burst of laughter. 'Who would have thought it? You *are*.'

'Don't make me sound like some kind of freak!'

Her voice fractured on the last word and she spun, her arms crossed, towards the wall. He took a step closer. 'I don't think you're a freak. I'm just surprised.' Very surprised, he thought, given her age and the kind of work she did and the people she'd mix with. It didn't seem the kind of work where you'd keep anything intact for too long, whether it was ethics, integrity or virginity.

But, notwithstanding her occupation, he was more surprised that someone as stunning as she was hadn't been seduced plenty of times, let alone once. Surprised and somewhat strangely, given the circumstances, even a bit pleased.

'Saskia?' he said, reaching out a hand to her shoulder.

'Don't touch me!'

She spun around to face him, her green eyes almost too large for her face, her lashes dark with moisture. But she was still coming out fighting.

'What kind of man are you? One moment you're accusing me of lying to you, of being here to drag Marla's name through the papers, and the next you've got me sprawled on the desk, pawing at me like you're some kind of animal.'

Her words sat uncomfortably with him, rankled with him. He didn't understand it either, but he sure as hell wasn't going to admit it.

'You're tired,' he said. 'Tired and emotional. Let's leave the guided tour until tomorrow. Maybe you should take a nap, and I'll have someone bring you dinner from the house a bit later.'

'Don't patronise me,' she spat. 'And don't bother with a meal. I don't want anything from you beyond one business profile. Nothing more.'

He felt a muscle in his jaw pop. 'A little while ago it was clear you wanted much more than that.'

She had the grace to colour at that. 'A little while ago I wasn't thinking. What's *your* excuse?'

* * *

Tahoe usually relaxed him. Even when he was working in his state-of-the-art office the lake and the woods and even the winter snows calmed him. It was a haven from Sydney and the office, but it was also a place from which he could rule his empire away from the day-to-day distractions of office life. It was supposed to relax him. That was the theory.

But he didn't have to look in a mirror right now to know that he was scowling as he walked back along the path to the house. Damn her. And damn his body's reaction. Though who could blame it? She'd been willing. So what was that she'd said about not thinking at the time? Hell, how much thinking was involved in knowing you wanted someone? It wasn't *University Challenge*.

What was it about her that made him want to forget why he shouldn't touch her—and why he shouldn't want to?

The portfolio she'd thrust into his hands before he'd departed slapped against his leg. He lifted it, regarding its burgundy cover critically. Did she really think a collection of her pieces was going to make a difference to anything now? Not a chance.

The morning was crystal clear, the air so chilled from both the elevation and the remnants of the season's snow that her breath turned to fog as she walked along the boulder-strewn shoreline. Saskia hugged her jacket closer around her and wandered out along the timber pier built into the water.

It was early, not long after dawn, but she hadn't been able to stay in bed. Her body clock was out of whack. Before her the lake stretched miles in every direction, the surface of the water almost polished smooth. Two ducks glided effortlessly across the small bay, their wake the only disturbance to the mirror-like finish of the water.

It was beautiful here. The water so clear she could see the rock-strewn sand below, the air so clean it hurt. If it wasn't for Alex she might almost imagine enjoying her stay.

'You're up early.'

She jumped and spun around. A woman stood on the shore, watching her, her hands deeply buried in her jacket pockets, her face framed with the fluffy fur lining of her hood. But she still recognised her immediately.

'Marla. I didn't hear anyone coming.'

The woman walked towards her, her fancy pink western boots clomping as she sashayed up onto the wooden deck. She stood alongside Saskia, took a deep breath and looked around. 'I just love it here,' she said, smiling. 'It's my favourite place in the world.'

'I didn't realise you were staying here.'

'I wasn't supposed to be. Alex had me booked into a clinic nearby, but I refused point-blank to go. I can't stand the kind of people they get in those places. Desperate movie stars, failed musicians—the whole nip and tuck set. *Ugh.* Don't get me wrong—I know I'm far from perfect, and I like a margarita just as much as the next girl—well…' She smiled conspiratorially and a little sadly and conceded, '…maybe just a tad more. But I know that if anyone makes me go to group therapy one more time I'm going to throw up.'

Saskia laughed for the first time in what seemed like for ever, and then looked over her shoulder self-consciously to where the house loomed up on one side. Could anyone see them down here?

'I'm not supposed to have anything to do with you, you know.'

'I know. Alex told me the same thing.' She pulled a manicured hand from a pocket and placed it on Saskia's, her eyes as brilliant a blue as the ice-cold depths of the lake. 'But I get so tired of being told what to do. Don't you?'

Oh, yes, she thought with a vengeance. But I need this profile. Otherwise things might be different.

'He doesn't trust me,' she told Marla by way of explanation. 'He thinks I want to do some sort of exposé on you.'

Marla laughed, throwing her head up high, and putting her hand back in her pocket. 'My brother is the consummate Mediterranean man—even though our mother was a true-blue Australian. He takes after his father and he doesn't trust anyone, let alone anyone from the press. I have to say I've given him fairly good cause to be wary over the past few years. He's probably entitled to a little paranoia.'

'So you're not worried I'm here to get the scoop on you?'

Marla shook her head. 'If you really wanted to interview me I figure you would have found a way before now. I'll risk it. Besides, I wanted to thank you.'

'Whatever for? Helping you get through the airport?'

'Partly. You don't know what a drag it is not to be able to move without cameras being stuck in your face.'

Saskia grimaced, remembering the melee at the airport. 'Oh, I think I have some idea. I'd hate it, I know.'

'But I really wanted to say thanks for whatever it is you're doing to Alex. You've really got under his skin—I expected more of a fight last night over my refusing to go to the clinic, but it's like he's lost focus. For once he's not permanently on my case. Thanks for taking the heat off me for a while.'

Saskia studied the almost perfect reflection of the trees and the mountains in the lake while she mulled over Marla's words. Alex certainly hadn't lacked any focus yesterday when he'd come on to her. Quite the contrary.

'You know he's told the press we're engaged?'

'Oh, God, I know. It's even made it into the papers here. Haven't you seen? I can get some papers sent over to the guesthouse.'

'Thanks all the same,' Saskia replied. 'But I really don't think I want to see them.'

They stood together at the end of the small pier, silently watching the sun lift over the mountains on the eastern side of the lake, until finally Marla sighed. 'I'd better get back before Jake returns from the gym, notices me missing and puts out an APB. That man really is driving me crazy. Will I see you tomorrow morning, before you leave for New York?'

It took a moment for Saskia to make the connection.

'Oh, you mean the fundraiser? Alex mentioned something before our flight here.' She shook her head. 'But I don't know any of the details.'

'He's taking you to show off as his new fiancée—another exercise in calling the press dogs off me. He's determined to take his brotherly obligations seriously, it seems. I guess I ask for it. It must be a real drag having a middle-aged sister who's totally unemployable and who's got no talent other than to get herself photographed in the most embarrassing predicaments with the worst guys she possibly could.'

'Oh, come on. You're too hard on yourself.'

Marla raised her perfectly sculpted eyebrows, but the ironic smile on her face looked genuine enough.

'Thanks. You're sweet, but I'm not too stupid to realise my own failings. Even though the press like to make more of them than they really are.' She looked up sharply. 'Oh, I didn't mean you.'

'I know,' Saskia conceded with a smile, surprised to find she liked Alex's sister so much. She hadn't expected to. With her bad press, and with her brother's rabid defence of her, she hadn't known what to expect.

'I really have to go, but I'll look out for you here tomorrow morning. It's so nice to have another woman to talk to for a change. And, Saskia?'

'Yes?'

'Do you think you could do a favour for me?'

'Sure.' She shrugged. 'If I can. What is it?'

Marla hesitated, her smile sheepish. 'Do you know anything about publishing—I mean book publishing?'

Saskia surveyed the woman suspiciously. 'Well, a little. I did do one writing unit in my business degree and I've got some connections in the industry. Why?'

The older woman had a hopeful expression. 'A friend of mine wrote down some stories—sort of snippets of her life in anecdotes, nothing fancy. I read it, but I really don't know if it's any good. Do you think you could look it over for her? Maybe even pass it on to someone if it's any good?'

Saskia didn't flinch, even though every cell was on red alert. 'For your *friend*?'

Marla nodded, her blue eyes large and pleading. 'She'd really appreciate it. Please? I'll bring it tomorrow morning, same time, if that's okay?'

'I'm not sure,' Saskia offered in response, not falling for that 'friend' story for an instant. 'I don't think Alex would like it.'

'Please?' Marla implored. 'It's so important to her. And he doesn't have to find out. It'll be our little secret. And it would make my friend so happy.'

She looked so hopeful, almost desperate, and Saskia felt for her. It couldn't be easy being Alex's sister, despite her wealth and creature comforts.

'Of course I will,' she relented, watching the other woman's expression turn to delight even while knowing she must be mad to even consider it. Whatever that book contained, it could be pure dynamite in the wrong hands. If Alex so much as got wind of what she was doing she'd be dead meat.

Which meant she'd just have to make sure he didn't.

# CHAPTER SIX

ALEX KOUTOUFIDES was not in a good mood. He couldn't blame it on the weather—at thirty-five thousand feet above the clouds the sun shone in a perfect azure sky as the private jet tracked to New York City. And for once he couldn't blame it on Marla. This morning she'd seemed happier than she had in years, her eyes bright and her smile infectious despite being 'locked away', as she put it, with her jailer, Jake. He couldn't even blame it on the fact he had to attend tonight's fundraiser. In the last few years he'd shunned all but the most select invitations to such events, but even the fact he was going to this one wasn't the reason for his deep-seated irritation.

No, the reason he felt so damned uncomfortable had much more to do with a certain file of articles he'd read last night.

He hadn't meant to read them. His intention had been to flick through and find enough evidence to support his prejudices before tossing the portfolio away, satisfied.

But that hadn't happened. His dismissive flick through had become hijacked by the very first article—a profile on Ralph Schneider, a senior member of the board of the World Bank, a man Alex had met on several occasions, and his interest had been piqued. Instead of finding the lightweight fluff he'd expected, he'd found the article in-depth and well researched, business information and facts balanced with a personal take on the man's character that Alex had found himself agreeing with. Somehow she'd meshed those different worlds to build a picture of a giant in business circles—a giant with a heart, and a giant you could trust to do business with.

But then he'd thought maybe Ralph had been an easy target? He was one of the business world's good guys, after all. He'd turned the page to the next profile—this time a billionaire UK property developer with a reputation for big talk and bigger buildings, and with almost celebrity status for his well-publicised charitable donations. Alex's attention had been riveted. He'd had dealings with a branch of this man's conglomerate back in Sydney, and there was no way he'd ever deal with any of his businesses again, after they'd cut corners on the contract and not delivered to specifications. Here was a man who would have tested her powers of perception.

But again Saskia's reporting of his business empire had been excellent, her coverage of the time she'd spent in his offices fascinating—and as for her profile of the man himself? Outwardly generous, she'd acknowledged, but, for all his popular media persona, definitely not a man to be messed with, and perhaps even one with whom to ensure more than ever that contracts were watertight.

It was a brilliant piece of journalism. There was enough in the article to make the property star feel good about himself, but there was plenty of subtext to make anyone dealing with him wary and cautious.

Alex had devoured the balance of the profiles, trying to find fault or a hint of gossip, but even while Saskia had taken measure of her profilees, she'd not touched on their personal lives. If they had mistresses—and he knew at least three of them who were so-called 'happily married' did—there was no mention of it. There was no mention of rumours of sexual preference, no hint of scandal. It was all extremely well researched and balanced.

In the end he'd flung the file away out of sheer frustration.

No wonder he felt sick. He'd accused her of wanting to get close to Marla. Time and time again she'd denied it, and still he hadn't quite believed her. But if the articles in that file were indicative of the kind of profile she intended to do on him, then he'd completely misjudged her from the start.

*Theos!*

He stole a look at her in the armchair alongside. Her eyes were glued to the window now, although she'd been busy for most of the flight, writing notes, or drafts, or whatever it was she was doing. What would she write about *him*? What would her profile say about *his* character after the way he'd treated her? It was hardly likely to be flattering. Would she stick to business, or would she be tempted to tell it how it really had been? A man who had promised her everything but delivered nothing? A man who had taken advantage and then taken nothing, and in doing so had left humiliation into the bargain? It was hardly the kind of analysis he wanted out there.

He'd rather not think about that right now.

Soon they'd be landing at JFK. Once this weekend was out the way and they were back in Tahoe he'd give her all the time she needed to get her profile done. And then she could go home, back to her life. Leave him to his. Let him get back to the way he liked to live.

But first they'd make tonight convincing. So what that Saskia wasn't interested in Marla's story? Plenty of others were, and the longer he could distract them, the more likely they were to let her go. He felt in his pocket for the object he'd removed from his safe earlier. He could put the profile off for a couple of days, but some things couldn't wait.

'Here—put this on.'

Reluctantly Saskia peeled her eyes from the window and the view of New York City coming into sight as the privately leased jet banked for its landing approach. They'd barely spoken on the way to the airport and through the flight—Alex seemingly locked up in his own thoughts. And if his mood was as dark as the glower on his face, she was glad he wasn't in the mood for conversation.

'What's that?' she asked as she turned, certain she couldn't have heard him properly. Then her eyes registered what he was holding and she plastered herself back against her wide armchair. 'Oh, no,' she said. 'I don't want it.'

'I'm not asking you,' he said impatiently, lifting the offending article towards her as if he was as keen to get rid of it as she was reluctant to take it. 'I'm telling you. You need to put this on. People will expect it.' She was still shaking her head as he continued, 'It'll be the first thing they'll expect to see.'

He was right. She knew it instinctively. But that didn't make the concept any more palatable. Pretending to be engaged to Alex Koutoufides was one thing. Wearing his ring, a concrete symbol of the promise they were supposed to have made to each other, of the vows they would make if this engagement had been anything other than a farce, was another.

*Concrete nothing,* she thought with derision. Concrete didn't flash and sparkle like these gems did. These diamonds would scream that she belonged to Alex Koutoufides—lock, stock and barrel.

'You don't like it?'

What was not to like? Its design was as masterful as it was spectacular. A large square cut diamond sat atop a two-tone band already filled to overflowing with a river of baguette-cut diamonds, flashing light and colour from hundreds of brilliant-cut faces.

'Does it matter what I think?' she snapped, knowing there was no point getting attached to it anyway. It wasn't as if it was hers to keep.

'No,' he conceded brusquely, his mood obviously not having improved recently. He reached for her hand before she could snatch it away. 'Not in the least.'

She swallowed as he took her hand in his, their palms brushing, his long fingers cradling her wrist. Why was it that just touching him set her temperature rocketing and jolted her heartbeat into double time? Or was she merely remembering the last time he'd touched her—and where he'd touched her—with those hands?

She must be shaking. His fingers suddenly gripped her wrist more securely. Could he feel her erratic pulse with his fingers? Could he tell how frantically her heart was beating right now?

With his right hand he slipped the ring on, gliding the gold and platinum band along her finger until it came to rest—an almost perfect fit. For a second he didn't move, just cupped her hand in his while in between them the ring sparkled and flashed, mocking them both with white fire.

'There,' he said at last, as if that solved everything. He let her go and sat back in his chair, his eyes closed while the plane made its final approach.

She lifted her hand, feeling the unfamiliar weight of the ring. 'How did you know?'

'Know what?' he asked, without opening his eyes or looking at her.

'What size ring to get.'

'I didn't,' he responded, almost as if he were bored. 'It was my mother's.'

Something squeezed tight in her chest. This was *wrong*! This was no quick purchase made on ebay. This was a family heirloom—an heirloom she had no right to be wearing.

'You can't expect me to wear this. Not your mother's!' She made to pull off the ring, but just as quickly he swung himself around and imprisoned both her hands in his.

'You will wear it. It's the ring she wanted me to give to my fiancée.'

'But I'm not—'

He moved closer, putting himself right in her face. 'When we're in public you are. It's expected of you. You might as well start acting like it.'

She tugged her hands out from under his. 'Fine. I can play the lovestruck fiancée. But let's not have a repeat of what happened at the airport. Pretending to be engaged doesn't mean you get to paw me in public.'

He glared at her, his charcoal eyes narrowing. 'If we're going to convince people that we're soon to become a happily married couple I'll do whatever it takes, and you *will* co-operate.'

The small jet bumped its way onto the tarmac and the engines screamed into reverse thrust. She knew just how they felt—having their efforts changed at the whim of someone who cared nothing but demanded all his machinery performed to his will. She felt like screaming too. But she was no machine. She deserved better than this constant frustration.

'I hope you're going to allocate me some time soon, to really get started on this profile. You've already wasted hours on today's flight, when you could have dealt with some questions I need answers for.'

He drew in a breath and let it out slowly. 'Where's the fire?'

*Right now, it's boiling my blood!* 'The sooner I get this profile done, the sooner I can get out of your hair and the sooner we can abandon this farce of an engagement you dreamed up. Surely that's what you want? But you've done nothing to help me yet.'

'I don't want to fight. Why can't you just enjoy a fun weekend in New York?'

'Fun? Pretending to be your floozy?' Saskia laughed, a laugh born out of frustration. 'I don't even know why you're persisting with this trip. I can't see that Marla is under any particular threat that you need to save her from, and our engagement story is old news by now. What are you even doing here? I can't imagine why they even invited you. I would have thought a fundraiser in New York was the last thing a known recluse would head for.'

'It is,' Alex agreed through gritted teeth, his indigestion getting worse by the minute as the plane came to a halt on the tarmac. 'Which is why it's so charming to have your delightful company.'

Saskia couldn't help but gasp as they entered the Starlight Roof of the Waldorf-Astoria hotel. If the grand marble rotunda in the entry foyer hadn't been impressive enough, the sight of the spacious art deco ballroom filled with tuxedo-clad men and stunningly dressed women stole her breath away. She'd been places in her career, accompanied businessmen and politicians while they went about their business in all manner of occasions and venues, but nothing compared to the rich opulence of this venue, with its two-storey-high windows framed by damask silks, its gilded ceiling and magnificent Austrian crystal chandeliers.

She gave up a silent prayer of thanks for giving in when

Alex had insisted on providing her with a gown for the evening. He'd already pressed upon her a closet full of clothes for their US trip, and she'd chosen from it a cobalt-blue silk pantsuit to wear—classy, but restrained, she'd thought. But this gown he'd had delivered to her room that afternoon, together with a tiara and a note that this was what she would wear for the evening.

The flash of rebellion she'd felt when she received the message had been short-lived once she'd taken a decent look at the over-the-top golden Oscar de la Renta silk taffeta gown and the diamanté studded tiara with it. Until then the cobalt silk suit had been the most gorgeous thing she'd ever seen. Now, looking around the ballroom, she knew that it wouldn't have cut the mustard. Not in this crowd.

It was sheer fantasy. A long, long time ago this would have been her deepest wish—to be seen in a dress such as this, on Alex's arm and wearing his engagement ring.

It was strange. She couldn't wait to get this profile done. She couldn't wait to get away from Alex Koutoufides and go home. But just for tonight she felt like royalty. Tonight she was a princess. And tonight she was here with the most handsome man in the room.

Why not enjoy it?

Alex tugged at her arm, wanting to get their entrance over. He hated events like this, though strangely for once he didn't feel so out of place. With Saskia on his arm, looking a million bucks in the gown he'd chosen from the shortlist Marla had come up with, for the first time since he'd begun attending the annual Baxter Foundation Ball he didn't feel the urge to leave within the first ten minutes. With Saskia to show off, he might even make it to twenty.

Cameras flashed in their faces, increasingly more so as

the reporters realised who they had in their sights. 'Mr Koutoufides,' someone called excitedly, trying to get his attention. 'Have you two set a date yet?'

Alex looked down at his partner who, surprisingly, instead of having to be reminded of her duty, he found beaming up at him, her green eyes sparking happiness and her lush lips turned into such a beautiful smile it completely blindsided him. Her hair was arranged Grecian goddess-style, topped with a tiara, leaving tendrils coiling around her face that he itched to wrap his fingers around to reel her face closer to his lips. If she kept playing the role as well as this he wouldn't make twenty minutes after all—he'd have her out of here and planted in his bed in under five.

As if sensing his hesitation, she placed a hand over his own—the hand bearing the ring he'd given her earlier—and the cameras took no time in focusing in on it as it sparkled and flashed in their lenses.

'As far as I'm concerned,' he said, feeling his own smile broaden, 'the sooner the better.'

Her eyes widened, her smile wavered, but she kept looking up into his eyes in that way she had, as if they were digging into his very soul, until he wondered once again if he hadn't done the very worst thing he possibly could by insisting she accompany him tonight.

And then the music started, and inspiration wiped out any regrets. Why bother thinking about the mistakes he'd made? Why think about who she was and what her father had done? Why bother beating himself up over things he couldn't change, things that could never be repaired, when instead he could simply take this woman into his arms and hold her close?

'Dance with me,' he said, taking her hand, already leading her to the dance floor. And silently she acquiesced, letting him lead her, letting him fold her into his arms as he drew her close and started moving to the music of the ten-piece orchestra.

She found her space in his arms as if it had been made for her, moulding to his body, moving with him like liquid warmth, and yet still turning him rock-hard.

He inhaled her scent, devoured it, letting it feed into his senses like a drug. Class and sweetness and lush, ripe woman combining in one package to make the ultimate aphrodisiac.

That number ended, the next began, and even the next after that. But still he didn't relinquish her. He kept her wrapped in the circle of his arms, drawing her even closer with every movement, until they were so close she rested her head at his neck. Their bodies were pressed together from head to toe, moving to the beat, moving with each other, until they were moving more to the primitive rhythm of their own bodies than the music of the orchestra.

Saskia didn't want it to end. She was barely conscious of the changes in the music, hardly registered when one number merged into the next, and then the next. If this was pretending to be Alex's fiancée, she'd volunteer for the job permanently. No pressure, no arguments, just the magic feeling of her body pressed up against his, the tang of his masculine scent winding its way through her, the feel of his arms around her, his hands on her—possessive, commanding, intoxicating.

*The way he used to feel.*

She could stay this way all night if he wanted…

'Saskia Prentice! I don't believe it.'

The familiar cultured girls' school tones knifed into her consciousness. She unpeeled herself from Alex in an instant, breathless and gasping, feeling the heat from every part of her body transfer to her exposed flesh.

'It *is* you! Wow, don't you look sensational?'

Saskia reluctantly blinked the last of her dreams away and plastered a smile to a face so obviously burning with embarrassment that not even the subtle lighting over the dance floor could save her.

'Carmen.' Quickly she recovered enough from her embarrassment to make the introductions. 'I didn't expect to see you here.'

Carmen smiled knowingly and took Saskia's arm, skilfully flashing the diamond lights of the engagement ring as she negotiated them away from the dance floor while raking her eyes over Saskia's dress in such a way that she could almost see the dollar signs ticking over. Not that Carmen's own gown was any slouch, wrapping her slim figure in formfitting backless silver satin.

'Drago's just gone to get us some champagne. I'm here working tonight—just like you.' Her words might have been intended for Saskia, but her attention was now one hundred percent focused on the man at her side. 'Or maybe not like you,' she said with a soft laugh that made the ends of her sleek black bob sway with her glittering diamond drop earrings. 'I hear congratulations are in order? I didn't quite believe it before, but seeing the size of those rocks on Saskia's finger, and the way the groom-to-be looks at his betrothed, maybe there's some truth to it after all.'

Carmen raised one perfectly manicured diamante-studded fingernail and pressed it to Alex's chest. 'So this is the great Alexander Koutoufides,' she whispered huskily. '*Lucky* Saskia. Who says you can't combine business with pleasure? *I* always try to.' Her smile was too wide, her eyes sharp and pointedly bright, and even the provocative tilt of her body combined to suggest an offer.

Saskia couldn't ignore the blatant messages Carmen was putting out, even though she knew the woman too well to be surprised—if marriage didn't render a man off-limits, then a mere engagement would hardly register. No doubt she'd have a field day if she thought there was anything false about their engagement. She'd be all over Alex like a rash. Just thinking about it had Saskia's hackles rising.

*Frustration,* she told herself. She was frustrated at the interruption, frustrated at having her rival reminding her of the task at hand, and frustrated at being ignored by the both of them.

She was definitely not jealous. Why would she be? She had no designs on Alex Koutoufides.

Alex smiled in return as he lifted one hand and snared Carmen's, holding it closely between them before touching his lips to her fingers and taking an age to lower it to her side. Saskia knew, because she was counting the seconds.

'You're colleagues, then?' he asked, his full attention focused on Carmen's smiling face, on her delight at his gallant gesture.

'We are. Or rather we *were*. I assume we won't be seeing much of Saskia any more, though, now that she has such a handsome man to keep her busy? Such a shame. I was really looking forward to this competition. But I guess this means she's out of the race?'

'Actually, I'm still very much *in* the race,' Saskia stressed, sick of being excluded from the private exchange going on in front of her and silently cursing the arrangement that was threatening to railroad her chances of success. But she was stuck. She wasn't about to explain to Carmen the nature of her arrangement with Alex. The board were aware of the situation, and that was all that mattered. 'Our engagement changes nothing—'

'What competition?' interrupted Alex.

Carmen smiled up at him. 'Hasn't she told you? The editor-in-chief's position is up for grabs, and we're both in the running for it. Whoever turns in the best profile from our latest assignments gets the job.'

Finally he dragged his gaze from Carmen's and looked down into hers. His eyes were seemingly expressionless, and yet still she could feel them scanning for the truth, searching for answers. She blinked a silent affirmation when in reality she wanted to yell at him, wanted him to know *that* was why she was so desperate to get this damn profile started.

'I've been assigned Drago Maiolo,' Carmen continued, oblivious to the exchange. 'Ah, speaking of whom…'

A squat greying gentleman joined the party, his heavy-lidded eyes flicking over them, cooling as they passed over Alex but warming considerably when he came to Saskia. He handed Carmen her glass and immediately conceded his own to Saskia.

'I see you've found your friends.' His voice was almost as thick as his features, and it seemed to rumble up from below like an approaching roll of thunder.

Carmen smiled her thanks and nestled into his arm on a shrug of innocence. 'Drago told me Alex would be here. I figured you might be too.'

'How did he know?' Saskia asked.

'Alex is *always* here,' Drago replied, answering for her. 'He's been the major benefactor of the Baxter Foundation for years. Isn't that right, Alex?'

'Alex?' Saskia asked, looking for confirmation.

'How are things?' he directed to Drago, without answering either question, tension obvious in the firm set of his jaw.

'Never better. Especially now I have Carmen here to brighten up my nights. I usually have no time for newspaper people, but this woman is something different. I had no idea an interview could be so…stimulating.'

Drago and Carmen both laughed, even while Carmen

squirmed and redirected one roaming hand from low behind her. 'Drago's been most co-operative,' she conceded. 'It's going to be a fabulous profile.'

'It had better be,' Alex replied. 'Or you won't stand a chance of that promotion. I've seen the work Saskia does and it's excellent. And now, if you'll excuse us, I've just seen someone I really should talk to before the speeches get underway.'

He ignored Saskia's open-mouthed response as he steered her away from the couple, leading her up the stairs to the balcony above. She didn't know who was the more dumbfounded—Carmen, at being so thoroughly and cleanly put in her place, or herself, at first learning that Alex was the foundation's major benefactor and then hearing him actually defend her.

She looked around as he backed her into a quiet place overlooking the ballroom from behind a screen of potted palms.

'What are we doing here? I thought you said you wanted to talk to someone.'

'I do. I want to talk to you.'

Saskia recovered in an instant. 'Good, because I want to talk to you too. Did you really read those profiles I gave you?'

His lips curved into a thin smile. 'Did you think I'd made up what I said?'

She blinked. 'But you stood up for me.'

He shrugged, as if he hadn't given it any thought. 'I needed a line to throw her so we could get away. I think it worked quite well.'

'Of course' she said, feeling suddenly deflated that his support had meant so much to her and desperate to change the topic. 'So why didn't you tell me you were the foundation's major benefactor?'

'You didn't ask.'

'But—'

'No. You tell me about this "competition" first.'

She raised her glass in irritation. 'It's like Carmen said. The one who turns in the best profile gets the promotion. They picked two businessmen nobody had managed to interview in more than a decade, and they assigned us one each.'

'Are you sure she's such a threat? She doesn't look it.'

'Don't be taken in by Carmen's appearance. She's got an MBA from Harvard and a cold barracuda mind to go with those curves. She's out to win. And, given the way Drago seems so accommodating, she's already got his full co-operation.'

'It looks like she's got one hell of a lot more than that.'

She looked up at him, remembering the way his lips had lingered over Carmen's fingers and how he'd taken his own good time releasing her. 'That could have been you, you know.'

He blinked into the pause. 'You mean you would have profiled Drago and I would have enjoyed the company of the vivacious Carmen?'

She did her best to ignore the 'enjoyed' part of his comment. 'It might have been easier for everyone. It certainly would have been easier for me.'

'You're forgetting something. You know why I agreed to this profile. You blackmailed me—remember? Said you'd go public on what happened eight years ago if I didn't go along with you. I doubt if even the very come-hither Carmen could have come up with something as creative as that.'

Saskia shrugged. 'Given the way Carmen fills that silver gown, she probably wouldn't have needed to. Creativity would have been the last thing on your mind.'

This time he smiled, lifting a hand and catching one looping tendril, winding it around his fingers, letting it slip through, winding it again. Her scalp tingled from the contact.

That much made sense—but why was it her breasts were suddenly straining, her nipples peaking? And why could she feel heat pooling inside, way down deep?

'I take your point,' he acknowledged, his voice unexpectedly husky, his eyes dark like a moonless night sky, the reflection from the chandeliers like the stars. 'But would you really rather I had Carmen? That wouldn't bother you?'

She swallowed as his face dipped lower, his eyes intent on her mouth. On her lips. And he could be doing this with Carmen? Oh, yes, it would bother her!

Was that what he was trying to prove right now?

'Of course not,' she lied, twisting away so that she tugged her hair from his fingers, carefully ensuring she avoided his eyes at the same time. What did he think—that she was jealous? Not a chance! She leaned her arms on the railing, looking out over the sea of brilliantly dressed guests in the ballroom below.

'If you say so,' he said. 'Although I for one am very pleased you ended up with me.'

Her heart did a slow roll and she turned her face up to meet his again. 'And why is that?'

'Because you'd be wasted on Drago. I didn't save your virginity for the likes of him.'

Shock rooted her to the spot as white-hot fury infused her veins, and only the fact they were in one of the top function rooms in the world, surrounded by the cream of society, stopped her from flinging the contents of her glass in his face.

'How dare you? I can't believe you just said that.'

'Why? You'd rather throw it away on someone like him?'

'How dare you pretend that you somehow "saved" me by what you did, and that that gives you the right to decide whom I make love to. It has nothing to do with you.'

Alex whirled around, pinning her between his body and the balustrade, his face close to her own. 'Now, that's where you're wrong. It has *everything* to do with me. I could have taken all you offered that night, I could have pushed my way into you. I could have deflowered you and used you and discarded you when I'd had enough. But I didn't. I let you go. But not so you could throw it away on some lecherous businessman old enough to be your grandfather.'

'Who says I would have thrown it away on him?'

'It doesn't matter. Whether you threw it or whether he demanded it as payment for his profile, it amounts to the same thing. A total waste.'

Her chest heaving, her temperature off the wall, and her body reacting to his coarse words as if she'd been shot with hormones, she spun around in his arms until she could rest against the balustrade and not be forced to look into those deep, dark eyes. 'I can't believe we're having this conversation.'

But turning around proved a big mistake. He moved closer behind her, so she could feel his warm breath on her ear, feel his body press full length against hers, wedging her tight against the balustrade. She gasped. He was aroused, and his hand snared her waist, dragging her even closer into contact with him, the sensation even through layers of fabric still shockingly intimate, irresistibly carnal.

'So tell me,' he urged, his voice low and thick in her ear, 'what would you rather be doing?'

Every part of her wanted to lean back into his heated strength. Even now her back ached to arch, ached to send that low part of her in motion against him, ached to feel his length caress her. What was he doing to her? Turning her wanton and reckless at the first hint of sex?

Purposefully she fought the battle going on inside her,

battled to quell the swelling of her breasts and nipples and secret places. Battled to suppress the need.

'I want…' she whispered.

'Yes?' he murmured, the tip of his tongue tracing the line of her ear.

'To get this profile done and go home.'

He stilled, and she could feel the disbelief blow holes in his sexual energy. 'The profile?'

'That's why I'm here, after all. Nothing more.'

He let go his hold on her and she slipped out of his reach, covering her relief at her escape by smoothing her skirts.

'So how important is it, this competition? Do you want to win?'

'Of course I want to win!' *I have to win.* 'Why else do you think I bothered to track you down? It certainly wasn't to chew over the fat and talk about old times.'

*Why else indeed?* He looked intently at her. She must really need this promotion desperately to go to the trouble she had, to risk another encounter with him. And, dammit, why had she walked back into his life? He didn't need reminders of the past. He didn't need the risk to his present. So why the hell couldn't he just leave her alone? 'What's so important?'

Saskia looked back over the crowd below—couples moving on the jam-packed dance floor, small groups gathered around the fringe, talking and laughing. 'What do you care? Isn't it enough that I want this promotion?'

'No, it's not enough.' He was angry now. Angry at all the old emotions she'd brought up. Angry that he couldn't forget them. 'What would make you desperate enough to come looking for me after what happened between us? You must have known the sparks would fly. So what is it that you want—the honour, the prestige?'

She shook her head as she leaned out over the highly polished brass railing. 'No, it's not the prestige.'

'Then it must be money. How much do you need? I can give you money.'

The words were out before he even realised, before he even knew that he meant them. But money was something he could do. Easily. He had more than enough for himself, and if it meant getting rid of her any faster then it would be money well spent.

She looked up at him, her green eyes filled with disbelief. 'You'd do that? You'd give me money?'

Hell, yes, if it meant getting her out of his hair and his life back to normal.

'How much do you need?'

She shook her head.

'I don't want your money. I'm expecting to win this competition. All I need is your co-operation so I can make this profile the best it can be.'

'And if you don't win?'

'I'm going to win.'

'Don't be so stubborn. If it's money you need, I can give it to you.'

'And why would you do that? Why would you suddenly want to give money to the woman you've accused of being the lowest of the low, somebody stalking your sister to get the goods to plaster all over the nearest gossip rag?'

'What was I expected to think, finding you sneaking around taking photographs outside my home at the same time the paparazzi were clamouring for Marla's blood?' He swiped a hand back through his hair. Damn! He was supposed to be trying to convince her to take the money and go, not rehash every problem they already had. 'Look, why not let me help

you? Consider it compensation for past transgressions, if
you like.'

Her face moved beyond shock to anger in an instant, her
green eyes vivid, narrowed in accusation.

'You want to give me *money* because you threw me out
of your bed before smashing apart my father's existence?
What are you looking for—absolution? Do you think you can
pay me off for what you did? That money somehow makes
it better? You don't even know how much I need. One
hundred thousand dollars? Five hundred? How about one
million? How much are you prepared to fork out to assuage
your guilt?'

'That's enough!'

'No amount would be enough!' she remonstrated, thankful
for the cover of music but still trying to keep her voice low.
'I was seventeen years old, bowled over by the attentions of
the best-looking man I'd ever seen. He made me feel like a
princess. For weeks he treated me like his queen—and it was
all such an outright lie. In one awful night he smashed my
hopes and dreams. The next day he smashed my father's. He
made a fool out of us both. *Totally humiliated us both.* And
now he thinks he can pay me off for what he did with cold,
hard cash? Not a chance.'

'Your father deserved everything he got!'

'So you say. Because he ruined your own family's business
more than twenty years before. What a nerve! But you sure
made him pay for that. What I don't understand is what I did
to deserve it too.'

He looked away, his teeth clenched, blood pounding in his
head, feeling his hatred for her father pulse through him like
a living thing. Feeling hatred for the man he'd been becoming

loom up like a gigantic shadow over his life. But what could he say? She was right. She'd done nothing to deserve it.

'It could have been worse,' he bit out at last.

'You think? How the hell could it have been any worse?'

'I could have finished off what I started. I could have made love to you that night after all.'

# CHAPTER SEVEN

A THUNDERBOLT of silence followed his remark. Finally she could speak. 'You're right,' Saskia said, but all the while her heart was screaming, *Liar.* 'Thank God I was spared that.'

The look in his eyes, shuttered and bleak, was satisfaction indeed. He glanced down at his watch.

'There are speeches coming up. And then we're leaving,' he announced.

'Already? And just when we're having so much fun.'

Scowling, Alex escorted her down the stairs, Saskia heading for the refuge of the ladies' lounge while he sought out the event's organisers.

The lounge was like a sanctuary inside, the velvet wallpaper, luxurious drapes and deep tub chairs making the room feel more like a sitting room than a bathroom.

She stood at the basins, holding a damp cloth to her heated face. What was it about that man? Lulling her into a false sense of security one minute, digging deep under her skin the next?

The door behind her swung open and she caught the flash of silver satin in the mirror. Saskia let her eyes fall shut and suppressed a groan. The last person she really wanted to see right now was Carmen. Her sanctuary had suddenly turned to hell.

'Things getting a little heated between you two lovers then?' she enquired.

'I've just got something in my eye,' Saskia responded, dabbing the cloth under her lowered eyelashes, uncomfortable with the thought that Carmen had been watching them. She pulled the fabric away, glancing down at the cloth. 'There,' she said smiling, *pretending*, before screwing it into a ball and tossing it into the waste. She turned around as if she was about to leave. 'Are you enjoying the ball? Alex said the speeches are about to begin. I must join him.'

'You're not going to win, you know. This job is going to be mine.' Carmen's face was set into a mask so tightly bound with loathing that Saskia felt the first stirrings of fear. They'd never been what she'd call friends, but this naked anger was something new. Something frightening.

'You seem pretty sure of yourself,' Saskia replied calmly, trying to avoid a slanging match and wishing Carmen would move away from the door so she could escape. 'Good luck with your profile, in that case.'

'So how did you do it?' Carmen asked, not moving an inch.

'How did I do what, exactly?'

'Get Alex to agree to marry you. I thought he'd be the last guy you'd want to get hooked up with after the way he wiped your father's company off the face of the earth.'

Saskia did a double take. 'You know about that? How the hell—?'

Carmen smiled—if you could call the way her lips thinned and curved nastily a smile. 'I do thorough research. It's a particular skill of mine. Or one of them.' She tilted her head, her eyes glinting dangerously even in the subdued lighting. 'Did you think I'd leave it to chance who we were assigned to profile? Who do you think suggested the subjects?'

Saskia laughed. 'You can't be serious. The board would hardly let *you* choose them.'

'Oh, it wasn't that hard,' she boasted, feigning interest in her long scarlet nails. 'A word in an ear here, a hint in another ear there. Pretty soon they get together to discuss things, and *voila!* They're all in agreement. Suddenly it's all their idea. Only you want to ruin it all. You weren't supposed to like the guy, let alone marry him.'

She smiled again, and Saskia imagined it must be how a shark looked before it headed in for the kill.

'But now that too is working in my favour. Already the board is thinking you're not such a good prospect, given you'll be doing the maternity thing before too long. If, indeed, you're not already…'

She let her eyes settle on Saskia's abdomen like an accusation, leaving her words to hang there, letting them drip their poisoned content down slowly.

'Is there already a bastard child of Alexander Koutoufides festering inside you?'

Saskia prayed for strength. Because if she didn't she might just slap the other woman right here, right now. 'Don't you think that's a little unlikely? We've been together barely a week, after all.'

'Enough time to become engaged, however. Tell me, what's he like in bed? Drago is enthusiastic, if nothing else, but he lacks a certain—*finesse*. I'll wager that Alex lacks nothing.'

'Who says I've slept with him?'

'Come on—you're getting married. No man in Alex's position would agree to such a thing without testing the merchandise.'

'And if I told you there was no engagement? That there will be no marriage?'

'Then I'd think you were clutching at straws. And that you were so very, very sad. Because that would mean you'll soon be without a job *and* a man.' She sighed theatrically. 'In that case, enjoy him now, while you can.'

Saskia reefed in a deep breath, trying to quell the mounting sickness inside her. 'You must want this job awfully desperately if you're prepared to lie and cheat to get it.'

'Oh, yes,' Carmen agreed brightly, not even making a pretence at disagreeing with Saskia's summing up. 'And I'm going to get it too.'

Saskia had heard enough. She gathered up her skirts in both hands and drove a straight line for the door, forcing Carmen to back off at the last moment as she soared past, leaving her parting words in her wake.

'Just don't count on it.'

'You missed the speeches.'

Alex slipped her wrap around her shoulders and she grunted her thanks. If he thought she must still be angry from their argument he didn't say anything, and she was glad he didn't pursue it. She was too tightly wound from her run-in with Carmen to make sense right now.

From across the foyer Drago waved and caught her eye, gesturing as if he wanted to talk. Alex steered her purposefully towards the door regardless. 'Come on,' he said.

'Drago—' she said, gesturing to her right in case he hadn't seen.

'I saw him,' he replied, and just kept going, directing her towards the doorman and a line of waiting limousines. The doorman pulled open the rear passenger door for them and waited for her to gather her skirts and climb in.

'Why do I get the impression you're not too fond of Drago?'

'Who says I'm not?' he rejoined, following her in, all lean grace and fluid movement.

The car drove away, and something about the way he'd answered piqued her interest.

'And yet you obviously have so much in common. Both of you hold status as business success stories who prefer to live life out of the public eye. And both of you share the Baxter Foundation in common.'

His jaw twitched markedly as he settled alongside her. 'Hasn't it occurred to you yet? Some people stay out of the public eye because they're naturally private people. Others simply can't stand up to public scrutiny.'

The meaning behind his words was more than clear. 'You're suggesting Drago is into something shady?'

Dark eyes collided with hers. 'I've done business with him in the past. And on the basis of that experience I would never choose to do business with him again.'

'Surely you're not suggesting there's anything underhand about Drago's business interests?'

The look he gave her was intentionally non-committal. 'Just be glad you're not the one doing his profile.'

He settled back into his seat, very relieved again that it wasn't Saskia who'd drawn the Drago Maiolo assignment. Just the thought of those squat diamond-encrusted and nicotine stained fingers anywhere near the sweet curves of Saskia thickened his breathing to growling point. She was still a virgin. Much too good for the likes of Drago.

Hell, she was far too good for anyone. And, no matter who her father was or what he had done, after the way Alex had treated her once before, he included himself in that number.

*But that didn't make him stop wanting her.*

She'd fitted into his arms tonight as if she was made for

him, her head tucked under his chin, her body pressed within a heartbeat of his, and no longer was she the teenage goddess-in-waiting who had been so hard to walk away from back then. Now she was the real deal, her body rich with the power of her femininity, ripe and lush. *Ready.*

Even now her scent worked its way across the space between them, calling out to him, tempting him. Even now the jade-green colour of her eyes was the colour he saw when he closed his own eyes. Even now, separated by several feet of the finest leather upholstery…

*Damn it!*

Even now she was making him hard!

'So which one are you?' she asked softly from across the car, cutting into his thoughts.

He turned away from the window and the unseen passing parade of Manhattan buildings. 'What do you mean?'

'Are you merely a naturally private person?' she continued. 'Or is there something you're trying to hide?'

He looked across at her. 'What do you think?' he challenged.

She looked at him for a moment, her features still, her eyes assessing, her lips slightly parted. 'I know you weren't always so media-shy. Something must have happened that made you go low-profile.'

He didn't like the direction this conversation was taking. She wouldn't like it if he went there. 'You're forgetting about Marla. Don't you think one headliner in any family is enough?'

She stared at him. 'Maybe,' she said, as if she'd already written off that possibility. 'Or maybe there's something else you're trying to hide. Why did you drop off the face of the earth like you did?'

Moments expanded into seconds. Seconds expanded into for ever. And a muscle in his jaw worked through it all. Should he tell her that it all went back to that night? That he'd seen what he was becoming, what he was turning into, and he'd run the other way?

Then the car pulled into the drive-through at their hotel, her door was pulled open, a bubble of sounds and light invaded their uncomfortable silence, and the moment was gone.

'I'll co-operate with you on the profile,' he said at last as they exited the car. 'And I'll give you all the time you need to give you the best chance of winning. But there's something I need in return.'

'What is it?' she asked, almost too enthusiastically. If Carmen was going to undermine her every attempt to win this job she was going to need Alex's full co-operation. That would be worth almost anything.

'I want your guarantee that you'll leave Marla out of it. I don't want you having anything to do with her and I don't want her mentioned. Understand?'

She was about to agree unreservedly before she remembered the notebook she had stashed in her luggage—the notebook she'd promised to read. It was a promise she'd made to the woman that she wasn't about to break, no matter what Alex demanded. Besides, it wasn't as if she was about to include anything from it in her profile. Alex might doubt it, but her sense of ethics went a little deeper than that. 'This has always been about you, not Marla. I intend leaving her right out of the profile.'

His eyes drilled into her, as if he were digging into her very soul for the truth.

'Just keep it that way,' was all he said.

It was only when she was alone in her plush suite and getting ready for bed that she realised he'd never answered her question. Why was that? What *had* provoked Alex Koutoufides's sudden departure from public view? What was he trying to hide, and why?

Saskia shrugged as she rehung tonight's gorgeous gown. Did it matter? At least she'd secured his co-operation. Tomorrow she could really start work. She'd assemble the additional reports she needed, she'd have her questions ready, and by the sounds of it he might even let her into the house to watch him at work in his study, managing his empire from half a world away.

Until then she had another job to do. She pulled the fluffy white hotel robe around her and flopped onto the wide bed, propping a pillow under her chest and picking up the red notebook. Her reviewing it obviously meant so much to Marla, but she really wasn't relishing the prospect. Even with a celebrity name behind it, the writing would still have to stand on its own merits, and the chance of publication was a long shot. Hopefully Marla understood that.

Reluctantly she contemplated the cover, where Marla had penned the working title *From the Inside*, expecting to be able to offer nothing more than an honest yet encouraging critique—something she hoped wouldn't crush the woman's hopes and dreams in the process. It was obvious she needed something in her life to make her feel worthwhile. Maybe writing was it.

Saskia turned the cover and started to read.

About a young girl finding her place in the world—a young girl whose perfect, cherished life changed when she encountered sex at the age of fifteen, at the hands of a much older man, a young girl who discovered how much she enjoyed the act and yearned to learn more, who *set out* to learn more.

It told the story of the impact when her parents died in a

horrific boating fire at sea, and how she'd lurched into her marriages. It relived the short-lived bliss and the disasters they'd became. It told of her endless flirtation with celebrity. It covered everything: her slide into drug and alcohol dependency, her time behind the walls drying out, having therapy, thinking she was sane, knowing she must be mad.

It told of a woman who needed to heal herself. A woman who had recognised that it was time to grow up.

The prose wasn't perfect. It was raw, and needed editing and organisation, but the account pulled no punches. It was brutally honest, and it didn't make the author out to be anything more than what she was, but it was funny and gritty and poignant at the same time, and touching beyond belief.

Hours after she'd started, and with tears in her eyes, Saskia closed the notebook. Marla was a remarkable woman. She'd claimed she had no talents, but the woman who'd written this was gifted and insightful and deserved to be given the chance to succeed. If Saskia could do anything to help her, she would. And while she was in New York she had the perfect opportunity—she knew just the person. A former colleague from her magazine now worked in editorial for a publishing house, and lived not far from here. She'd be doing her a favour and getting Marla a second opinion.

In a fizz of excitement she'd reached for the phone at her bedside before she noticed the time. It wasn't long till dawn. She snuggled into bed and snapped off the light, feeling better than she'd felt in ages. She'd call after she'd snatched a few hours' sleep.

Alex was pounding on her door when she raced out of the lift shortly before noon.

'I'm here,' Saskia said breathlessly.

'Where the hell have you been?' he demanded, as she used her room key to unlock the door and pushed it open. 'I've been calling for ages.'

'Nowhere special. I just…went out for a walk.'

'Our car will be here in ten minutes.' His words trailed her into the room.

'It's okay. I'm just about packed.' She didn't bother to take off her jacket even though she felt as if she was burning up after running back. Instead she just threw her purse on a chair and grabbed the last of her toiletries from the bathroom. She zipped them into a bag and turned straight into a wall. The wall of his chest. His hands went to her shoulders, anchoring her before she could step away.

'What's the rush?'

'You said the car—'

'There's time.' He touched a hand to her chin, lifting it so her eyes had no choice but to collide with his. 'Your face is pink.'

She knew full well that her colour couldn't only be attributed to her race to get back. A large dollop of it was relief at completing her task this morning. Her former colleague had been as keen to see Marla's story as she'd expected. Her excitement at reading the first chapter had mirrored Saskia's own, and right now she couldn't wait to get back to Tahoe and let Marla know an editor was considering her work.

As for the rest of her colour? It was due entirely to the way he was making her feel right now, pressed so close to her, his fingers adding an electric thrum to her overheated skin. 'I ran,' she said, when she'd located the thin thread of her voice at last. 'A few blocks. That's all.'

'Maybe you should calm down a little.'

His voice had a husky quality that didn't fit with a rush to the car. Where was his urgency? Where was the panic she'd seen when she'd found him pounding on her door?

She laughed, a half-hearted attempt that sounded as pitiable as it felt. How the hell was she supposed to calm down with him standing over her—touching her?

'Thanks. I will. Now…if you'll excuse me…I'll finish my packing.'

This time he let her go, standing in the doorway, one arm behind his neck, as she stashed the toiletries bag and locked down her luggage.

'I'm ready,' she said, her senses reeling once more from experiencing the let-down after a close encounter with Alex: the sensual build-up, the pull of his body on hers, only to be let go, to be spun out like wreckage from a hurricane, thrown out to crash wherever it landed. It was crazy. How could he have this effect on her when she didn't want anything to do with him?

He pushed himself away from the door to follow her. 'Before we go,' he started, 'last night I offered you money. You objected then, but maybe overnight you thought about it. Maybe you re-considered. I want you to know my offer is still open.'

She closed her eyes for a second, breathing in deep. She'd said too much last night, way too much. She'd reacted too violently to his offer of money and she'd made it sound as if her pain was still raw, that it still mattered.

But it didn't matter any more! She was over it. And if it wasn't for Alex, scraping back the intervening years, peeling back time as if he was ripping off a thick scab and revealing the wound, raw and stinging and deep, the past would have stayed safely where she'd buried it.

'No,' she said at last, slinging the strap of her purse over her shoulder. 'You should never have offered me money.

Especially not for the reason you did. But let's not talk about it any more. It's in the past. Let it stay there.'

He took a step closer, bridging the gap between them. 'Saskia, think about it. You could forget all about this bizarre contest.' He reached out a hand to her arm. 'You could leave now.'

She reeled back. 'Don't touch me!'

A muscle twitched in his cheek, his eyes turned hard as steel. 'You'll never forgive me for what happened, will you?'

'Why should I?' she insisted. 'You can't buy me off. It simply should never have happened in the first place.'

His dark eyes glinted, his jaw square. 'I had my reasons.'

'What? Now you're telling me you had *reasons*? You really have a nerve. I have no idea what kind of sick reasons you think would excuse the way you acted, and I really don't want to know.'

'No,' he muttered, trying to control his anger-coated breathing as she marched out of the room ahead of him. 'I don't imagine you do.'

Marla must have been anxious for news. She was already waiting for her early the next morning, when Saskia took a walk along the lake's edge. Her jeans and thick sweater were keeping out the early-morning chill, although she was already regretting not tying her hair back against the breeze that whipped her curls around her face and turned them to stinging tendrils.

'How was the ball?' Marla asked, a nervous excitement in her smile.

Saskia nodded. 'It was entertaining in places.'

'Good,' she said brightly, and Saskia could see that for all her anxiousness she was too afraid to ask.

'Marla, about that writing…'

'Yes?'

'I know it was yours.'

The older woman looked contrite and laced an arm through Saskia's as they walked out onto the pier. 'Oh, I'm sorry. I thought you might say no if you knew it was mine. And I did so want your opinion on it.' She looked up at Saskia, hope in her eyes. 'So…did you get a chance to read it? What did you think?'

Saskia smiled. The older woman's enthusiasm was infectious. 'Well, first of all, you know how hard it is to get work published, don't you? Some people struggle for years and years and never make it.'

Marla's face dropped. 'Are you saying it was no good, then?'

'No. I thought it was very good.'

'Really? You really did?'

She laughed. 'I really did.'

Still with their arms entwined, Marla clapped her gloved hands together and jumped up and down. 'That's fantastic. So where's the problem?'

'I just don't want you to get your hopes up too high. I've left the book with an editor friend of mine in New York. She was very interested, but it still doesn't mean—'

'You've got an editor reading it? My book?' Marla pulled her arms free and slapped both hands over her mouth. 'That's so fantastic. Oh, Saskia, thank you so, so much!'

She threw her arms around the younger woman and hugged her tight.

'It's great news,' Saskia agreed. 'But don't be too disappointed if they can't use it—okay? There are plenty more publishers out there after all. I'm sure there's one for you somewhere—it might just take a while.'

'Oh, my, I just can't believe it,' Marla said, giving Saskia another squeeze. 'I'm so glad you came. This is the best news I've ever had.'

They walked along the shore, talking companionably, Marla pumping her for comments on various parts of her story, and all the while the wind was picking up. Getting more frustrated with herself for not tying it back, Saskia pushed her hair off her face one more time. 'This hair is driving me crazy.'

Marla looked up at her. 'I love your hair. Those curls make it look so alive, and I just love the colour.' She pulled back the hood of her jacket and ran a hand over her own silvery blonde mane. 'Do you think that colour would suit me? I think it's time I had a change.'

Saskia smiled, recognising immediately that the warmer colour would suit Marla's skin tones perfectly. 'I think it would look great.'

'You wouldn't mind if I tried?'

'Why should I mind? I think you'd look sensational.'

They talked for a while together, about hairstyles and colours, and families, getting to know more about each other, building an easy camaraderie. Until a voice called out through the pines.

'Marla!'

She spun around. 'Oh, God, I've been too long. That's Jake, looking for me. That guy is driving me totally crazy, you know. I'd better run.' She kissed Saskia quickly on the cheek, gave more hurried thanks, and headed off quickly for the house.

Finally Saskia had a chance to get some much needed work done. Alex had been true to his word and had invited her into his large state-of-the-art office, complete with computers, fax and even teleconferencing facilities. 'Wow,' she said, contemplating the screen and taking some shots with the digital camera he'd finally conceded she might need to do her job. 'What a set-up. You've got everything you need to do business anywhere in the world right here.'

'That's the idea. Now that my portfolio is spread so widely, I can't be in every place at once. This is the next best thing.'

He pulled some files out of an oak filing cabinet while she looked at the photographs on his desk. There was one very old one of his family alongside a fishing boat. She picked it up and smiled. Alex must have been around ten or so, his arms crossed and his stance wide, as if he was the boss, but his smile was cheeky as he looked into the camera. Marla stood alongside, looking like a young colt, not that much taller for her years, but all long legs, unbridled energy and classic beauty, even though she must have been just a young teenager. His parents stood behind, his olive-skinned father with an arm around his fair mother's shoulders. Marla's story mentioned they'd died in a boating accident. Had it been that same boat they'd died on?

'My parents,' Alex said softly, pulling the photo from her hands and placing it back on his wide desk.

'How old were you when they died?'

He sighed, at the same time dropping a stack of glossy reports and financial statements on the desk before turning to look out through the large windows into the distance. 'Fourteen.'

'That's so not fair. My mother died when I was still too little to remember her. I can't imagine what it would have been like to have lost her as a teenager.'

He looked over his shoulder at her. 'What happened to her?'

'Breast cancer, apparently. She was too scared to see the doctors, and by the time she did it was too late. But I was a baby, so I don't have any memories of her at all. I think in some ways that's easier. I can't imagine losing both of my parents in such a horrific accident, though. That must have been devastating.'

He turned around completely, his brows drawn together. 'You know how my parents died? How is that? I don't remember telling you.'

She swallowed, suddenly guilty because it had been Marla's memoirs that had filled in the details for her. 'I must have read it somewhere. In my background notes, maybe.'

He considered her answer for a while, his eyes holding hers, locked in the past, swirling with pain. 'Sometimes I think they really died after the takeover. It broke them, you know.' Then he seemed to snap back to the present. He grunted and sat down opposite her. 'If you want this profile, we should get started. Here's what I've got for you to look at already…'

They were still in his office hours later, when the call came through. The late afternoon sun slanted through the long windows and a fresh breeze stirred the curtains, making one think of closing up windows and doors—that the best part of the day would soon be over.

Alex listened for a moment before handing the receiver over. 'It's for you, from London,' he said. 'A Rodney Krieg?'

She accepted the phone while Alex pushed back in his chair, his arms behind his head, his feet crossed on the desk. 'Sir Rodney? I didn't expect to hear from you so soon.'

'Saskia, my dear.' Sir Rodney's gruff voice churned down the line. 'How are you getting on over there?'

'Great. The profile's going really well.' She nodded at Alex. 'I've got Alex's full co-operation—I should be finished within the week.'

'Ah…' blustered the voice at the other end. 'About that profile…'

A cold shiver of trepidation shimmied its way down her

spine. 'What about it?' she asked, her voice tight with concern. 'Is there a problem?'

Alex leaned forward in his chair and she swivelled her own away, so she didn't have to look at him. She didn't need him in on this conversation.

'Well, it's just that the board's more than a little concerned…'

Trepidation gave way to dread.

'About what?'

'There's some talk that you might be going to withdraw from the contest.'

'Why would I do that? I've been working towards this job for at least the last twelve months. Why would I suddenly give it all up?'

'You might if you were worried about taking on such a demanding role in London when you're thinking about settling down and starting a family somewhere else. This is a demanding role. It's no place for a part-time employee or commuter. I expect you realise that. Now in this day and age we can hardly discriminate against you on such grounds—that wouldn't be right at all, of course. But we can ask if you seriously want to proceed to with this application or not—and if not, then it might be wiser to withdraw.'

Her heart skipped a beat. She couldn't be hearing this.

'No, no, Sir Rodney. I explained all that. There is not going to be any marriage. This engagement isn't real. It's just for show—just a diversion for the press to get the focus off Marla. Obviously it must be working, or the board wouldn't be thinking it's real.'

'Now, now,' he soothed, with no conviction at all. 'I know that's what you told me. But you're forgetting one thing. Carmen saw you together at that Baxter Foundation night, looking very much the part, and now the papers are reporting

Alex as saying you're going to be married as soon as possible. There's even some talk that a family might not be too far distant.'

Saskia's blood froze. There was no mistaking where those whispers would have come from. 'Did that come from Carmen? Because she's told me she'll do anything to win that promotion. Can't you see what she's doing?'

'Does it really matter where it came from when it only serves to verify what the board already suspects?'

'Of course it matters! Please believe me, Sir Rodney, there will be no wedding! I told you, it's not a real engagement.'

'I'm sorry, Saskia.' Sir Rodney was sounding impatient. 'I know how much this promotion means to you, and I know how hard you've worked, but the board is having trouble accepting that this engagement to a man like Alex Koutoufides can be anything but real—it doesn't make sense. They don't want to find out after they've made a decision that you've decided you're no longer available for the job. This role is too important.'

'But I wouldn't!'

'Besides which, Carmen has already handed in a preliminary report. It's excellent—just what we're after. Frankly, the board are wondering if there's any point proceeding with the contest.'

'But Sir Rodney…'

There was a moment's hesitation. 'I'm sorry, Saskia. It might be for the best if you get notice of your withdrawal into the board sooner rather than later.'

Saskia held the phone to her ear even after the final click had signalled he was gone. Because even just holding it felt as if she wasn't giving up on her dream. Once she put down that phone it would be like acknowledging her chances were dead. And they couldn't be dead.

She'd done everything she could possibly do for this job—

she'd agreed to profile the person she detested more than anyone in the world, the person who'd destroyed her family and whom she held responsible for setting her father on his decline to despair and illness. She hadn't wanted to profile Alex, but she'd agreed because it was the only way that would ensure she had the means of providing the kind of care her father needed and deserved. That or she'd drag him down in the process.

She'd done everything she possibly could, and it was still not enough. Once again her hopes and dreams had been thwarted.

And it was all down to one man.

The man sitting opposite her right now.

*Alexander Koutoufides!*

She took a deep breath and turned her chair back round, replacing the long-dead receiver, finally acknowledging what she'd known all along—there was no lifeline. No lifeline, no white knight to ride out on a charger and save her, no fairies at the bottom of the garden. This was real life, and if she needed saving she was going to have to do it herself.

'What's wrong?' he asked from across the desk. 'What's happened?'

She lifted her eyes to meet his, momentarily taken aback at the level of concern she saw there—but only momentarily. He didn't mean it. He didn't care about her or her job, and least of all her father. He'd used her once again and this was the result. Another disaster. Another nightmare. And all at the hands of Alex Koutoufides. Oh, Carmen Rivers might have taken advantage of the situation, but it had been manufactured by this one man.

She stood—unable to sit, unable to control the buzzing forces that screamed for release inside her, unable to control the trembling fury that possessed every muscle.

'You bastard!' she seethed. 'You total bastard. If you hadn't insisted on all this engagement garbage—if you hadn't told every reporter going that you couldn't wait to get married—'

'Hey,' he said coming around the desk towards her. 'What am I supposed to have done?'

'I'm out of the running for the promotion. The board has decided that it can't give me the position—regardless of the profile I turn in—because it wouldn't be fair to the magazine or to *our marriage*.'

'I thought you'd already explained what was going on.'

'I had! And I thought he finally believed me. But you had to insist on taking me to New York. You insisted on me wearing a fortune in your mother's diamonds to flash in front of everyone, including the one person I was competing with for the position. And then you had to tell the press that we were getting married as soon as possible. Now there's no chance I can get that job. It doesn't matter what I do, or how this profile turns out, they won't give it to me. And it's all your fault!'

'But they can't do that, surely? Whether or not you're married is irrelevant. They can't discriminate against you on those grounds.'

'They're not! They're expecting me to withdraw. Especially now Carmen has already given them a teaser of *her* profile. They're not even interested in anything I might present.'

Her chest heaving, her breathing ragged, she battled to control her thoughts. There had to be an answer. There just had to be.

He rounded the desk towards her and she spun away as he spoke. 'Maybe things aren't as bad as you think?'

'You have no idea how bad!' That job should have been hers. The chance to see her father was cared for decently—it had been within her grasp. She'd fought so hard for it. She'd more than paid the price. Only to have success snatched cruelly and bitterly from her. 'You have no idea what you've done or what you've cost me. You ruined my life eight years ago and you've ruined it all over again. You couldn't have ruined it more thoroughly if you'd tried.'

She felt a hand on her shoulder and spun back round, lashing out with her hands, wanting to beat her fists against his chest, wanting to strike him and pound him and hurt him so that he'd know something of what she was feeling. Something of the pain. Something of the despair.

'I hate you Alex Koutoufides. I hate you to hell and back!'

She couldn't see him, but still she struck out. Tears distorted her vision and anguish distorted her mind, but still she pounded away. Only the pain was focused, sharp and deep and burning hot. And the pain tore through everything, savagely slicing open old wounds, jaggedly ripping through her heart, fuelling her beating muscles, screaming out the truth.

*She'd failed.*

She'd been so close to succeeding, so close to success that she'd been able to taste it, and yet still she'd failed. Now she would have nothing to offer her father. Now there would be nothing she could do for him. Nothing.

There was no point any more. There was no reason to fight any more. Everything she'd battled for, everything she'd held precious, was worth nothing. And now she had nothing left to lose. There was nothing left to fight for.

She was like a hurricane in his arms, unpredictable, unstoppable, a powerhouse of energy and emotion that had to spin itself out. All he could do was hold her, let herself work it out of her system and take it out on him.

Except he couldn't wait.

She was in his arms, passionate, desperate, and he was passionate and desperate enough to take advantage of it. How could he resist the erratic pounding of her heart, the frantic rise and fall of her breasts, her scent, and the sweet press of her feminine curves so close to his own? Why should he even bother?

He dropped his head, pressed his mouth to the top of her head, burying his lips in her mussed hair, inhaling the warm scent of woman—this one special woman.

Her breathing caught and she stilled her fight momentarily, giving him a chance to reach a hand under her chin and turn her face up to meet his. Her eyes were cloudy and damp, but warm, like the sky after a tropical storm, her lips moist and pink and slightly parted.

He shook his head. What the hell was he thinking? But then, what did it matter anyway? These thoughts skipped through his brain before he decided that thinking was surplus to requirements and dipped his mouth to hers because it seemed like the most natural thing in the world.

The most obvious thing.

The most inevitable thing.

Her breath caught and she froze, fought for an instant, and then relaxed as his mouth refused to let go of hers. She tasted of that storm and its aftermath, of maelstrom giving way to peace, of tempest followed by calm. And her lips moved under his. And as they did her body changed again, her breathing quickening, her energy returning, so that he could feel it as a living, pulsing force.

And soon the storm was back.

She was giving as good as she got, her lips demanding more, her tongue seeking his own. Her arms found purchase around his body and she pressed herself up against him, so close it was as if she wanted to be part of him, and he ached to make her so. Then she forced her hands up between their bodies, her nails raking against his shirt, unzipping his desire, before pulling his mouth down on hers again. Did she realise what she was doing to him? Did she have any idea what her body was inviting?

'*Sto thiavolo,*' he murmured against her ear, her answering shudder feeding into his wants and desires. To hell with it, indeed. The rush of blood through his veins told him he was going there for sure.

She wasn't asking him to stop, and somehow he knew he was no longer capable of it anyway.

'What are you doing?' she asked, her voice thick with need, as he swung her into his arms and carried her through a short passageway to a sprawling bedroom.

He pressed his lips to her forehead and let them linger, sampling her sweetness, tasting her desire. Then he drew back and lost himself in her green, green eyes.

'Something I should have done a long time ago.'

# CHAPTER EIGHT

LIFE didn't come with second chances, let alone third. Alex knew that. All his life he'd taken his opportunities when and wherever they appeared and not relied on waiting for a second chance to come around. He'd clawed his way back from having nothing because of it. He'd built his success around it. And in the unlikely event that he'd missed an opportunity he'd lived with the consequences.

He'd had his chance with Saskia Prentice eight years ago. He'd had it and he'd blown it, and he had been happy to live with the consequences. Well, maybe not happy, but resigned. He knew the way he'd treated her back then had been a mistake, he knew what he'd lost before it had been gained, but then this was the price he'd had to pay.

But now life was giving him a second chance. And what with second chances coming around so rarely, no way was he going to mess this up.

It was like a gift from the gods. He laid her down on the bed, intending to shrug off his clothes before he joined her, but one look into her large green eyes and he knew that his place was there, alongside her, right now. He took the time to lever off no more than his shoes before he lowered himself, fully clothed, gathering her close. *'Agape mou,'* he told her, because right at this moment the English language didn't seem large enough to describe what he felt. 'You're so beautiful,' he said, echoing what his eyes had already told her. Then it was the turn of his lips and his hands to prove it.

The sun moved lower in the sky, the breeze carried more of a chill, but inside the room temperatures were soaring exponentially with need. He wanted to feel every part of her, to taste every part of her, all at once.

And she was hungry too—her hands reaching out for him, reefing out his shirt, seeking out his skin. And knowing she wanted him only ramped up his own need tenfold.

She was a virgin. He'd had the opportunity before to accept her gift eight years ago and he'd blown it. And yet here she was, still entrusting him with the heady responsibility of showing her the full magic of being a woman, and the supreme power of what she could do to a man.

And that was a gift indeed. A gift he wasn't about to turn away again. Not when he could have his fill of her and get her out of his system at the same time. Because if he had her he wouldn't crave her any more. It was worth making love to her simply for that.

His hands moved over her, hot and hungry, falling on her breasts, unpeeling clothes and lace and anything that got in the way of his need and his purpose. He cupped her breasts in his hands. He suckled her nipples, one after the other, feeling her body arch underneath him as she cried out in torturous pleasure, and she wrenched off his shirt, clamping him to her, demanding more.

He dispensed with his own jeans, then with her trousers, peeling them from her like a second skin, revealing the pearl-like skin of her long legs to his hungry gaze.

He ran his hands up their length as his kiss preceded them.

They were smooth legs, firm legs. Legs made to wrap around a man and draw him in close.

And right now he was that man.

His hands reached the top of her thighs, toying with the band of her silk panties, while her hands reached his head, her fingers raking through his hair, tugging, insistent.

'Alex,' she cried.

But he wasn't through with her yet. She hadn't felt all he could make her feel. He pressed his face against her and breathed in her rich feminine desire, a scent made just for him, just for this time. A scent that filled every remaining part of his mind and body with need.

He stripped away the underwear in an instant, parting her tenderly with his fingers, dipping his tongue and circling the lush pink bud within, dipping his tongue further and tasting her honeyed sweetness.

She cried out again, her hands clutching at his head, then pounding at her pillow as she bucked, then back again as he anchored her to her mouth, drawing out the sweetness, teasing out the pleasure.

'Please...' she pleaded.

He wanted to please her. He wanted to show her how good it could be. How good it *should* be. But it was so hard not to be waylaid by how perfect she was. He lifted his head and touched her gently with his fingers, feeling the liquid heat welcome him. He raised his eyes and watched her face as his fingers stroked her entrance and then entered her, first one and then another, feeling her tight silken heat envelop them, tugging, insistent, inviting, as his thumb continued to circle that tight bud.

'Alex!'

He wanted to take his time. He meant to. He knew she was

a virgin and he should go slowly. He knew he should take his time and make it as wonderful for her as he knew it was going to be for him. But the desperate edge to her voice, the keening note it contained, was his undoing.

Driven by need, compelled by desire, he moved between her thighs, spreading them wide, remembering only at the last instant to take precautions. He fumbled with the details. Any delay now was far too long. He'd waited eight long years as it was.

And then he was there. She held onto him, her arms entwined around his neck, her mouth working with his, welcoming his tongue inside as she would soon welcome him.

And he entered her, smoothly, cleanly, in one swift, painless thrust that took both her breath and her virginity away. And as she gripped him with new-found muscles that held him tight and dared him to go deeper, he heard in his heartbeat a distant echo of a former time. It made no sense, its rhythm drowned out by the force of what was happening between them, the power of his thrusts, the magic receptiveness of her body, tilting, angling to receive him even deeper. And deeper.

He was lost, her power taking him where it wanted, drawing him over the edge even as it took her. She stilled and came apart in his arms, her muscles contracting all around him like firecrackers until he had nowhere to go but to explode in the aftermath.

And it was only in the quietening minutes after that his heartbeat settled down once again into a steady rhythm that he could recognise. He listened to the beat, his limbs heavy in his post-sex state. He listened to what it told him. And it approved of his choice of bed partner. With her wild hair and lush curves and her too-wide mouth, she was a woman to hold onto, a woman you could love.

*Theos!* His body tensed, his spine chilled and his senses went from drowsy to red alert.

Where the hell had *that* come from? He couldn't love her. It would never happen. This was an exercise in taking what she'd offered, in getting her out of his system. Nothing more.

He shifted to one side, wanting suddenly to get away, yet strangely moved when she followed him, nestling in close. He looked at her, her eyes closed, her hair spread on the pillow like some coiled mantilla, a spiral curl of it falling over her cheek. Unable to resist, he lifted a hand, smoothing it back from her face, and her eyelids fluttered open.

Green eyes greeted him, moisture laden green eyes, and an unexpected guilt bit deep.

'Did I hurt you?'

Suddenly he realised that it mattered. That he didn't want to make her cry. And that made him even more unsettled.

'No,' she said. 'Were you supposed to?'

'I'm glad,' he said, more brusquely than he'd needed, avoiding the issue altogether. He didn't want to know why she was crying. He didn't want to muddy the waters any more when he didn't understand why sex should suddenly felt like something else entirely. But he wouldn't have to think about it for long—not if he could get her out of here quickly.

'I'm taking you to England tomorrow,' he said, his hand unable to resist sweeping gently along the dips and curves of her body even while planning his escape route

'England?' It was hard to think with him doing that, stirring her flesh all over again. Saskia had thought it couldn't be any better than that first time, but the way he had her feeling already made her think otherwise. But a trip to England? If they were anywhere near London she might have a chance to visit her father. 'Do you have business there?'

'No. We both do. I'm taking you to see Sir Rodney and the

board. I'm going to tell them the truth. I'm going to make them believe there never was an engagement.'

Something inside her chilled and set.

'You'd do that for me?' she asked. It was more than she'd ever expected from him, and yet still it was hard to sound excited about it.

'That promotion means so much to you. And it's because of me that you run the risk of losing it. It's the only thing I can do.'

It's not the only thing you can do, she wanted to argue. You could… What? What did she expect him to do? Admit his undying love for her? Marry her? On the strength of one hasty if spectacular sexual encounter? She didn't want that herself.

*Did she?*

But, no, she was no naïve teenager any more—and now she was no naïve virgin. She'd shed a tear as she'd waved one part of her life behind, even as she'd embraced the new. Because how could she feel the same and yet feel so different at the same time?

Right now it was too hard to think—much too hard to think. Especially when his mouth was weaving its magic on her skin and his hands were moving hot and heavy over her flesh. And when he entered her again she forgot all thoughts anyway.

He flipped her over in his arms until she was sitting astride him, his hands curving from her hips to her waist and up higher, till he took both breasts in his hands, cherishing them, taking pleasure in them, celebrating their fullness, his thumbs rolling the pebbled peaks of her nipples between them.

And then he moved inside her and she gasped, her back arching. The feeling was different, fuller, deeper than anything before, and pleasure roiled within her. Pleasure and aching heat. He moved again, his hands on her hips, guiding her along his length till she was almost at his limit and then letting her fill herself with him again. He let her find the rhythm, sometimes achingly slow, sometimes descending like a woman possessed. As she must be. Possessed by him.

Absorbing him.

*Loving him.*

It was back, she realised on a gasp, and worse than before. She'd been but a teenager, totally inexperienced in the world, when she'd first fallen in love. Now she should know better than to fall in love with a man like Alex Koutoufides. But that still didn't stop her.

Damn her, but she loved him. She wanted him. Every part of him.

And it frightened her, this new knowledge of loving him, of new experiences and new sensations. Of his hard length even now swelling inside her, and how much power she held over him. She watched the sweat break out on his brow as he searched for control even while she battled to retain hers against the mounting forces that felt as if they were trying to split her apart. With a sudden cry he grabbed for her hips, flipping her underneath him and lunging into her, each time bringing her closer and closer to that shattering conclusion she craved, taking her there in one final thrust and going with her into that gasping, yawning chasm of release.

Saskia felt a mounting sickness inside her. After a night of making love and a morning spent waking up to it, he'd organised a jet to take them to London. They had finally touched down in the evening, too late for anything but a late dinner in the plush hotel restaurant. An appointment had been requested with Sir Rodney first thing in the morning and if all went well there Saskia planned to visit with her father later in the afternoon. Hopefully the news would be good.

Now, Saskia toyed with her wine glass, turning the stem between her fingers, looking absently out of the large picture windows overlooking Regents Park while she waited for Alex to return from making a call. If she received this promotion she'd be based near London permanently, her time primarily taken up with her new role with the magazine, her weekends taken up with caring for her father. And whatever was happening here between her and Alex would be over.

*Thank goodness.*

How she'd managed to even look at herself in the mirror this morning she didn't know. She'd thrown herself upon him like a desperate virgin incensed that he'd rejected her once before. She'd fallen for the man who'd destroyed her father's life.

How could she even face her father after that?

Cramps squeezed what little she'd eaten into a tight ball inside her.

Thank God this would soon be over. Alex had been tense all day. He wanted her gone just as much as she needed to flee. Why else would he be pursuing any chance to help her win her job? He was pulling out all the stops to ensure she had a chance for this promotion.

Alex returned to the table and smiled tensely down at her, apologising for taking so long as he lifted a bottle of champagne from the ice bucket and filled both their glasses. And in spite of the churning in her tummy she couldn't help an uneasy smile back. Because right this minute it didn't matter if he didn't want her beyond tonight. Already muscles she'd thought well spent made themselves felt, making their interest clear to her in a way that brought heat and colour to her cheeks. She had this night to look forward to—why spoil it?

He picked up his flute and slanted it towards her. 'It's confirmed. We meet Sir Rodney at eleven. Here's to a successful outcome. Here's to getting what you want.'

They touched glasses, the expensive tink of crystal against crystal a total contrast to the sensation of her stomach crunching into more knots.

How could she get what she really wanted when she didn't know what she wanted herself?

She sipped from her glass, tiny beads sparkling in the fine wine, her heart strangely heavy.

'Would you like to do something after the meeting? Maybe take in a river cruise or visit a gallery?'

'Thanks,' she said, 'but I've got plans for the afternoon already.'

Surprise gave way to a resigned shrug. 'I see.' He picked up his glass. 'What have you arranged?'

She took a deep breath. 'I'm visiting with my father.'

His glass stilled at his mouth, mid swallow, before slowly he replaced it on the table. 'Your father lives here? In London? When did that happen?'

Her eyes challenged him. 'Where did you think he lived? Still back in Sydney? He came with me when I got my scholarship to the London School of Economics. Did you really think I'd leave him alone in Sydney after everything that had happened? He couldn't wait to get away and make a fresh start.'

'And has he?' Alex demanded, his tone suddenly aggressive. 'What kind of "fresh start" has he made?'

Saskia twisted her serviette in her lap. He had tried—at least in those first years. He'd started out in a new country with determination and a whole new zest for living. But when proposal after proposal for new businesses had been knocked back, with partners pulling out at the last minute, finance continually declined, then so had he. His dreams to start another business curtailed, he'd searched for employment. But jobs for aging executives with experience half a world away were thin on the ground. Soon he hadn't even been trying, and it had been only then that she'd found him spending more time with the betting pages than the employment guide. Before long she had discovered he'd gambled what little they'd had left clean away, and the debts were already mounting.

'These last few years,' she admitted, 'it's been hard.'

'*Life's* hard.'

Her sadness evaporated in an instant, incinerated in the harshness of his pronouncement. 'I certainly didn't expect any sympathy from you! Not after you'd done your bit—pulling the company out from under his feet the way you did.'

'In exactly the same way he ruined *my* father's business. If he could dish it out, you'd think he might have been able to take it.'

She stood up to go, placing her napkin on the table. 'I really don't want to sit here and listen to this.'

Alex snared her wrist in one hand. 'Sit down,' he snapped. Then, softer, 'Please. I shouldn't have said anything. Let's not argue tonight.'

She stood there, torn between leaving his man with a hatred for her father she couldn't understand—a man she shouldn't be with, not if loyalty to her father meant anything. And yet the very thought of walking away from Alex right now almost ripped her in two.

In the end it was only the thought that she would have to leave him anyway, and soon, that allowed her to sit down. That and the fact she still needed his help tomorrow with the board if she was going to be able to help her father at all. But soon enough she'd never see Alex again. Soon enough he'd be gone from her life. What was one more night of passion to steal before then?

A tense meal stretched into tense coffee, stretched into a tense journey to the penthouse suite. Alex hadn't even made a pretence of booking two rooms for them this trip, and both of them knew what was in store.

Inside the suite's welcoming lobby he pulled her straight into his arms. She came reluctantly, like a piece of board, all angles and stiffness and attitude. And then his mouth met hers and he felt the resistance drain out of her, her lips parting and welcoming, his tongue meeting hers, tasting and duelling. And somewhere in the midst of it their mutual resentment gave way to mutual desperate need, and clothes were tackled, peeled off, shucked. He manoeuvred her through to the magnificent bedroom and they hit the four-poster bed, a frenzy of entwined lips and tangled limbs and frantic grabs for air. He barely had time to sheath himself before he was inside her, driving, thrusting, seeking that place that wiped all others away, finding it in her and spinning them both over the abyss.

For a while they lay gasping together, their bodies humming, their senses slowly returning to something approaching normality. 'Stay there,' he said, kissing her forehead before easing away, padding to the bathroom and turning on the gold-plated taps over the large oval-shaped bathtub. A bottle of hotel bubble bath followed. When he came back he found her wrapped in a fluffy robe at the dressing table, removing her jewellery.

He growled and caught hold of her and spun her towards him, taking hold of the tied ends of the robe and unlooping them. He let the sides fall open, exposing a long window of shimmering skin, of womanly curves and golden blonde curls, and he felt himself start to get hard all over again.

She watched him with those green, green eyes, watched him drink her in, watched him take his fill of her and smile. And he saw sadness in those green eyes, mixed in with her desire. And he saw his own desire reflected back at him.

And then he buried his mouth on her neck, where her pulse jumped ragged for him. 'I'm running a bath for us,' he said. 'So you won't be needing this.' He let the robe drop from her shoulders, leaving her naked in his arms, his hands scanning her surface, cherishing every dip, memorising every curve.

'You go ahead,' he said at last, while he knew he was still capable of letting her go. 'I'll get us a drink.'

Still he turned to watch her go across the carpet, the gentle sway of her hips like a seduction in itself. He breathed in a groan and threw his head back, reefing his hands through his hair. She was going to walk out of his life the same way she'd just walked to the bathroom.

Eight years after he'd sent her packing, he was about to lose her again. And he was doing his utmost to ensure it happened.

Eight years ago he'd been sure about his decision. Now he didn't know what to think.

But he couldn't let her just walk out of his life as if she'd never been there. He'd been given a second chance—a second chance to get things right, not merely a second chance to make love to her. What the hell was wrong with him? Why hadn't he been able to see that before?

He *would* make things right. For both of them. Starting now.

She didn't have to take that job. Whatever it was that meant so much to her about it, he'd give her that tenfold. She didn't want his money, she'd made that clear, but he could make up for what had happened in the past with more than mere cash. She could come and live with him. She wouldn't need to scrimp and worry about money again. They could pretend the past had never happened. They could start afresh.

And he'd take care of her.

Starting tonight.

A bottle of champagne stood chilling in a crystal ice bucket on a silver tray, two crystal flutes alongside. He popped the cork on the champagne, filling the flutes only halfway. He'd just picked up the bottle and glasses when a flashing light caught his eye. Someone had left a message while they were out.

He almost didn't bother picking it up, but if Sir Rodney and his cronies had changed the appointment time they would be better off finding out tonight, before the two of them embarked on what he expected would be another long night of sex. It wouldn't do to be late for the meeting, even though now his own agenda had taken a slight change of direction. If he played his cards right tonight, Saskia would no longer have to plead for a chance at this promotion. She'd be handing in her resignation. He put the bottle down and picked up the receiver, pressing the message bank button as he happily contemplated tomorrow's meeting.

'Saskia!'

He blinked as he recognised the voice, a prickly suspicion crawling through him, congealing in his gut. Why the hell would Marla be calling Saskia? He focused on the message she'd left.

'I have such exciting news. They've made an offer on my memoirs. They recommended I get an agent straight away, so I need your help. When are you back? Call me when you get a chance. I can't believe it—they're going to publish my book! And I owe it all to you!'

# CHAPTER NINE

THE bath was liquid heaven, the bubbles up to her chin, the spa jets gently massaging muscles sore in places from abilities she had never dreamed possible. She closed her eyes and let her head loll back against the rim. But she wasn't about to go to sleep. Not a chance. Soon Alex would join her, and another chapter in her sexual awakening would begin. And in the slippery oil-scented water she was very much looking forward to this particular chapter.

Tonight she wouldn't think about anything but what he would teach her and what she would learn. Tomorrow there would be time enough for recriminations.

Saskia sensed rather than heard the door open. She opened her eyes and looked around, expecting him to be still naked, expecting him to join her. But he was wearing jeans and a buttoned shirt, and the look on his face was dark thunder. She frowned, lifting herself a little higher in the water.

'Alex?'

'You bitch,' he snarled. 'How the hell did you think you'd get away with it?'

She sat right up now, turning around to face him, ignoring the sluice of water and the slide of bubbles from her skin. 'Alex, what's wrong?'

'All the time you demanded to be trusted. All the time you pretended to be something you're not. All that crap about a profile. All that rubbish about suddenly not being in the running for the promotion. It was all one big con. There never was any promotion. There never was any competition. It was all one big cover-up for what you were really doing.'

'I don't understand.' She pushed herself up and out of the bath, securing one of the enormous bath sheets around her while he continued to stand like some gunslinger looking to shoot her down. 'What are you talking about?'

'Marla's memoirs are what I'm talking about!'

Fear sent shivers down her spine. He'd been bound to find out some time, but why now? Why now, before Marla had had a chance to speak to him about it herself? 'How did you find out?'

His lips turned into a sneer. 'And you're in so deep you can't even deny it.'

She shook her head, grabbed another smaller towel to wipe away the foam that still clung to her shoulders and hair. 'Why should I deny it? She asked me to read them.'

He grabbed the towel and whipped it out of her reach, forcing her to focus on him and him alone. 'You're lying! You've been stalking her from the start.'

'You don't know what you're talking about. Marla asked me to read them. So I did, and they were good. And I passed them onto a friend of mine who works for a publisher in New York. Like Marla also asked me to do.'

'I told you to stay away from her!'

'And I did. She sought *me* out. I didn't go looking for her.'

'You're lying.'

'It's the truth! Don't blame me. Blame yourself. Marla and

I might have been confined to different cell blocks, but you were the one who had us living in the same prison compound.'

'You promised me in New York that you'd stay away from her.'

'No! I promised you that this profile would be about you!' she reminded him. 'Besides, I'd already told Marla I'd read her manuscript, and I wasn't about to break a promise I'd made to her.'

'You didn't tell me.'

'Why the hell should I? I knew what you'd say, how you'd react. So did Marla. But she pleaded with me to read it and I did.' She glared up at him, waiting for the next explosion. 'So what's happened?' she asked. Sick of being confined to the bathroom, she shoved past him and made her way to the dressing room, needing the security of clothes. She couldn't hold this conversation wearing only a towel.

'Did Marla call?'

'She left you a message,' he responded, following her. 'Some sleazy publisher has offered her a contract to publish them.'

She spun around, her hands full of clothes, the significance of his message overshadowing his insult. 'They want to make her an offer? But that's great news. She must be so excited. Surely you can see how wonderful an opportunity this is for her?'

'What I can see,' Alex said, coming towards her so fast he seemed to rise up like a mountain over her, 'is that you've succeeded in getting my sister to splash the sordid details of her entire life to the papers.'

'This isn't the papers, and it's not about sordid details. If what you say is true, and I hope it is for her sake, then it's a book deal. She's actually scored the heady achievement of selling her first book. Do you have any idea how rare it is to have your first book published?'

'Sleaze will always find a market.'

'How *dare* you say that? This is your sister's writing we're talking about. And if you bothered to read it you'd see it's an amazingly well-written account of one person's life and her struggle to find herself. *In her words.* Noone else's. And it's funny and witty and touching and wise. Did you know your sister was so talented? I doubt it. I bet you didn't even know your sister was a writer.'

His eyes slid away and she knew she'd hit a raw nerve.

'Marla's a gifted writer,' she continued, 'and now she might even have the start of a career. Don't you want that for her? Don't you want her to have a real life? Or are you so determined to keep up this big brother act, keep her locked away, that you can't even see what's good for her any more? Can't you see that's why she breaks out? Because she wants freedom—not to be treated like a child!'

'She needs my support.'

'No, she needs her freedom. You keep her locked away in a gilded prison. No wonder when she breaks out she seeks every bit of attention she can find. You've got her so locked away she doesn't even know who she is.'

'And you think *you* know what's good for her?' His face was severe, his mouth twisted, and Saskia knew she'd hurt him.

'Look, I know you care for her. She's your sister and you love her. But maybe you should back off a bit. Maybe you should give her a bit more responsibility and freedom. I know she wants it.'

'And splattering her life in print is the way to do it? Why couldn't you leave her alone? I told you to leave her alone!'

'Alex, listen—'

'Marla was fine until your family came along. What business do you have in trying to ruin her life? Don't you think your father's done enough to her already?'

His words shocked her into silence, and he stood over her, his chest heaving, the words hanging between them like a damnation. Why should he hold such deep-seated hatred for her father? Sure, their families had history, but so did just about every other family engaged in business in Sydney. It was an occupational hazard.

'Look, we both know my father took over your family's business. And I know it must have been difficult for your family. But it was such a long time ago. Maybe it's time you got over it.'

He laughed—the sound of the devil, evil and poisoned with acrimony—and fear flared out from her spine. 'I'm not talking about the takeover,' he sneered, his face now only inches from her own.

Dread rooted her to the spot. But if it wasn't the takeover… 'Then, what?'

'I'm talking about when your father raped my sister!'

Cold shock drenched through her, dousing her in disbelief. She was unable to speak, unable to respond, the shaking of her head the only movement she was capable of.

'You don't believe me? You don't believe your precious father could do such a thing?'

'No,' she protested. It was too revolting, too ugly to have any measure of truth. Dear God, not her father. It was a lie. It had to be.

'Believe it,' he said. 'Your dear sweet father wasn't content to strip my father's business bare. He decided to strip Marla of her virginity as well.'

'No! It can't be possible.'

'More than possible. It happened. And your father waved the fact he'd stolen Marla's virginity in front of my father like a trophy.'

'It can't be true.'

'She was *fifteen* years old!'

Every revelation was worse than the one before. She cowered before him, reeling from his accusations as if they were body blows. Marla had been a teenager—little more than a child. It couldn't be true. It just couldn't.

*Until she remembered the memoirs*—how Marla had lost her virginity at the age of fifteen—to a much older man.

*Could that man have been Saskia's own father?*

Could he have acted that way? Her own father? How could he have done it? Surely he could never have committed such a horrendous act, only then to turn around and flaunt the fact in front of Marla's father? It would have destroyed them.

But then, it *had* destroyed them, hadn't it?

What had Alex told her? His parents had never recovered from the shock of the takeover. Only now she could see that it hadn't been the takeover that had destroyed them, it had been despair at what had happened to their young daughter.

Why else would Alex hate her father so much? He must know it was true. And so far nothing else made sense. Nothing else fitted.

She'd always known her father had prided himself on his ruthless business skills, but she'd never seen him in that light. Saskia must have been only about one year old at the time, and to her as a child her father had been her gruff teddy bear, who'd sent her into fits of laughter by teasing her with his whiskers when wishing her goodnight.

How could the same man who had tickled her and kissed her goodnight do something so hideous to someone else's daughter? She shuddered. Had he kissed her goodnight after what he'd done to Marla? Oh, God, she hoped not.

With a cry of grief and disgust she bolted for the bathroom, losing what little she'd managed to eat of her Michelin three-star meal.

He stalked up behind her, throwing her a towel that she grabbed hold of and clutched to her mouth. 'I know,' he said, his voice hard and remorseless. 'It turns my stomach too.'

She was shaking, her body too weak to stand, her breathing ragged. 'Alex,' she croaked. 'I had no idea. I didn't know.'

'So now you do. And now you know why I didn't want you having anything to do with Marla from the start.'

'You were protecting me from discovering what my father had done.'

'I was protecting *her*! This was always about Marla, about keeping her safe.'

Oh no, she suddenly thought. *Marla*. The woman had trusted her, had sought out her help. She looked up at him, 'Does she know? I mean, about me… I mean…'

'That you're *his* daughter? Of course she doesn't! Why the hell else would she have anything to do with you?'

'I don't know what to say,' she said, blotting her face on the towel, wishing it could soak up the horror, wishing it could mop up the past.

'Then do me a favour and don't say anything.' His face had moved beyond fury. The heat had dispersed and now it was ice that met her gaze—cold, unforgiving ice that chilled her heart and soul.

'You know, I actually believed we could forget the past because I thought you were different. For a while there you had me so taken with sleeping with you I even forgot who your father was.' He laughed, this time a self-deprecating sound that smacked of how much of a fool he thought he'd been. 'But you're no different than he is—preying on the naïve and vulnerable for your own sick purpose. Now I can see you're truly your father's daughter. You two really deserve each other.'

He disappeared once more into the suite. A few seconds later she heard him talking, barking orders into the phone.

She stood, still shaky, and washed her face, shocked at how pale her skin looked in the mirror. She saw movement behind her and turned. Alex had his leather briefcase and suit bag in his hands, and her heart—something she hadn't thought could get any lower—took a dive.

'You're leaving?'

'I'm moving to another suite. I'll be flying back first thing tomorrow. I'll ship over anything you left.'

'What about tomorrow morning's meeting?'

'Oh, come on, Saskia. Enough's enough. You don't expect me to believe that rubbish still. You've got what you wanted. You've already got Marla bending over backwards to spill her guts to the tabloids, or wherever else you want her to, even if I do manage to get that manuscript back. You don't have to convince me now. It's too late.'

She thought she saw something move across his eyes—a sad look, almost of regret—but it was fleeting and too quickly blinked away. And too easily misinterpreted, she thought, knowing that looking for something in his eyes, hoping for it, would not make it so.

Like he said, it was too late.

And it was no wonder he didn't want anything to do with her. She was a constant reminder of what her father had done.

'Oh, and when you see your father tomorrow…'

She waited a few seconds, then, 'Yes?'

'Let him know that he's the only man I ever felt like murdering. Tell him that under the circumstances he ended up getting off lightly.'

Saskia closed her eyes against the bitterness of his parting jibe, and by the time she'd opened them he'd gone. Seconds later she heard the cushioned thunk of the suite's solid front door closing.

He was gone.

Again.

For the second time in her life he was casting her aside. And for the second time in her life she felt as if her insides had been ripped out of her body, shredded into ribbons and hung out to dry.

# CHAPTER TEN

THE meeting with Sir Rodney and the board had gone as well as could be expected. At least that was what Saskia told herself, trying to find some positive angle as she stood outside the Snapmedia building, wrapping her coat more tightly around her and battling back tears under the grey, sleet-threatening sky.

Because, in all seriousness, what had she expected? The board were bound to have been unimpressed with the fact that the man who'd insisted they all get together for a meeting to convince them their engagement had been a farce from the start hadn't even bothered to show up.

If she'd slept last night, if she hadn't lain awake in the empty suite, being tormented by the awful knowledge that her father was not the man she thought he was, that he was suddenly a stranger, then she might have been able to argue her case. But she'd been shattered by both the news and her sleepless night, and part of her wondered if she'd even wanted to fight anyway.

In the end the board had conceded that if she could get her profile in within the week there was a slim chance she might still be considered for the position, but it would have to stack up against Carmen's excellent in-depth report.

She'd almost laughed in their faces. How could she turn in a profile when her subject had just walked out on her? She didn't stand a chance. But then, why did she even need a chance?

Why did she need this job to pay for a house for her father when right now she wasn't even sure she ever wanted to see him again?

She sniffed against the heavy cold air, blinking away the tears from her scratchy eyes as engaged cab after engaged cab cruised past. Of course she wanted to see him—he was her father, after all. The only father she'd ever have. And he was old and frail, and he had no one else to take care of him, and she had no one else to take care of.

But if it were true…

If he'd committed such an unforgivable act…

Oh, where *were* all the empty cabs in London?

She rubbed her hands together, wishing she'd worn gloves and suddenly missing Alex, with his limousines and jets on tap. He turned travel into an art form, not this battle for survival.

Finally she managed to coax a black cab to the kerb. She pulled open the back door and jumped inside.

'Where to, luv?' asked the driver.

It was warm in the cab, much warmer than outside, and it took her a moment to register that she needed to make a decision—now.

She took a deep breath and gave him her father's address.

Twenty minutes and half a lifetime of dread later the taxi pulled up opposite her father's dingy block of flats.

He's an old man, she told herself as she climbed the stairs to the second floor.

He was still the same old man she'd spoken to a week ago.

And, whatever else he'd done, he was still her father. But it was hard to convince herself of that—so hard to feel warm for the man who'd tucked her in at night at the same time. God only knew what else had been happening.

It was after the third time she'd knocked that she started regretting the fact she hadn't let him know she was coming. But then she hadn't known what she was going to say. And what *could* she say?—*Hi, Dad, what was it like to have sex with Alex Koutoufides's sister?*

Maybe it was just as well he wasn't home. Maybe she wasn't ready for this. But then, where was he? The last time she'd rung he'd been too ill to leave the flat.

The door of the adjoining flat opened and a woman peered out.

'Mrs Sharpe,' Saskia said, relieved to see the neighbour. 'I've come to visit my father, but he's not answering. Do you know where he might be?'

Enid Sharpe's face creased into wrinkles deep enough for caverns and her bird-like frame shuffled out through the door towards her. 'Oh, Saskia, my luvvy, haven't you heard?'

Alex was in a foul mood by the time he got back to Tahoe, and it didn't help matters when Marla came outside to meet the car, the smile on her face broader than he'd seen in years. She rushed up to kiss him on the cheek, and then looked around the car, puzzled.

'Where's Saskia?'

'London,' he snapped, snatching up his bags from the boot of the car himself, before the driver could collect them.

'But why? When's she coming back?'

'She won't be,' he said, noticing Jake standing by the door, waiting. He nodded. 'Jake.'

'Good to have you back, boss.'

*You won't think that when I'm done with you.* 'Meet me in

my office,' he told him. They had a few matters to discuss concerning Marla's secret liaisons. 'Fifteen minutes.'

Marla trailed him through to the massive timber-beamed living area. 'But…'

He turned around alongside the stone fireplace, ready to snap her head off, and then something struck him as different about her. 'What have you done to yourself?' he asked. 'You look different.'

She reached a tentative hand to her hair and shrugged. 'I coloured it, that's all. Do you like it?'

What was not to like? It was honey-gold, just the way he liked it. Just like… He growled, clamping down on the thought.

'I got your message,' he said. 'I know about the book.'

She blinked. 'Oh?'

'And I want you to know I'll do everything I can to get it back.'

'What do you mean?' Her hands clutched his arm. 'They want to buy it. It's going to be published.'

'Not if I can help it.'

'No! You don't understand. Saskia said—'

He shrugged off her hands. 'I don't care what Saskia said!'

She stood watching him, her breathing fast and furious. 'How did you find out? I left that message for Saskia, and she wouldn't have told you. I asked for Saskia's room…' Her eyes suddenly widened. 'You two shared a room. You slept with her, didn't you?'

Alex swung his bags around and resumed walking past the fireplace towards the master bedroom wing.

'You slept with Saskia. I *knew* you would. It was obvious you wanted to. Is that why she hasn't returned my calls? But what did you say to her? What did you do to her to make her stay in London?'

He spun around, incensed at what his sister was saying—

doubly incensed at what she'd perceived. 'I told her from the very beginning to stay away from you. But she couldn't, could she? She pretended to be here to interview me, when all along she was angling to get the dirt on you. I trusted her to keep away from you, and she couldn't.'

'You've never trusted anybody in your life!'

'She told me she was here to do my profile.'

'And she was.'

'Then how did she end up selling *your* story?'

'Because I sought her out! I saw her walking along the lake shore in the early morning and I went down to talk to her. I liked her. It was nice to talk to another woman for a change, and that's when I asked if she'd be willing to read my manuscript.'

'I'm sure that's how it was.'

'She told me you wouldn't like it. I had to beg her to read it. I even had to pretend it was written by someone else. She didn't believe me for a minute, though. And I know she was thinking it was going to be hopeless, and she really didn't want to know, but I was desperate. I made her take it.'

Alex looked at his sister, weighing up her words. Marla had done plenty of things in her time that he didn't like, but she'd never lied to him. And wasn't that exactly what Saskia had told him—that Marla had sought her out?

But so what? It didn't matter in the scheme of things. She was still who she was. Nothing would ever change that.

'It doesn't change the fact that you have to pull that manuscript. We have to get it back.'

Marla crossed her arms and stamped her heel down hard. 'What if I don't want to?'

'Then it's getting pulled anyway. You know I'm only doing what's best for you.'

'No, you're not. How can you know what's best for me?

Have you ever *asked* me what I'd like? And, given the way you've obviously treated Saskia over this, you don't even know what's best for you. How can you possibly think you're any judge of what might be good for someone else?'

Alex sighed and raked the fingers of one hand through his hair. He was tired and hungry and he'd had enough of women lately—especially women who couldn't see what was obvious and yet imagined all sorts of other things. But maybe he'd come on too strong all the same. There was no point taking out his frustrations over what had happened with Saskia on Marla.

'Look, I just want you to be happy, okay?'

'Fine. That makes two of us.'

'Then there's no point publishing a whole lot of stuff that's going to hit the fan big time.'

'How do you know that's going to happen? You haven't even read it.'

'Come on, Marla. Since when has anyone published anything about you that hasn't caused trouble?'

'But *I* wrote this. Don't you even trust me to get it right?'

'This isn't about trust—'

'Yes, it is! I'm nearly forty years old, and still you don't trust me to tell my story my way and not screw it up. If you just talked to Saskia—'

'*No!* I will not be talking to Saskia—and if you know what's good for you, neither will you.'

'And yet it was okay for you to sleep with her?'

Breath hissed through his teeth. 'You don't understand. You don't know what kind of person she is.'

'I know she's not the gutter press you'd like to make her out to be.'

'It's not just what she is; it's *who* she is.'

'Because she's Victor Prentice's daughter?'

With his brain still fogged from too much travel and too little sleep he had to take a second to assimilate what she'd just said.

'You knew?'

'Of course I knew! I mean, not straight away, but it wasn't too hard to work out—not with her photo and her name plastered all over every paper in town.'

'But her father…'

'You don't have to remind me who her father is or what her father did! I was there—remember?'

'You were only fifteen!'

'And you were only twelve! What could you have really known about it at the time? I wish you'd never found out. I wish Dad had never said anything to you.'

'I knew something was going on even before he did. So many hushed conversations. So many tears. And when I found out he'd raped you I wanted to kill him. I swore I'd have my revenge for what he did.'

She looked at him open-mouthed. 'What did you just say? He *raped* me? Is that what you've believed all these years?'

'He took your virginity. You were only a teenager. What would you call it?'

'I'd call it sex. I'd call it satisfying a mutual need.'

*'Tsou!'* The word exploded from him as he reeled away. When he turned he was pointing his finger at her like an accusation. 'He was old enough to be your father! Why would you feel any such need with *him*? How would you even know what you needed?'

She shrugged. 'Who can explain attraction? He was older, and I thought he was so dashing and powerful. I was drawn to him, and curious about sex. And he was so lonely and sad—with no wife and a tiny child. I guess I felt sorry for him.'

'But why would you agree to do such a thing?'

'I didn't agree. *He* did.'

She gave him time to let the words sink in—time that he desperately needed to make sense of it all.

'But that would mean…'

'Exactly,' she said. 'I *asked* him to make love to me. I chose him to show me what it was to be a woman. I know what he did was wrong, and so did he, but I begged him—even forced myself on him, if you must know.' She tilted her head, her brow furrowed slightly. 'Is this why you've been so against Saskia from the start? It wasn't just that she was a journalist? It was because she was Victor's daughter? How could you possibly hold that against her, when she was still in nappies at the time?'

He reached his arms up, pushing his neck back against his knotted fingers. 'It doesn't matter. He still had sex with you. He had no right—'

'Forget about Victor! You have to let this hatred go, Alex! It's history. Besides, Victor's little more than a broken man now. He's frail, and needs constant help.' She stopped when she saw his double-take. 'You mean you didn't know? Didn't you speak to Saskia at all while you had her here? Or were you too busy angling her into your bed? Why else do you think she's so desperate for this promotion of hers? It's the only way she's going to be able to afford decent care for him.'

'*Theos!*' he said, closing his eyes as he spun around, feeling suddenly ill. He couldn't have managed this more badly if he'd tried.

'What have you done?' Marla came closer, put a hand to his arm. 'Didn't you go over there to help her? What happened?'

He looked down at his sister, but he saw nothing but the pain on Saskia's face—the pain he'd savagely inflicted when he'd accused her father of committing the most hideous of crimes, of raping his sister. He heard Marla's rapid intake of breath, registered her shocked withdrawal.

'Oh, my God! You didn't tell her... Please say you didn't tell her that...?'

He shook his head. He couldn't deny it. Just as he couldn't deny he'd sent her packing for the second time. He'd used her and insulted her and then thrown her to the wolves, discarding her like a piece of dirt. And he'd felt so righteous. In spite of everything there had been moments in that hotel room in London when he'd wanted to keep her, wanted to have her in his bed and by his side, when he hadn't wanted to let her go. But at the last minute he'd been saved from those weak urges by hearing Marla's news and proving he'd been right not to trust Saskia all along.

What the hell had he done?

Alex stood in his study, his hands in his pockets, gazing unseeingly out of the floor-to-ceiling cedar-framed windows. He knew what the view looked like from here. He knew every tree and boulder leading down to the lake. He knew every mountain rising on the far distant shore.

So why today did everything look so different?

The morning was sharp and crisp, the lake water so still and clear he could see right down into the boulder strewn shallows. He'd given up on sleep and spent most of the night in his study, catching up on business he'd neglected over the last few days.

But his mind hadn't been on business either.

Sleep eluded him. Business escaped him. Only one thing stood as stark and clear as the towering pines that framed his view. Only one thing accounted for the sick feeling in his empty stomach.

He'd been wrong.

Totally, completely, unforgivably wrong.

And that was just about his sister.

For years he'd thought he was protecting her, wrapping her up in cotton wool, trying to keep her safe and wondering why she'd escape his protective custody at every opportunity. Who could blame her? He'd never trusted her. He'd never let her find her own way. He'd taken her mistakes as signals that he should make all the decisions, not that she just needed the space and time to learn.

It was a wonder she still deigned to call him her brother.

But if he'd done wrong by Marla, his own sister, then what he'd done to Saskia was one thousand times worse.

He'd misjudged her, he'd mistrusted her, he'd damned her to hell—a hell that he himself had crafted for her—and then he'd left her there to rot.

Hell, if he ran his business this way he'd be bankrupt in a minute.

And wasn't that word appropriate?

*Bankrupt.*

Morally and ethically, when it came to Saskia, he lacked the most basic resources. He'd misjudged her from the start because of who she was and what she reminded him of. He'd misjudged her motives, he'd mistrusted her, he'd refused to believe her. And when he'd learned about Marla selling her memoirs all his vile prejudices had thrown a party and celebrated. He'd been right all along!

And yet he'd been so wrong.

He'd taken the moral high ground, thinking that ground was solid, not realising how thin a crust he was standing on.

And that crust had crumbled into chalk dust when he'd learned the truth about her.

She hadn't lied to him. She hadn't betrayed his trust. She'd recognised things about his relationship with his sister that he'd been blind to, that he hadn't wanted to hear. And she'd come here, dealing with the one person she'd never wanted to see in her life again, not for personal gain but to ensure she could care for her father.

*What a damned fool he was!* He fisted his hands to his forehead as the trees, the lake, the mountains all faded away before him. All he could see was her body slumped on the bathroom floor, her hand clutching a towel to her face, her eyes large and fearful like a wounded animal's. He'd dumped the news of what her father had done to his sister like a victory. It had been his *pièce de résistance* and he'd made the most of it, twisting it like a long, sharp-bladed knife in deep.

He'd trashed her father. He'd trashed her career by not staying to support her in front of her board. He'd trashed her life. And then he'd coldly walked away.

He'd had his second chance with her. He'd had a chance to put things between them to rights. And for a brief time he'd thought he could—that they might even have a life together, a future.

But he'd blown his precious chance sky-high.

Now there was no hope.

Saskia squirmed to wakefulness in the vinyl chair, its wooden arms cutting into her legs where they tucked under her. She opened her eyes and looked over at her father, hoping to see some improvement. Her heart sank as rapidly as it had risen.

No change.

After three days at his bedside she knew what to look for. After three days she was beginning to wonder if the coma that had claimed him after his inoperable brain stem haemorrhage was ever going to let him go. Would he ever be able to breathe without that tube down his throat and a machine to fill his chest with air?

'It could be five days before he wakes up,' the doctors had warned her. 'Or it could be five months. And even then…'

She clamped her eyes shut, trying to keep back the glum prognosis they'd issued, but the painful truth seeped through. She had to be ready, they'd told her. Even if he woke up he'd need months, maybe even years of rehabilitation. And that was the up side.

She didn't want to think about any of it. She'd already tied herself up in knots thinking, but right now what was the alternative? Trawling over the train wreck of the last couple of weeks with Alex? Not likely. There was no joy down that path. Only self-recrimination. Because for the second time in her life she'd offered herself to the man she'd fancied herself in love with. And for the second time she'd been discarded like something stinking stuck to his shoe.

But how utterly stupid of her was it that it had been the same man both times?

Hadn't she learned *anything* the first time around?

Saskia looked over at her father. The machine alongside him was ensuring the constant rise and fall of his chest, keeping him alive until such time as he could breathe on his own again. She looked at his creased sunken cheeks and his closed eyes as he slept, and he just looked like an old man.

When she'd gone to see him at the flat she'd been sick to the stomach over how she would greet him. What would she say? How could she believe what Alex had told her was true, and that her own father was capable of such an act? Because she was so very scared it was.

But now he was lying there in a coma, critically ill, possibly dying. Now only one fact mattered.

He was her father.

The only father she had.

And, God forgive her, she still loved him.

Tears slid down her cheeks. So what kind of person did that make her? Maybe Alex had been right. Maybe she truly was her father's daughter.

The door swung open and a nurse bustled into the room, flashing her a compassionate smile as she breezed by to check her patient's vitals. 'Beautiful day outside, Miss Prentice, but they're predicting it'll rain later. Maybe you should grab a cup of tea and get some fresh air while you can?'

Saskia stretched, and eased her feet into her shoes.

'Maybe you're right,' she agreed, swiping away at her own precipitation. There was precious little she could do here.

It was dark when she made it back to her tiny one-bedroom flat, bone-weary and wanting nothing more taxing than to lose herself in a long hot bath. She'd been at the hospital for five and a half days, refusing to go further than the gardens outside, refusing to leave her father's side for any length of time. He had nobody else—what if he woke up?

But the doctors were right. It was time to go home.

She swung the door open and let herself inside, snapping on the light. A neat pile of mail sat on the dresser and she gave silent thanks—as usual, her landlady had been keeping an eye on the place while she'd been away. Then she turned to see an untidier stack of boxes filling one half of her living room.

She looked at them, blinking as she moved closer, checking for the forwarding address.

*Tahoe*. That explained it. Alex had said he'd send her things. But why so many? She'd left barely anything there. And what she had left she really didn't care if she never saw again.

She slit through the tape on the first box and peeled back the flaps. Clothes. The outfits he'd bought her in Sydney—the boutique full of clothes he'd had delivered so she could look the part of his fiancée. Clothes she'd never considered hers. The beautiful silk-chiffon dress she'd worn at the airport that first day ran through her fingers. The ballgown she'd worn in New York was folded like treasure, and everything else was in between. There were clothes she'd never worn, and shoes and bags and underwear.

She sat back on her heels and contemplated it all, absorbing the shock of her discoveries, trying to come to terms with the sheer cold-bloodedness of it all. She began to laugh.

It was funny, really. They'd never been her clothes, but he'd cleared the cupboards and sent everything to her as if they were. There was a box of ballgowns here! A boutique in a box there! 'Here a box, there a box,' she cried, whooping with laughter as an old nursery rhyme came to mind. 'Everywhere a box, box.'

She laughed and laughed, unable to stop the hysteria welling up inside. He'd dispensed with every trace of anything she might have breathed on, let alone touched. He'd wiped her existence from his life as if she'd never been there, and he'd bundled up and sent her the crumbs, so she would know just how little he wanted to be reminded of her.

It was too funny for words. Because what made Alex think for a moment that she wanted to be reminded of *him*?

And she kept on laughing, the tears streaming down her face, unable to recall later, when she'd dragged herself off to bed, just when it was that her laughter had given way to tears.

\* \* \*

Twenty-four hours later she was functioning again. If you could call it that. The doorbell rang and she pulled her still wet hair into a ponytail, calling out that she was coming. The charity group she'd called to take away the boxes obviously hadn't wasted any time—but that was good. The sooner they were gone, the sooner she would be rid of the physical reminders of her time with Alex. The memories she knew would take longer.

She pulled open the door wide to let them in, and froze.

'Hello, Saskia.'

## CHAPTER ELEVEN

SHE blinked, took a breath, but when she opened her eyes again it was still Alex standing on her threshold—and it was still an angry knot that was tangling up and pulling tight inside her.

'What are you doing here?'

'I came to see you.' She noticed the tight lines around his jaw, the lines between his brows. She took in the creases in his chambray shirt and the slight slump to his shoulders. He looked tired, maybe a little shattered. Even so, he looked a darned sight better than she knew she did.

'Aren't you going to ask me in?'

'Why should I?'

'Because we have to talk.'

She shook her head. 'I don't think so. I don't think there's anything left to say.'

Two men, one middle-aged and wearing overalls and one in his twenties in baggy jeans and a sloppy T-shirt, appeared behind Alex's shoulder, trying to get her attention. 'You got a pick-up for Charity Central, luv?'

'That's right,' she said. 'Just through here.'

Alex didn't move out of the way, she noticed with irritation. Instead he moved inside the room to let them pass.

She indicated the boxes with a sweep of her hand. 'All of these.'

Alex looked at the boxes and then back at her as the first box was lugged into strong arms and disappeared out through the door. 'Hang on a minute,' he protested. 'Aren't these…?'

She nodded. 'The very same.'

'Those clothes cost a fortune.'

'Your fortune,' she said. 'Not mine. But if you want them…'

The older man stopped midway to the door. 'So are they going or staying?'

'They're going.'

'They're staying.'

They spoke together.

The man huffed and put the box down, tapping his returning assistant on the arm to stop him picking up the next box. He drummed his fingers on the top of one box. 'So what's it to be, guv?' he said, deferring to Alex.

'I bought them for you,' he told Saskia accusingly.

'You bought them for your fake fiancée,' she replied, 'who is now surplus to requirements. As are these clothes. If I don't want them, and you don't want them, charity seems the perfect solution.'

'Fine,' Alex said, as if he was speaking through gritted teeth. 'Take them away.'

The man looked from one to the other and then nodded at his colleague. In three trips they'd cleared the living room, smiled their brief thanks and disappeared, before either of them could change their minds.

Saskia breathed a sigh of relief as she boiled the kettle for a long-deserved cup of tea. The boxes were gone. If only Alex, still occupying her living room as if he belonged there, could be dispensed with so easily.

'What was that all about?' he demanded, coming up behind her.

'This is my home,' she warned him, spinning around. 'You might rule the roost in your own fleet of houses and hotel rooms, but here, in this flat, what I say goes. Have you got that?'

She knew her voice sounded thready and weak. Hell, she *felt* thready and weak. But she couldn't just let him take control. 'Besides which,' she said, 'I don't actually remember inviting you in.'

His eyelids dipped, almost as if he was shutting out her protest. 'Nevertheless, I'm here.'

She turned to look at him, saw the hurt and ache that coursed through his eyes and suddenly wished she hadn't. What right did he have to want sympathy? After everything he'd done?

She turned back towards the bench, squeezing out her teabag, twisting it around a spoon to wring it out, and finally dropping it in the bin, all her actions running comfortingly on autopilot. Then she stirred in a heaped teaspoon full of sugar, just for good measure. Right now she could do with all the fortification she could get.

'What if I don't want you here? Did you consider that?'

'Oh, yes. I considered that.'

'And?'

'It wasn't an option.'

She laughed, feeling the lingering hysteria of the night before revisiting her. Only now that hysteria wanted to be magnified by his presence. 'Now, that sounds like the great Alexander Koutoufides.'

'No!' he said, grabbing her arm and sending boiling liquid sloshing over the rim floorwards, thankfully not over her.

She looked down at his hand, then up at him. 'Let me go.'

'I didn't come here to argue with you.'

'Then why *are* you here, Alex? What could you possibly want after all that's happened?'

He looked at her, and the longer he did so the more she wished she'd never let him in.

'I came to tell you I was sorry.'

She drank in a deep breath, plastering a thin smile to her face. 'Well, that makes up for just about everything, then.'

She forced herself to take a sip of her tea, knowing it was still too hot but needing something to do. Something that didn't involve interaction with him. And yet, even scalding hot, her tea was no competition for the heat generated by his presence.

'Marla told me she pursued you about getting her memoirs published. She said you didn't come after her at all.'

She barely threw him a glance. 'Oh, and isn't that what I'd told you already? I had the distinct impression you didn't believe me.'

Her accusation hung heavy in the air, but even though his head was bowed his eyes still held hers.

'I realise you don't have to make this easy for me, but I am trying to apologise.'

'Of course. Apology accepted,' she said brightly, clearly throwing him off balance. 'Now, if there's nothing more…' She gestured to the door.

'Dammit, Saskia! Of course there's more—lots more.' He wheeled away, forcing hands rigid like claws through his hair. When he spun back he was holding out his hands almost in supplication. 'I left London because I thought you'd betrayed my trust. I thought you'd gone behind my back to get whatever dirt you could on my sister. And when I spoke to Marla and found out how wrong I was, do you know how bad I felt?'

'No,' she said frankly. 'I have no idea.'

'I'd not only accused you of a lie,' he continued, ignoring her snippy reply, 'I'd abandoned you to face your boss and your board alone for probably the most important meeting of your career. How bad was it?'

'Oh, it was just peachy,' she told him. 'And they were good enough to give me a few days to get my profile in. Only problem was, my subject had walked out on me.' She shrugged as she took a sip of her sweet tea. *C'est la vie.*'

'You'll get that job, if you still want it, with or without my profile.'

She looked up at him. 'How sweet of you to say so.' Then, just as his eyes were starting to relax and warm, she held one hand up and waved it in the air. 'But I don't care any more. I've decided to let Carmen have the job. She wants it so badly—frankly she must do, to have poured herself all over Drago the way she did—and she'll be good at it, I know.'

'Saskia, Carmen won't be needing that job.'

'What do you mean?'

'You haven't been listening to the news today? Drago Maiolo had a heart attack and drove his Ferrari through a barricade and over a cliff.'

'Oh God, that's awful. But what's that got to do with Carmen?'

'Carmen was in the car alongside him. She didn't stand a chance.'

It was too much. When would it all stop? She squeezed her eyes shut and swayed, letting herself slump into a chair. No matter how much Carmen had done to hurt her, nobody deserved to die like that.

'I'm sorry,' he told her. 'There was no easy way to say it. But don't you see? Now that job can be yours.'

She rested her forehead against her hand. 'And don't *you* see? I don't want that job!'

'But I thought you needed it for your father.'

She looked up at him, blinking blindly, her stomach yawning open into a whirlpool, sucking her down further into that dark, fetid, bottomless place.

'I know all about it,' he explained. 'Marla told me he was sick. She said you need money to fund his care. And she told me more—'

From somewhere she dredged the energy to stand. 'And now I'm supposed to believe you suddenly care about my father?' Her voice was accusing, though her senses were still reeling as she swiped up her barely touched cup and transferred it to the sink.

'Listen to me,' he urged. 'I spoke to Marla. What I said in that hotel—'

She spun round, ignoring him, cutting him off. 'I'm awfully sorry to have to tell you I didn't get to pass on your message.'

'Message?'

'About how much you'd always wanted him dead.'

'*Theos!* Saskia, I never should have said that. I lashed out at you. I didn't mean—'

'Of course you meant it! You meant every word. And all the time we were together, all the time you were making love to me, you still hated my father so much you wanted him dead. How you must have hated having anything to do with *me*, the daughter of the man you hated so deeply. Frankly, I'm surprised you could bear to touch me.'

'It wasn't like that.'

She held up a hand to silence him, her smile thin. 'Don't worry. It doesn't matter. What does matter is that you got your wish.'

Silence hung over the small kitchen like a shroud.

'What are you talking about?'

'Didn't you know? My father died yesterday.'

All of a sudden the dark circles around eyes almost too large in the unearthly pallor of her skin of her face made sense.

Victor Prentice was dead.

'Saskia,' he said, automatically reaching out for her, thinking back to when his own parents had died, remembering the awful sense of loss, knowing how terrible she must be feeling without him having unceremoniously dumped the news of Carmen's death on her as well.

Clumsily she darted out of his reach across the kitchen, putting the dining table between them and crossing her arms defensively in front of her. 'Don't you dare touch me!'

'Saskia…'

'And please don't insult my intelligence by pretending you're sorry! You wanted him dead all along. You must be so relieved he's finally out of the way.'

'No. I'm not going to pretend I ever liked or respected your father,' he said honestly, 'but I was wrong about him. And I was wrong to tell you what I did. I hurt you, and I shouldn't have.'

She blinked, her green eyes glossy and as hard as jade. 'What do you care about me anyway? I never meant more to you than a means of revenge—somebody you could thoroughly humiliate in order to satisfy your own personal need for vengeance.'

'That's not true,' he argued. 'The last thing I ever wanted was to humiliate you.'

Her eyes looked bigger than ever. Brilliant green pools of disbelief.

'And you don't think you did? I don't believe you. You led

me on, you took me out and made me feel like a princess—
and I did—I've never felt so special in my life. And once
you'd got me in the palm of your hand—*whammo*—you not
only pulled the rug out from under my feet, you did it when
I was at my most vulnerable, when I was naked in your bed.
Don't you have any concept of how humiliating that was?'

He bowed his head, knowing every word of what she said
was true. 'Believe me, I didn't want that.'

'Then what the hell did you think you were doing? Don't
you remember how you used me? Oh, my—' She stopped,
clamping one hand over her mouth. 'Why didn't I see it before?
All this time I thought you just wanted to humiliate my family
because of what my father had done in ruining your father's
business. But you had an even better reason. You took me to
bed because you were replaying what my father had done to
your sister. As if what he did wasn't bad enough, you had to
repeat the act! What kind of monster does that make you?'

'Listen, Saskia—' He moved in closer.

She moved back, every movement strained and wary,
screaming muscles on red alert.

'That was why you took me to bed, wasn't it? You were
performing the ultimate revenge. You took me to bed—purely
to get back at my father for what he'd done to Marla!'

He stood motionless. 'It's true. I was going to take your
virginity just as your father had taken Marla's. But I couldn't
do it. I couldn't go through with it. That's why I stopped.'

'You didn't stop! You threw me out of bed.'

'Because I didn't want to hurt you.'

'Don't give me that. You threw me out of bed because you're
a cold-hearted bastard. You don't care about anything or
anyone apart from your own sister, who doesn't even want your
help. And you're too arrogant and full of yourself to realise it.'

'No! Don't you see? If I'd been the cold-hearted bastard you accuse me of being, I wouldn't have thrown you out of bed. I would have stayed there, forced my way into you and finished the deed!'

'But you told me—'

Oh, yes, he remembered only too well what he'd told her that night. Hadn't she reminded him of it only recently? 'I didn't throw you out of bed because you were a virgin.'

She swallowed, her throat scratchy and dry. 'Then…why?'

'Because I couldn't do what I'd planned to. I'd worked it all out like a military operation. I had your father's business in striking distance and I had you exactly where I wanted. I had *everything* I wanted, all lined up like ducks in a row.'

'I trusted you!'

'I know. But you have to listen,' he implored. 'Because all the time I was with you—taking you out to dinner or the movies or dancing, supposedly getting you ripe for the picking so I could reap my revenge—I started to care for you. I wasn't expecting to. It was the last thing I wanted. But you were bright and fun and so beautiful, and it was no hardship to be with you. You were easy to like. But I had the memory of what your father had done to Marla and I had a goal—and I was determined that *nothing* was going to keep me from that.'

He paused, looking at her face, at the pain of the past merging with the pain of her recent loss, and he wished he could rewrite the past to make the present somehow more tolerable for her.

'I had it all planned,' he continued. 'I took you to the beach house. There'd be no interruptions—nobody would know we were there because I never took anyone there. And, just like I'd planned, you were ready for me. When I asked you to make love to me you came willingly. You let me take off your clothes and lie you down amongst the pillows.' He held up one hand, his index finger and thumb a bare millimetre apart. 'I was *this* close to taking what I wanted. I was *this* close to exacting my revenge.' He sighed.

'What happened? What changed your mind?'

'It was something you said that suddenly made me realise what kind of person I was becoming. All of a sudden I understood what I'd been doing ever since I was twelve years old and clawing my way up the ladder to get back everything my parents had lost and more. I'd never realised it for all those years, but you made me see just how far I'd sunk.'

'And that's why you dropped out of business society? It wasn't Marla?'

'No. It wasn't Marla. It was me, and the man I'd made myself into. And it was an ugly revelation. You made me realise that in seeking my revenge, in becoming a ruthless businessman and committing the same atrocious act your father had, I was turning into the very man I hated most in the world. I was so ashamed that from then on I knew I had to live a different life. I could still be successful, but I didn't need the ruthless tactics. I didn't need to be front-page news. I chose to hide away. Just like you guessed while we were in New York I had things I never wanted anyone to know, because it was hard enough facing them myself.'

He moved closer, and this time she didn't back away. He reached for her hands, cradling them in his own. 'Don't you understand? I knew I was going to hurt you, whatever I did that night, and I knew you would hate me. But I figured that at least I wouldn't rob you of everything. At least you'd still have something to offer someone else. Someone who might even deserve it—God knows, I didn't.'

She swallowed, the action pulling his attention to her lips and the long smooth ride of her throat. 'What was it I said?'

He smiled weakly, remembering the way she'd lain under him, her eyes so full of trust, her arms wrapped so tightly around his neck, her body so welcoming. 'You told me you loved me.'

Silence followed his words, allowing the sounds of the ticking mantel clock to fill the void, unnaturally loud in the ensuing silence.

'I thought I did back then,' she said softly at last, her voice barely more than a whisper, her use of the past tense slicing through his flesh like a scythe. 'I thought I was the luckiest woman on earth.'

He reached out, putting a hand to her hair, still damp and fresh from her shower, resting his forearm on her shoulder. Her scent, fresh and unadulterated, wove its way through him—the scent he'd missed so much since he'd walked out of their hotel suite days ago. He inhaled it, drinking her in, worried that this might well be the last time.

'Saskia, I'm so sorry.' Sorry for what he'd done. Sorry for what her words revealed. She *had* loved him—in the past. Was there no chance of rekindling that love? Was there no hope at all for their future now?

'You were so angry with me that night. I don't think I've ever been more afraid.'

He toyed with the loose spiral ends of her hair, running them through his fingers. 'I know. You bore the brunt of it, but I was furious with *me*—disgusted for letting myself sink to such depths. I'd been so completely blindsided by my desperate need for revenge that I couldn't see what was in front of me—that I cared for you and that it meant something that you loved me. But I knew that I'd just ruined whatever chance I might have had with you. I knew I had to find a reason to throw you out of my bed and that it had to be one that would make you hate me for what I had done. Can you ever forgive me?'

'It's okay,' she said, closing her eyes to his ministrations as two fat tears rolled down her cheeks. 'Under the circumstances, I guess I should thank you for sparing me the same fate as your sister.'

Her words speared into his conscience. He touched the other hand to her cheek, brushing the tears away, feeling her tremble and feeling his own guilt build up by another layer. 'It's not okay. Because I never should have had you in my bed. Not for the reasons I used. I got it all wrong. Your father never raped my sister.'

Her eyes widened and she leaned back away from him. His hand was still on her shoulder. She anchored a hand on his forearm as if to steady herself.

'What did you say?'

'I spoke to Marla. It wasn't how I thought.'

'What do you mean? Are you saying they didn't have sex?'

He took a moment to steady her. 'They did, and she *was* only fifteen, but Marla insists it was hardly forced. In fact she maintains that he was reluctant but she pursued him—that she all but threw herself at him.'

Saskia sniffed, and touched the back of her hand to her nose.

'But what about him flaunting the fact he'd taken her virginity in front of your parents like you told me? Was that not true either?'

Alex sighed. 'That much he *did* do. He told my father he'd taken Marla's virginity as part of the deal.'

'But why would he do that?'

Alex ground his teeth together. 'Apparently he wasn't proud of what he'd done, but there was no way he wanted the truth to come out. He let my parents think he'd stolen her virginity so that they would hate him and not turn against her. In his own way, it seems he was protecting her.'

She blinked her haunted eyes, and he could see how much effort she was putting into holding herself together, but there were at least the beginnings of something like hope in her features.

'So you're saying my father was never a rapist?'

'No,' he said quietly. 'And I wish I could take back all those ugly words I hurled at you. I wish I could have saved you that. I was so wrong.'

'You thought you were avenging your sister. I can't imagine anyone going to such lengths for *me*.'

*I would,* he thought. If only I had a chance.

Saskia took a deep breath and moved across the kitchen, wiping her face with her hands. 'I should thank you for coming and explaining everything. Especially for what you just told me. I appreciate you coming so far to clear it up.'

He froze. She was dismissing him. And he hadn't finished what he'd come here to tell her. But she was still raw from her father's death, and she'd had enough to assimilate for one day.

'Then I'll go,' he said.

Saskia tied her ponytail with a black satin ribbon and stood back to survey her reflection, tugging on the hem of her black jacket. The dark circles were still there under her eyes. Make-up had made them less obvious, and lipstick had given her face some much needed colour, but overall… She grimaced. How was she expected to sleep anyway? She would have to do as she was. It was hardly a fashion parade after all.

She glanced at her watch and took a deep breath. It was time. In a strange way she was looking forward to the funeral. These last two days she'd done a lot of thinking about her father—missing him dreadfully, contemplating life without him, but thankful also that he had been spared possibly months in a coma. At least the end, when it had come, had come blessedly quickly.

And the funeral would be some kind of closure. She knew now how it must have been with Marla and her father—a pretty young girl, a lonely man missing his wife. It hadn't been the right thing, but thank heavens it wasn't as bad as she'd first feared. At least now she knew.

She gathered up her handbag and keys and pulled open the door to meet the gloomy grey day, heading out to meet the cab that would be here any minute.

'Can I offer you a lift?'

She took a step back. The dark-suited figure leaning against the sleek black Jaguar was the last thing she'd been expecting to see outside her door.

'What are you doing here? I thought you'd gone.'

He *had* gone. She'd sent him away herself, and he had left as smoothly as the chiffon dress she'd sent to charity had slipped through her fingers. He'd done what he'd come for. He'd made his apologies and given her plenty to think about.

Surely he should already be back ruling his empire from Sydney, or Tahoe, or wherever it was that he was based right now? Why was he still hanging around here?

'I came to take you to the funeral.'

'I don't think so,' she said, knowing she wasn't strong enough today to deal with both the loss of her father and Alex's presence. 'You spent your entire life hating my father. Do you think there's a chance in hell I'd let you take me to his funeral?'

He straightened and looked her in the eyes, his charcoal gaze steady and direct.

'I told you why I felt that way. And I told you I was wrong.'

'Yes,' she agreed. 'You were wrong.'

'But my being here today has nothing to do with how I felt about your father. This has everything to do with how I feel about you.'

She was too tired to work out what he meant. Instead she looked up and down the street. 'I've ordered a cab.'

'And I've sent it away.'

'You did what?' She shook her head and dived into her purse for her keys. 'Then maybe I'll take my car after all.'

'You shouldn't drive—not today. Do you have someone else to take you?'

Her sideways look told him everything he needed to know. There was no one else. She was alone. And she'd had no intention of driving.

'Then I'll take you,' he decided.

'You might have asked if you could come.'

'And you would have let me?'

'No.'

Ten minutes later he pulled into a parking space outside the small funeral chapel and killed the engine. She made no move to get out of the car.

'You'll feel better once it's over.'

She looked at him, her eyes so filled with grief and despair he just wanted to take her in his arms and hold her. But instead he took her hand and squeezed it gently. 'Come on,' he said.

There were few in attendance. Enid Sharpe from next door, his visiting nurse and a couple of old cronies he'd played bridge with. Throughout the brief ceremony she held herself together, the strain etched in lines around her eyes and mouth as she contemplated the flower strewn coffin bearing her father.

*Bearing the man Alex had hated for almost a quarter of a century.* And all for what? A pointless exercise in revenge for something that had never happened. And now what did he have to show for all that hate? What had it produced but more problems? Marla had been so right. It was time to let it go.

At the end of the service he felt Saskia's hand slip into his, and he looked down into the green pools of her eyes. 'Thank you for bringing me,' she said, before Enid came up to give her a hug.

Afterwards they stayed only long enough for a cup of tea, exchanging small talk with the minister.

She slumped back in her seat when he got her into the car, her head tipped back, her eyes closed. 'Thank God that's over,' she said on a sigh.

She looked exhausted, and from the way her black suit bagged around her he suspected it was days since she'd eaten properly. She was just about asleep before they made it back to her flat. He carried her in, despite her protests.

'Would you like me to run you a bath?' he asked.

She shook her head. 'No, just bed,' she muttered sleepily, her arms around his neck, her face nestled into his chest.

He carried her to her room and pulled back the covers, placing her gently down. He slid off her shoes and peeled away the baggy suit without protest from her, shocked at how much flesh had wasted from her bones. She shivered, and he tucked the blankets closer around her.

'So cold,' she whispered, trembling.

He couldn't leave her like that. He pulled off his own shoes and stripped off his suit in a moment, joining her in the bed, collecting her into his arms and wrapping himself around her. She clung to him and cuddled closer, her head resting on his shoulder, her legs scissored between his, and he willed his heat into her, feeling her trembling gradually subside and her breathing steady as she drifted towards sleep.

He kissed her hair, breathed in the sweet scent of her and tucked her closer.

'I love you,' he said. *'Agape mou.'*

# CHAPTER TWELVE

SASKIA woke up feeling better than she had for days. She must have slept for hours, filled with dreams of warmth and loving. And then she remembered. *Alex.* She spun around, but she was alone and her heart pitched south. He'd been so good to her yesterday, so gentle and understanding. Surely he couldn't have left? But why had he been here in the first place? He'd made his apologies. What could he still want with her now?

Her bedroom door swung open. 'Perfect timing.' Alex smiled at her as he came around the door, still wearing the dark suit trousers and white shirt of yesterday, but with the sleeves rolled up and the buttons left undone, exposing a tantalising glimpse of firm olive-skinned torso. But right now it was the tray he was carrying that snagged her attention, piled high with plates and cups and from which the most heavenly smells were coming. 'Are you hungry?'

She took another long look at that patch of skin, and the whirl of hairs that disappeared down into his trousers. He looked good enough to eat himself, but her stomach was sounding a definite protest. 'Famished,' she said, surprised at how true it was. She hadn't felt like eating for days, and suddenly her body seemed to want to make up for it.

'You go wash up,' he said. 'I'll get the coffee.'

She skipped out of bed, grabbing her robe and making for the bathroom, horrified at her reflection. Hair everywhere, and yesterday's make-up sliding wherever, but at least her eyes didn't look so hollow any more. She rinsed her face and attacked her curls with a comb.

'Back into bed,' he ordered when she reappeared, and she didn't think to argue, too busy contemplating the plates piled with eggs, bacon and tomatoes, the racks of toast and dishes of butter and jam.

He loaded up a plate and handed it to her, and it was all she could do not to inhale it all in one delicious whoosh.

'Oh, my,' she said, sipping on a coffee as she leaned back against her headboard. 'That was wonderful.'

'You've had enough?'

'Hold the dessert,' she joked as she patted her tummy. 'Seriously, thank you,' she said. 'Not just for breakfast, but for everything you did for me yesterday. I was so tired last night, so cold, and you kept me warm and safe. And I didn't think I wanted you at the funeral but I'm glad you were there.'

He topped up her coffee and set the plates aside. 'It was important for me too. I carried around that hatred for so long—too long—it was time to let it go. I'd been so wrong about everything, so damned stupid, but all along he was your father, and he'd made a beautiful daughter in you. How could I hate him?'

She smiled, tears springing into her eyes. 'Oh, hell,' she said, reaching for a box of tissues. 'I thought I was done with the tears.'

He laughed softly, moving closer, taking the tissue and touching it gently to her eyes, soaking up the moisture. She blinked her eyes open, studying his eyes, so close to her own.

'Why are you still here?'

He leaned back, his charcoal eyes so desperately focused on hers she could feel the communication between them. 'There's something I have to ask you. I want to know if you can ever forgive me for what I did and for all the hurt I've caused you.'

'You've apologised already.'

'No,' he said. 'That wasn't enough. I need to know if you forgive me, because only then can we really put what's happened behind us.'

She hesitated. 'And that's important because…?'

'Because then we have a chance at a future together. If you want one. Because I love you, Saskia. God knows I don't deserve you, but I don't want to spend my future apart from you.'

'You love me?' She blinked, remembering those words from a dream, warm and loving and happy. But this was far better than the foggy memory of a distant dream. Far better. This was real.

He smiled. 'I love you. It took me a long time to realise it—much too long. But I want to spend my life loving you, if you'll have me.'

'You love me,' she said again, in awe and wonder, her lips curling at the sound of the words, at their taste on her tongue, at the way they fed her soul.

He laughed, a rich, deep sound that radiated warmth. 'Can I take it you don't mind, then?'

'Don't mind? Do you know how long I've waited to hear those words from you?'

'And do you know how much I've missed hearing those words from you? You said it to me once. But I'll understand if you can never bring yourself to say it to me again.'

'Oh, Alex.' She shook her head. 'I tried not to,' she said. 'I really tried to stop loving you. For so long I told myself I hated you, that I couldn't possibly love you. But, damn you, I've always loved you, Alex Koutoufides. I never stopped loving you, and I never stopped hoping one day that I'd hear you say those words to me. Of course I love you.'

'Saskia,' he said, pulling her into his arms. 'You don't know how good it is to hear that from you. Because I love you so very much. And I have so much to make up for.'

And he kissed her, a kiss so achingly sweet and full of love it moved her soul. This was the man she was destined to be with. This was her mate. This was her destiny. All those years ago, as a seventeen-year-old young woman, she'd known it. And all these years later it was finally coming to pass.

His kiss told her how much he loved her and how much he wanted her. His hands moved over her, his touch like worship, cherishing her, seducing her, setting her body alight while her hands pushed their way under his shirt, desperate to get closer, itching to feel more of the muscled wall of his chest.

'About that dessert…' he whispered, his breathing already choppy as he ripped off his shirt and tugged at the ties of her robe.

'Bring it on.' She chuckled as she dragged him back down to her lips. 'Didn't I tell you I was famished?'

# EPILOGUE

BLISS. Life could never get better than this.

Saskia paused as she looked out onto the enclosed patio of their Tahoe home, watching Alex cradle the tiny bundle that was his month-old daughter on his jeans-covered legs.

Their daughter.

The daughter they'd made together in an act of love.

He looked down at baby Sophie so adoringly that she sucked in a lungful of pure happiness. She loved him so much. Even now she got a thrill thinking of her name aligned with his. Even after a year of marriage the wonder was still there.

And tiny Sophie's arrival had magnified that wonder tenfold.

She picked up two of the salads the housekeeper had prepared earlier and stepped out onto the deck, placing them on the table, watching his face light up with warmth as he welcomed her approach.

'What time are our visitors arriving?'

'Any minute now. I hope you've got the champagne chilling. Marla told me they've got an announcement to make.'

He looked up quickly, still with Sophie's tiny hands clinging to his fingers, as Saskia sat down in the chair alongside. 'Are you thinking what I'm thinking?'

She nodded. 'Oh, yes. Jake's the one. They've been

together a good while now, and he's good for her. He's solid and loyal, and she'll need that stability—especially now she's going to be doing this book tour. It's obvious they've been crazy about each other for ages, despite all her protests to the contrary. I'm glad they're planning on making it official.'

'She's so different now,' he said, gazing back into his baby's big dark eyes. 'So much more self-assured. The book's success has been amazing.'

'I think Marla's found herself. She has her own career now, with her writing. You know she's picked up another national monthly column? She actually feels like she's making her own way in the world, and she's loving it.'

'And you're responsible for that.'

She shook her head. 'No, Marla is. She's the one who took control of her life. All we had to do was help her make it happen. And you letting go the reins had as much to do with it as I did.'

He looked at her with equal measures of respect and love. 'You will never stop astounding me, you know. I think I might just love you, Mrs Koutoufides.'

'I think I might just love you back, Mr Koutoufides.'

He snaked an arm around her neck and pulled her in, kissing her over the squirming baby below. 'So, what's next for your own career? Have you given Marla's offer any more thought?'

She nodded. 'I'm going to tell her today. I'll take on her press work—it should be fun—and I'll fit in my own freelance articles when I get a chance. It should be the perfect stay-at-home job.'

'You don't miss *AlphaBiz*?' he asked, when finally he let her go.

She smiled, and touched a finger to the baby-soft curls adorning Sophie's head. 'What kind of a question is that? No. I wasn't happy with the way they seemed to be going anyway—increasingly chasing the celebrity angle. I don't want to write that way. Besides,' she said, smiling into the dark eyes of her young child, 'why would I rather be seeking out crusty old businessmen to interview when I can have the best of both worlds—doing freelance work and looking after this little one and her father?'

He scowled. 'Crusty old businessmen, eh?'

'Present company excluded,' she added with a grin. 'Anyone as gorgeously talented and virile as you can't be too crusty.'

He pulled her close again, measuring the ripe sway of her breasts in his free hand. 'Maybe later on I might be able to convince you just how virile and uncrusty I am.'

'I warn you now,' she said, already feeling her body awaken and stir at his sensual caress, 'I might take some convincing.'

He growled and pulled her close, and they shared a kiss so deep and rich with promise that it was only the plaintive cry of the child on his lap that broke it off. He turned his attentions back to his child, scooping her up into his arms, kissing her softly on the forehead.

'Was I neglecting you, sweetheart?'

Her cries stilled, her eyes locking onto her father's, her tiny mouth stretching into a wide, gummy smile.

'She smiled at me!' He looked at Saskia. 'Look at that! They said she wouldn't do that until at she was at least six weeks old.'

'Of course she smiled at you,' she responded, stroking the downy dark hair of little Sophie. 'How could she resist? I never could.'

He beamed back at her. 'And, when it comes to the women in my life, that's just the way I like it.'

He contemplated the child in his arms again, and breathed in deep as he looked back at the woman he loved. 'I love you,

Saskia, for your warmth and your beauty and for giving me this child. But most of all for your forgiveness and your love. You've made me the happiest man in the entire world.'

She wrapped her arms around both the man she loved and the tiny baby cradled in his arms, feeling the love radiating out from him and breathing in the magic scent of pure one hundred per cent male mixed with the sweet, innocent smell of a newborn.

It was a mix that moved her like no other.

It was love she could sense.

It was intoxicating.

It was simply…

*Bliss.*

# THE ITALIAN BILLIONAIRE'S VIRGIN

BY
CHRISTINA HOLLIS

**Christina Hollis** was born in Somerset and now lives in the idyllic Wye valley. She was born reading and her childhood dream was to become a writer. This was realised when she became a successful journalist and lecturer in organic horticulture. Then she gave it all up to become a full-time mother of two and run half an acre of productive country garden.

Writing Mills & Boon® romances is another ambition realised. It fills most of her time, between complicated rural school runs. The rest of her life is divided between garden and kitchen, either growing fruit and vegetables or cooking with them. Her daughter's cat always closely supervises everything she does around the home, from typing to picking strawberries!

You can learn more about Christina and her writing at www.christinahollis.com

**Don't miss Christina Hollis's exciting new novel, *The French Aristocrat's Baby*, available this month from Mills & Boon® Modern™.**

To my darling Martyn –
a perfect gentleman who makes dreams comes true.

# CHAPTER ONE

BALMY afternoons in Tuscany were made for people-watching, although Rissa tried to hide her curiosity as Signor Mazzini guided her through the crowds.

'I am sure the late Count will have introduced you to the joys of the *passeggiata*, Contessa. It is that time when we all like to take the air.' Pink and perspiring, Mazzini threaded his client through the press of people strolling around the village square.

'My husband never brought me to Italy, *signor*. After our marriage, we rarely left America.' Rissa tried to keep the disappointment out of her voice. She had a lot of catching up to do. When Luigi had been alive, there had only been one, unhappy visit to her home in England. Now she was a free agent, her husband's debts were keeping her just as much a prisoner. Luigi's extravagant lifestyle had drained the Tiziano fortune of everything but the long-abandoned *palazzo* that bore his family's name. Rissa had only seen the place from a distance so far. Today was her first opportunity to enter the estate and look around the sole remaining Alfere-Tiziano property.

Trying to avoid actually being touched by Signor Mazzini's guiding hand, she walked across to the tall gates that protected the Tiziano estate. As Mazzini fumbled for his keys, Rissa got the strangest feeling that she was being watched. She had expected the villagers to be curious about her, but this felt somehow different.

She turned with a ready smile, but it faded instantly. A man was watching her from one of the many café tables set up around the village square.

*'Buongiorno?'*

She had felt bound to say something, but her observer stayed silent. He was only a few yards away, and could easily have replied, but he did not. He was well dressed, and might have been called handsome if not for his expression. He was piercing Rissa with a challenging glare. She caught her breath. No wonder she had sensed someone was looking at her. The intensity of that stare was enough to put anyone on their guard.

With a shiver, she followed Signor Mazzini into the safety of the estate. She was glad when he locked the gates behind him, but her relief was short-lived. Looking around the rampant wilderness, she saw that fallen trees had brought down the surrounding wall in several places. Her heart sank. Big repairs would mean big bills.

She had been blinded with love when she married Luigi. That love had changed over the years, as they'd come to terms with their secret sadness. Then his dazzling personality, which had kept her trapped like a rabbit in headlights, had been extinguished when his sports car went off the road at one hundred and twenty miles an hour.

Luigi's death had shocked Rissa out of her trance-like existence. Her next trauma had come when she'd discovered there was virtually no money left in any of Luigi's accounts, and that she was the last person in the world to bear the name of Alfere-Tiziano. That had given her a strong feeling of responsibility.

She *had* to keep up appearances, for Luigi's sake, and she *had* to see this mysterious *palazzo*. She had spent almost all her ready cash on a one-way ticket to Italy, and fallen instantly in love with the romance of the place. But she knew that this rundown estate could never pass to a rightful heir.

For a few weeks after Luigi's death, the heartbreak of their childless marriage had all but overwhelmed her again. Despite Rissa's shaky finances, when the office of AMI Holdings—apparently a great international construction company—had made her an exceptionally generous offer for the *Palazzo* Tiziano, she refused it point-blank. The sale would have given her more than enough money to move back home to London, but she felt she still had a duty to her adopted family name.

Her cash was now running dangerously low. Rissa had been almost tempted to reveal her problems and ask Signor Mazzini to contact AMI Holdings again, but two things stopped her. Luigi had been a proud man, and his heritage was at stake. She could not bear to think of his ancient family home being pulled down to make way for luxury holiday flats, which seemed to be the fate of every other historic house. There was another reason, too. A house in her name would give Rissa some security.

She knew that living in rented accommodation had been a terrible worry for the elderly couple that had brought her up. The only things Rissa possessed now were their love, and this place in the middle of nowhere. If somehow she could hang on to the house, and eventually earn enough to bring her adoptive parents out to live with her, she would do it.

Rissa had decided to give herself one year. If she had not succeeded by then, she would sell the *palazzo* and try to buy somewhere in England to share with her Aunt Jane and Uncle George, as she called her adoptive parents.

This romantic wreck of a house and its fairytale setting in the rolling Tuscan hills was her big chance to make a success of something. It was lovely, and there could be no question of selling. She *had* to improve on the hand fate had dealt her, so that she could bring her adoptive parents out to live here and bury her own demons of the past. Giving up was not an option.

It was a problem worthy of Sherlock Holmes, and Antonio Michaeli-Isola was not a man who liked puzzles. Brooding over his untouched *caffè freddo*, he observed the mating rituals of Italian youngsters. It was deceptively easy for them. The girls and boys eyed each other up in the hormone-drenched heat. Lack of money was the only obstacle to their happily-ever-after. Antonio had the opposite problem. He had all the women and all the money anyone could ever want— but he needed something else.

That 'something else' was the *Palazzo* Tiziano. He looked across the crowded village square to where high stone walls concealed his ultimate prize. He was not to be denied, and only one thing stood between him and his ideal home. The Contessa Alfere-Tiziano.

Without even meeting her, Antonio knew her type exactly. Women who had clawed their way into society were all the same. They were idle, amoral clotheshorses, who did nothing but tumble their male staff and bully their maids. Sex and money were the driving forces behind them. With Luigi Alfere-Tiziano dead, and the *palazzo* reputed to be a ruin, Antonio had expected 'her ladyship' to convert the dump into cash and disappear to the Hamptons as fast as her Manolo Blahnik heels could carry her. Instead, she was apparently determined the keep the old place.

It was inexplicable. In Antonio's experience, women simply did not behave like that. Getting the *palazzo* was obviously going to cost him more than money.

He watched a well-dressed man escort a girl across the street towards the *palazzo* gates. He tensed. Then his spirits soared. It must be the Contessa, being let into the estate by one of her staff. Antonio had expected a hard-faced Manhattan harridan. Instead, a slender, pretty girl glanced around nervously as she was led into the overgrown gardens beyond the estate walls.

Things are looking up, Antonio thought.

Getting his hands on the treasure of the Tizianos might be both easier and more enjoyable than he had expected.

A copy of the *Financial Times* was waiting for Antonio when he got back to the Excelsior hotel in Florence. Before checking the mail on his laptop, he flicked through the newspaper, and stopped when he saw his name in centimetre-high type.

*Billionaire to fund new hospital,* he read, grim-faced at the inaccuracies that underestimated his generosity and overstated his age. Antonio was not a vain man, so there was no question of demanding a retraction, but it showed how the media's Chinese whispers could distort facts. He read again the same old story, which they delighted in repeating. His mother was the daughter of a refugee. In acknowledgement of that family history, Antonio Michaeli-Isola still used part of her maiden name alongside that of his father, who had been a fisherman in Naples.

Unlike the glossy magazines, the *FT* did not linger over descriptions of Antonio's good looks and brooding Italian heritage. Unfortunately, like all other publications, it was still obsessed by the size of his bank balance. Antonio hated that.

Growing up in the shadow of poverty had taught him the need for hard work and self-reliance. Now he enjoyed putting something back into the community, but other people's fixation with the way he spent his money never failed to amaze him.

His expression flashed a warning. His features demanded respect rather than admiration. Growing up in the streets of Naples had left its mark on him. The dark eyes reacted with anger more often than merriment, and were rarely touched with a smile even when he appeared to be amused. He had learned as a child that the only person he could truly rely on was Antonio Michaeli-Isola. *If a job is worth doing, do it yourself* had been the maxim which had catapulted him from a two-roomed flat to corporate superstardom.

Now, men fawned over him when they were introduced. Women could not wait to paw him, and attached themselves to his arm like unlucky charms. Antonio had grown up on the wrong side of the tracks, where prostitution was often the only way some women could feed their children. He was not squeamish about the seamier side of life, but when wealthy women offered themselves to him like whores he found it difficult to disguise his disgust. His natural good manners were often tested to the limit.

He picked up the other newspaper the hotel had delivered and glanced through it, looking for the business section. Then a face on the society page caught his eye. It was she. The woman who had twice refused his company's offers for the *Palazzo* Tiziano. Antonio's expression hardened. Normally he never bothered to read the gossip columns. He knew everyone who was anyone in business, and preferred truth to speculation, but today he absorbed every word with relish.

*From Riches—to Designer Rags?* ran the headline.

*Is the Contessa Alfere-Tiziano frittering away her late husband's millions?*

*Larissa Alfere-Tiziano has been selling off her inheritance at a rate of knots. Widowed by Count Luigi's love of fast cars, tragic Rissa has been getting ready for a little retail therapy by turning her late, lamented husband's property into hard cash.*

The article included a photograph of the fawn-like beauty Antonio had watched walking into the estate that should, by rights, be his.

Antonio did not show emotion easily, but his brow lowered with every line. Appearances could certainly be deceptive. The girl he had seen following her flunkey into the *palazzo*'s grounds had looked as mild as milk. Antonio had foreseen no problem in sweet-talking her out of the house in a face-to-face meeting. Now he learned she was as shallow and greedy as all the rest of her sex.

With a thoughtful expression he folded the newspaper carefully and laid it down. Antonio might be rich, but he was not stupid. Two generous cash offers for the property had failed. Pushing more money at her would simply make the girl suspicious, and all the more likely to sit tight, hoping to push the stakes to ever more ridiculous heights. No, Antonio would have to employ guile. He would get his own way by more subtle means. Sex would feature, of course—he would never pass up such a delicious opportunity—but he would use it as bait to discover why she had sold off luxurious and better-placed properties for the greater glory of her bank balance, but not this one. Once he knew her motives, he could calculate the best way to move in for the kill.

Antonio leaned back in his chair and allowed himself a wolfish smile.

'I am delighted to make your acquaintance, Contessa.' The elderly woman made a creaking curtsy.

'Oh, please don't do that—Livia, isn't it?' Rissa shot a quick look at her land agent, Signor Mazzini. He nodded.

'Livia has looked after this place for as long as anyone can remember.'

Mazzini tried to oil his way past the housekeeper. He was eager to start a tour of the *palazzo*, but Rissa was more interested in the old lady.

'Thank you, Livia. The Alfere-Tiziano family must have been very grateful.'

'Ha!' The walnut-faced housekeeper muttered something else under her breath.

Despite her imperfect grasp of Italian, Rissa gathered that Luigi's aristocratic mother had been as generous towards Livia as she had been to Rissa. Both were commoners. As such they had been beneath the old Contessa's contempt, even though Rissa had married the last of the Alfere-Tiziano line.

Rissa did not know what to say in the face of Livia's discontent, but Mazzini came to her rescue.

'Come, Contessa, before the light fades. You will want to see around your new home.'

With a smile for Livia, Rissa allowed herself to be ushered from the draughty entrance hall into a warm, bright kitchen. One side of the room was almost filled by a huge, old-fashioned range. Reflections of its open fire danced across the gleaming copper pots and pans which hung over an enormous kitchen table. Seeing a plate set with chunks of ciabatta and a cone of goats' cheese, Rissa instantly turned to find the housekeeper. She did not have to look far. Livia was glowering at them from the threshold.

'I am sorry to have interrupted your meal, Livia. Come back to the table—Signor Mazzini and I can go somewhere else first.'

'No. This is meant for you, Contessa. It is your supper,' Livia announced with a look of triumph.

Rissa swallowed hard, wishing she had not been too proud to accept Mazzini's offer of a meal at the village trattoria.

'That's lovely, Livia. Shall I eat it now, or should we continue the tour, *signor*?' She looked to Mazzini for help, but Livia was quicker.

'You should eat now, so that I can wash up and still get home to the village before dark.'

Pulling a pitcher of milk from a bucket of cold water in the corner, Livia slopped some into a chipped mug and banged it down beside the makeshift meal. There were sour flakes floating on the watery white surface. Rissa looked back through the doorway into the hall, at the nearest portrait of one of the nobles who had lived in this house before her. There were huge pictures of them hanging all around the vestibule, each with raven-dark eyes and a piercing, humourless expression. *If this sort of food was good enough for them, then it will have to be good enough for me,* she thought, with more certainty than she felt.

Sitting down at the table, Rissa worked her way steadily through everything. She was determined not to turn up her nose at the stale bread or the sour milk, and managed it all.

'Thank you, Livia,' she said eventually, handing the house-keeper her empty plate and cup. Luckily her mobile rang before she had to add the words *That was lovely*.

'Auntie!' All the strain of the past weeks fell away and Rissa laughed with genuine pleasure. 'I was going to ring you as soon as I had a moment to myself—yes, I'm finally moving into Tiziano today. And as soon as I've sorted out a good room for you and Uncle, you can come here!'

Mazzini grimaced, and Rissa had the awful feeling she had said the wrong thing. Covering the mobile's mouthpiece, she questioned him with her eyes.

'A surveyor needs to check the upper floors before they can be trusted, and only two rooms on the ground floor are cur-rently in use—this kitchen is one of them,' he hissed. Rissa's spirits sank.

'I hope you like camping.' She spoke to her aunt again. 'Apparently the house is all to pieces, but Signor Mazzini tells me it stands in ten hectares—'

'—of scrub and desolation.' Mazzini shook his head dolefully.

'So things can only get better!' Rissa reassured her aunt, with an attempt at cheerfulness. 'The couple who brought me up haven't had a night away from home in ten years,' she ex-plained to Signor Mazzini when the call was over. 'They helped me through college, and they mean the world to me. I can't wait to see them again. It's been too long,' she said sadly.

'You have an *education*, Contessa?' said Mazzini, and Livia stared at her.

'Oh, yes—I studied Marketing and Media Studies. After graduating, some friends and I decided to spend a few months travelling before starting our careers. It didn't last long. I wanted to work my passage, sending money home when I could. I couldn't afford much socialising, so the other girls drifted off to LA and Las Vegas in search of more exciting company. Then one day Count Alfere-Tiziano's car got a flat tyre while he was burning up Route 66. He was marooned in the diner where I happened to be working. The rest, as they say, is history!'

Mazzini and Livia watched her warily. Not for the first time Rissa realised she had gone too far. Luigi had always scolded her for being too friendly with the staff. She shrank at the thought of what he would have said about her cheerful chatter. Then she decided that what Luigi would never know could not upset him. She straightened up, cleared her throat, and looked them both straight in the eyes.

'But that's all behind me now. I only have Aunt Jane and Uncle George to worry about. And the *Palazzo* Tiziano,' she added with a slight frown. 'You had better start my guided tour, Signor Mazzini. My world has been shrinking rapidly for the past few weeks, so I shall have to get used to it!'

Three hours later, Rissa was alone. Mazzini had swept off to Florence in his Alfa Romeo, while Livia had limped back down to the village. Thunder was growling around in the distance, and Rissa did not fancy sitting alone in the kitchen. She retreated to the tiny room that had been prepared for her. It must once have been a pantry, she decided, for the small, high window was barred and there was an underlying chill about the place. This was not helped by the inch-wide gap at the bottom of a door that led straight out into the garden.

In one corner of the room an ancient electric fire glowed. It added a bit of warmth, and Rissa sank down into a bed that was cosy, with soft blankets and sheets scented with lavender.

It was a pleasure to be hugged by a proper bed, with real linen and clouds of pillows, rather than struggling with ergonomically designed neck supports and a synthetic crackly duvet.

The only problem Rissa had was that her enjoyment could not be dimmed by sleep. She lay awake for hours, alert to every new sound. The ancient mansion creaked on its foundations as it settled for the night. From the kitchen next door she could hear noisy nibbling. Rissa did not know if it was a mouse…or something bigger. She did not feel like investigating. She could only lie in the darkness and wonder if it was a single creature, or whether it had company.

When the hands of her alarm clock crawled around for another hour and she still could not sleep, Rissa gave up. Getting out of bed, she switched on the light. Walking as noisily as she could over to where her suitcase rested across the arms of a squashy old armchair, she hoped that any four-legged residents of the house would be scared away before she could catch sight of them.

Among her favourite possessions was a small radio. She carried it with her everywhere. If she could tune into the World Service it would at least fill the lonely hours until dawn. Things never felt so bad in daylight—although how she would feel after a whole night without sleep, Rissa didn't like to think.

She had retrieved her transistor and was about to switch it on when she heard a plaintive cry from outside. The wind was getting up. Sounds of a gate on rusty hinges and a shutter swinging somewhere in the breeze made her more apprehensive than ever, but she was sure a cat was mewing out in the darkness. It was not a sound Rissa could ignore. She froze. The poor animal sounded like she felt—lonely and unsure. She waited. The sound grew closer, and more wavering.

There was nothing for it. Cautiously, Rissa went over and opened the door. The shaft of light she released lit undergrowth that crept up on the house from all sides. It also showed a big ginger cat, only feet away from where Rissa stood on the threshold. The creature had one front paw raised, and was jiggling its head to look past her, eyeing up the room beyond.

'Puss, puss, puss?' Rissa called. The wind whipped her words away like autumn leaves.

Greatly daring, Rissa took a few steps out into the night. The cat shrank into a half-crouch as she approached. As Rissa drew nearer, she could see that blood was staining the white toes of the cat's up-raised paw.

'You poor thing—let me see.' She reached out, but the cat sprang away. Even on three legs it was faster than Rissa could hope to be, but she followed it out into the darkness just beyond her lighted doorway. It was a mistake. Brambles tangling over the steep bank beyond the house snatched at her arms and legs. She tried to stop and go back, but the gradient and gravity swept her feet out from under her and she crashed into darkness.

Bruised, battered and out of breath, Rissa tried to drag herself upright, but gasped as a stab of pain shot through her ankle. A flash of lightning threw the undergrowth into sharp relief for a moment, before darkness returned, blacker than before. A spatter of icy rain scrabbled through the leaves. Now she was in the same position as the cat—or rather, worse. Rissa had no idea where she was. At least the cat must be local.

She sat down on the hard ground. The scent of pine resin and peppermint rose up from all around, and helped clear her head. She had to get back to the house. The door had been left standing wide open! Rissa could not bear to think what might be happening up there, but she tried to be optimistic. Perhaps the cat would go in and sort out the mouse in the kitchen? Based on her experiences so far, Rissa was not too hopeful *that* would happen.

A less-than-delicious supper, a depressing tour of the *palazzo* and now this tumble should have been enough to put her off the place for life. Instead, it sparked a new determination in her. Hauling herself upright, she managed to scramble painfully up the bank. It was a long way, etched with prickles and splinters. Rissa kept her head down and concentrated on where to put her feet, but she needed a boost to get her up the last little climb to the top. When she lifted her head, reassurance was the last thing she got.

Towering above her, silhouetted by the light from the open *palazzo* doorway, was the tall, muscular figure of a man.

# CHAPTER TWO

'THIS is a dangerous place, Contessa.'

Rissa shrank back as he crouched down beside her. He was so near to her she could feel the warmth of him.

Thunder rolled a warning around the hills. She wondered whether she had more to fear from this stranger than she did from the weather and her new home combined.

'How do you know who I am?'

'This is a small village.' His voice was low but melodious. 'Everyone saw you arrive. They are hoping that by moving into the *palazzo* you will bring work to the village, but I know differently. There is not much hope of that, is there?' Seen in a flash of lightning, his face was hard and grim.

Rissa recognised him instantly. 'You were there—in the village square this afternoon. You were seated apart from the others, looking at me—'

Lightning crackled from the clouds again, giving Rissa a glimpse of his even white teeth. They were bared in a smile.

'That is so. I have returned here after…a long absence.'

'But what are you doing in my garden?'

Rissa might have been surprised by the sharpness of her tone if she had not been frightened half to death.

He put his head on one side, that interrogative stare pinning her down again. 'I wanted to have a look around, to see if the old place is still as my grandmother used to describe it to me.'

He continued to bend over her. Rissa reasoned that if he had been going to attack her he would have done so by now. She decided to try and stand up, then make a dash for the house.

'You aren't going to see much in the dark, *signor,*' she began, getting to her feet. But as she took a step she gasped.

He grabbed her as she crumpled, and stopped her from falling.

'Do you mind? Let go of me!' Rissa tried to shake off his hands, but he had a firm grip. The thunderstorm released a sudden spatter of huge raindrops in shining sheets, adding more urgency to her predicament.

'No—if you have an injury, Contessa, you may aggravate it further by trying to walk on it. Let's get you into the house.' Without waiting for her to agree, Antonio swept her up in his arms and began striding towards the lighted doorway.

'No—wait! There's a cat out here—it's injured—we can't leave it!' Rissa squirmed urgently in his grasp, made more desperate by the increasing deluge. It had soaked them both to the skin within seconds. He took no notice of her and strode on, an irresistible force. It was hopeless to try and fight. Shouting against the noise of the storm would be futile, too, and when they reached the sanctuary of the house he got in first.

'I shall go out and look for the animal as soon as you are—' He stopped. Then he laughed, water coursing from his rain-darkened hair across the subtle gold of his skin.

Rissa tore her gaze from her rescuer for long enough to see that the ginger cat was stretched out on a rug before the electric fire. It had beaten them back to the house and was basking in warmth while it licked its injured paw clean.

'I don't think you need to worry about him, Contessa. On the other hand, I must check to see if your injuries should be giving cause for concern.'

He was holding her indecently close to his body. She could feel his heart beating through the thin transparency of their wet clothes. It aroused a strange feeling within her. Hiding her uncertainty beneath a brisk tone, she spoke without taking her eyes off the cat.

'As you can see, this is my temporary bedroom, *signor*. Take me straight through that far door and into the kitchen, please.'

It had been a long time since she had been in the arms of a gorgeous man, and even longer since it had taken place in a bedroom.

'Very well,' her rescuer said sharply. 'And as you give orders as if I am your servant, Contessa, I should introduce myself. I am Antonio Isola.'

Closing the outside door, he crossed Rissa's room in a few easy strides and entered the kitchen. For an instant the storm threw enough light through the windows to let him place her down safely on a chair. Then he found a switch and flooded the room with harsh electric light.

Rissa blinked. The tall man standing in her doorway was shrink-wrapped by his sodden shirt and jeans. His clothes clung to every contour, leaving nothing to the imagination. Biceps and pectorals thrust against thin cotton made almost invisible by the rain. With a gasp, Rissa saw a full pelt of dark body hair casting a shadow beneath his white top. The spell was only broken when she realised that his slow, spreading smile meant that the hard beads of her nipples must be equally visible through her negligee. She threw one arm protectively across her chest.

'Could you fetch me my robe please, *Antonio*? It's draped over the bedhead.' Rissa waved her other hand dismissively towards her bedroom.

'Is the cat all right?' she said, when he returned with the less-than-practical dressing gown Luigi had bought her for their honeymoon. That time in her life had been such a whirlwind of high hopes, dreams and expectations. If only they had been fulfilled. Luigi would have left the *palazzo* with a legitimate heir and not just *me*, Rissa thought sadly.

'The cat has settled himself down to keep watch on a mouse hole. I think we can assume he will be OK, Contessa.'

He spoke in heavily accented English, a musical sound that did nothing to settle Rissa in her chair. She looked away quickly. Focussing on her ankle, she probed it gingerly.

Antonio advanced and crouched in front of her. 'Try wiggling your toes.'

Rissa did as she was told. Slipping his hand around her ankle, Antonio cradled her heel. Gently but firmly he used the fingers of his other hand to test for movement. The pain had almost disappeared, but Rissa still flinched.

'There is nothing broken, but you will have some magnificent bruises, Contessa.' He surveyed her with practised eyes.

Before Rissa could complain, they both stiffened at a sound from outside.

Antonio vanished towards the door, and a minute later Rissa heard Livia's voice, raised in agitation. Trying out her left foot with care, Rissa made her way over to her bedroom.

The housekeeper had the ginger cat gripped in her arms and was scolding him and crooning by turns. She was speaking so quickly that Rissa's Italian could barely keep up. Antonio obliged with a translation.

'Fabio escaped from Livia's new lodgings at her sister's house in the village, tearing a claw in the process. He made straight for his old haunts. Livia has been frantic, so she arrived for work early in the hope she would find him here.'

Rissa looked at her travel clock in amazement. 'It's five o'clock already and I haven't slept a wink!'

'A beautiful *contessa* like you will not have to worry about that,' Antonio said silkily, with a smile that did not reach his eyes. 'Rich women are well known for their ability to spend whole days languishing in bed, are they not?'

'Not *this* one,' Rissa said firmly. She was careful not to mention that Livia probably had more disposable income than she did. 'I've got a busy day ahead. I need to sort myself out a new room, because it sounds like Livia has given me hers and I cannot allow that. You must come back here to live, Livia. This is your home.'

The housekeeper beamed, squeezing Fabio around the midriff until the cat's eyes bulged.

'In the meantime, would you mind providing Antonio with some breakfast, please?' Rissa went on. 'He was kind enough to help me. The least we can do is to offer him some hospitality.'

'I don't know, Contessa.' The housekeeper stuck out her lower lip and looked Antonio up and down suspiciously.

Rissa was not entirely taken in by Antonio's charm either, but she had to repay him in some way. A stand had to be made.

'He will be happy with whatever you were going to make for me, I am sure.'

'He is a stranger, Contessa,' Livia grumbled, still eyeing Antonio.

'And so am I,' Rissa said firmly. 'Now, if you would both

excuse me, I must get ready for the day and find myself a new room.'

There were warm towels in a cupboard beside the range. Rissa took out an extra one and handed it to Antonio. He looked momentarily surprised before resuming his air of amused indifference.

By the time Rissa returned to the kitchen, showered, and dressed in a short-sleeved shirt and jeans, breakfast was ready. Breads and cold meats were laid out on the table, together with glasses of fresh orange juice. It looked far better than the miserable meal that had greeted her the day before.

Rissa stopped and stared—but not at the breakfast. It was the shock of seeing Livia smile. It was the first time since Rissa's arrival that she had seen the housekeeper grin at her. Then she saw what was amusing the old woman. Antonio had stripped off completely and was standing beside the range, pouring out espresso. A thick white towel was wrapped around his narrow waist. He looked amazing.

Giving both Antonio and Livia a casual greeting, Rissa sat down at the big old kitchen table. As she took a roll from the bread basket and began her breakfast, she saw that Antonio's skin was the same tone of clear light gold all over. It did not take much to visualise that glorious colour continuing beneath the tightly wrapped snowy towelling. Rissa found herself drawing in a long, appreciative breath. Reluctantly she realised that, despite all her enforced celibacy, female hormones were a law to themselves. Antonio was a perfect Alpha male, from the lean lines of his muscles to that mass of dark chest hair.

Rissa passed the tip of her tongue over her lips. Her breasts were tingling. Her nipples pressed against the lacy bra she was wearing beneath her tee shirt, and became painfully obvious. She felt heat rising to her cheeks. How could her body betray her like this when it had been so long since Luigi had shown any interest in her? She had thought all passionate feelings had died in the early days of her marriage. The memory of how Antonio had held her close when he carried her into the house must have triggered some sort of reaction. It had certainly alerted all her senses.

Antonio placed a small cup of dark coffee beside her, then offered one to Livia. The housekeeper looked aghast, and took a step back.

'You are *that* sort of employer, then, are you, Contessa?' Antonio announced, putting his own cup down on the table and taking a seat opposite Rissa. His eyes locked with hers. He seemed oblivious to the effect he was having on her. As a respectable widow, Rissa knew she should be glad he was so detached, but while her head told her one thing her body rebelled with feelings of its own.

'Livia is quite welcome to sit and have coffee while I discuss the day ahead with her,' Rissa said briskly.

'I'm glad you want to get down to business straight away. The quicker we get started, the quicker this place can be restored.'

Rissa looked at him blankly. *'We?'*

Antonio concentrated on cutting himself a square of focaccia. He had to hide a cynical smile. If everything went according to his plan, the *Palazzo* Tiziano would soon be returning to its rightful owner, not just its former glory. Naturally he would not be telling the Contessa that. He intended that she would be far, far away by the time he took possession.

'You speak reasonable Italian, Contessa.'

'Thank you—'

'But that is not enough to deal with tradesmen and artisans. Livia tells me the house and grounds need a great deal of repair—indeed, I must come with you to choose your new room to make sure it is structurally sound. It is lucky we met when we did. You have great need of someone who is experienced. In property development,' he added, after a significant pause.

'Do you have anyone in mind, Antonio?'

She wanted him to persuade her, he thought caustically. The wiles of women always annoyed him.

'I am fully qualified in every department.'

Rissa did not doubt it.

'That is, I could become your project manager, Contessa. You need someone to tell you what work must be done, in what order, and who can be relied upon to get those things achieved quickly and efficiently. My first task will be to conduct a detailed survey of this house from top to bottom.'

'Wait a minute, Antonio! How do I *know* that you are the right man for the job? And can I afford you?'

'The Palazzo Tiziano cannot afford to lose me.' Antonio took a leisurely sip of coffee. 'This house needs me… you need me,' he added, but at his own, slightly suggestive pace.

'I shall have to ring Signor Mazzini.' Rissa was uneasy. She didn't know if she should tell him quite everything about this Antonio. Although he sounded the part, and the place definitely needed a good manager, she didn't quite trust him.

However, the sooner she could get the house into a fit state for her aunt and uncle to move in, the happier Rissa would be. Her adoptive family had taken her in as a baby, but their desperate desire to give her the best of everything had meant they had little left for themselves. As soon as she'd grown old enough to appreciate the sacrifices they had made for her, Rissa had been determined to pay them back. She had taken her first Saturday job at fourteen, waiting at tables. When she had been offered a university place it had been natural for her to contribute to the expenses. She had sent as much money home as possible—until the day when…

As well as being a fairytale romance, it had seemed such a wonderful opportunity at the time. Luigi Alfere-Tiziano had walked into the diner where she'd worked and it had been love at first sight—at least as far as Rissa had been concerned. In Luigi's case it had been more a cocktail of lust and rebellion against his mother. The love had come later.

A whirlwind courtship of champagne, gifts and starry nights had made Rissa feel like a princess. She had been Cinderella in the arms of her very own Prince Charming. Only when Luigi had taken her home to show off her multi-carat engagement ring had Rissa realised she'd fallen into a trap.

Antonio watched her as carefully as Fabio the cat had been watching that mouse hole. She was miles away, he thought, noticing emotion drawing down over her eyes like a veil until she blinked it away.

'I am the perfect man for your job,' he announced brusquely.

Shaking off her memories, Rissa came down to hard, un-promising earth.

'So you say, Antonio. But how do I *know* that? Magazines like *Harpers & Queen* and *Country Life* have beautiful build-ings like the Palazzo Tiziano in them all the time. It will take expertise, time and a great deal of money to return my house and estate to the condition they should be in. How do I know that you have the knowledge and expertise it needs?' She was frowning. After settling with Luigi's creditors, Rissa now had to watch every penny—but there was no way she was going to tell Antonio that.

'You also mentioned time, Contessa. You and I both have plenty of that.' Antonio flexed his powerful shoulders. 'Hard work never killed anyone. You can plan the restoration and detailed budgets—under my guidance, of course. I will organise the workforce, and together we shall work to make the Palazzo Tiziano the beautiful place it should be. Of that I am certain,' he decided. 'To convince you to agree, I shall work for nothing.'

He smiled to himself. 'Billionaire for hire' had a good ring to it—but what the hell? He didn't need the money, and it would be sheer pleasure to help put this house back into shape, knowing it would soon be his. He would work on her from the inside, he thought, with considerable satisfaction.

Finishing his breakfast, he pushed away his plate and stood up. Rissa had been silenced by his generous offer, but now she had to stifle a gasp. He loomed over her in a way that brought warmth powering through her veins again. With an effort she collected her thoughts, then wished she hadn't. They involved the sensation of his hands grasping her again, perhaps even pulling her across the table for a passionate kiss.

She cleared her throat and looked up at him. It was a mistake. The intensity of his expression caught her heart and slammed it against her ribs. His lips were parting in a half-smile, a hint of white teeth gleaming against gold skin. It was an expression that said: *Come on, kiss me. You know you want to…*

Rissa's hazel eyes became dark pools of sensuality as she wondered what it would be like to have her own lips pressed against that firm mouth, to be silenced by—

'Contessa—' Antonio's voice cut through her feverish thoughts. With a shock, Rissa realised her breath was coming in little gasps, and she could only imagine the guilty depth of her blush.

'This will be a formal working arrangement, Contessa.'

'Of course!' Rissa jumped to her feet, shocked to discover the effect he was having on her body. She felt as frail as a kitten, and had to grip the tabletop for support.

'I assume you have no objection to employing me on that understanding?'

'Of course not, Antonio. Although I will reimburse you as soon as the house is in a fit state to be mortgaged, so please keep a note of all the hours you work and any expenses you may incur.'

He had not expected that. Looking down at the good, yet understated watch on his wrist, he thought quickly.

'No. That will not be necessary. Work on the Palazzo Tiziano will stop me getting bored, and keep my skills current. And now—I think Livia's clothes-dryer should have finished with my things.'

'I'll fetch them,' Livia said quickly, heading out to the ramshackle laundry area.

'Good—that allows me the chance to give you some advice, Contessa.' His voice dropped to a whisper. Planting both hands firmly on the table, he leaned towards Rissa. As he did so, her eyes fixed on the discreet crucifix swinging gently from a fine silver chain around his neck.

'Yes?' Rissa managed to sound detached, but only because she was not looking directly at him.

'There is no need to undress a man with your eyes when he is wearing only a towel.'

'*What?*' Rissa squeaked. Livia returned at exactly the wrong moment, and exploded with laughter.

'I saw the way you were looking at me. Running that glance over every centimetre of my body.'

'Never!'

Although the kitchen table was between them, Rissa took a step back.

'All English women desire our men.' Livia chuckled unhelpfully. 'And Antonio is surely a prime specimen, *signora*!'

'You see?' Antonio arched one dark eyebrow. 'Livia acknowledges your feelings, even when you cannot. It is an accepted fact that those in power like to dabble with the lower orders. *Droit du seigneur*, I think it is called.' He shrugged. 'So, if during the long, cold nights here you need a few personal services to warm your heart, and perhaps a few other places—'

'No!' Rissa snapped, desperate to regain some sort of authority.

How on earth was she going to make her new home a fitting memorial to the great house of Alfere-Tiziano when her staff enjoyed so much fun at her expense?

Antonio had dressed and left an hour before, but Rissa still could not get him out of her mind. Any woman would have to be made of stone not to be moved by that body, and his charmingly dangerous attitude. She walked through the *palazzo*, trying to decide where she wanted Antonio to survey with a view to providing her with a proper room, but she could take nothing in. Restless and uncertain, she was troubled by the feverish ache running through her body. It would have been unusual enough if this handsome stranger had only tempted her. The real shock was the extent of her physical arousal. For years marriage had persuaded her that she was sadly lacking in that department.

Thoughts of Antonio super-heated her in a way her late husband had never warmed her. Rissa had been married for five difficult years, but Antonio had worked some sort of magic within seconds. She felt a frisson of fear at the way he had summoned thoughts and desires she had never experienced before. Her marriage, and her position as Contessa Alfere-Tiziano, had taught Rissa the importance of putting on a good show for others. She had always been careful to do the right thing, and had never given in to temptation or emotion of any sort in public.

*Frailty is for little people*, Luigi had said.

Rissa certainly felt frail now, and guilty. Wicked thoughts crowded in upon her which she could not understand. After all, she had never made a success of sex with Luigi, and Antonio had made no secret of his scorn for her title and position.

This dark stranger was forbidden and forbidding at the same time. It was a frightening combination—but exciting.

# CHAPTER THREE

'AH...SO many beautiful clothes!' Livia murmured next morning as Rissa began to unpack.

They were standing in the rooms that Antonio, not Rissa, had chosen as her suite. He had probed the upstairs rooms in detail the day before, working with the air of an expert. Most of the first floor had been pronounced sound enough for immediate use. The remaining salons and the top storey would need work, but for the moment Rissa could breathe again. Perhaps the place wasn't in such a desperate state after all.

At the moment her new rooms were nothing more than large, dusty spaces with breathtaking views out over the surrounding hills. Looking straight down, the prospect was not so lovely. Rissa's overgrown estate would need a lot of work before she could bear to gaze on what should be palatial gardens. The wrought-iron balconies outside her windows were too delicate with age to walk on, but at least Antonio was more optimistic than Mazzini had been about the *palazzo*'s interior.

Rissa's self-appointed project manager had been going over the house with great care. In here, he had made a list of things to be done, but they were only cosmetic touches like decorating and minor repairs. That could wait. The main aim was to get the whole place as habitable as her new bedroom.

Not that it seemed very habitable to Rissa, as she gazed around at all the dust and cobwebs. Two huge oak cupboards took up most of one wall, flanking a marble fireplace. These would have taken all her belongings with room to spare, but when Livia had opened the cupboard doors stale, musty air had rushed out and put both women off the idea. Instead of storing everything in the cavernous interiors, Rissa and Livia had rigged up makeshift shelves from bricks and old floorboards. Clothes by Armani and Moschino now had to hang from the curtain rails. They did the job of curtains far better than the old moth-eaten drapes, and were much more colourful.

'There will not be room here for a fraction of your things, *signora*,' Livia said sourly. Antonio had persuaded the housekeeper to thaw a little, but when he left the room he always managed to take Livia's smile with him.

'That won't matter, Livia. I shall be selling most of it. There must be stores dealing in second-hand designer clothes in Florence.'

'There is a charity shop in the village…'

'Yes, I noticed it. Unfortunately I must be practical. There is far too much stuff here—you've said that yourself. I might as well sell some to help fund repairs to the *palazzo*. Any proceeds left over when this place is perfect and we open to the public can be pledged to the charity shop. How's that?'

'I do not know what your agent, Signor Mazzini, or for that matter Signor Antonio will say to such an idea.' Livia clicked her tongue. 'Foreigners! *Ha!* It was bad enough when the place was going to be knocked down and the estate filled with holiday homes. I suppose we should be grateful that you only wish to fill the gardens with elderly English ladies!'

Rissa was so horrified by Livia's earlier words that she let the slur on her own plans pass without comment.

'Somebody wanted to demolish the *palazzo*?' Astounded, she looked around at its shabby grandeur. 'But this house is so beautiful—and it must be full of history. What would have happened to all the family portraits downstairs?'

'No family—no portraits.' Livia shook her head heavily. 'Signor Mazzini was approached by an office in Cardiff— where they play the rugby. Although not as well as in Italy, of course,' she added with defiance.

Livia's hidden depth of sporting knowledge impressed Rissa, but she was more interested in what might have been going on behind her back.

'Signor Mazzini told you what has been going on?'

'Things become common knowledge in Monte Piccolo very quickly. Some billionaire property developer wanted to come here and change everything,' Livia's tone showed she had little time for the rich. 'Signor Mazzini did not want that. On the day of your husband's funeral he told the company you would never sell.'

Rissa was puzzled. 'But at that time I didn't know anything about the *palazzo*…'

'Signor Mazzini knew the village would not want change. He must have been answering in everyone's best interests, Contessa.'

'Yes…' Rissa frowned. 'And he was quite right. Everything must be done to secure the *palazzo*'s future as it stands, for the good of the village.'

The housekeeper looked at her sideways. 'But you are not a local, *signora*. Why should you care?'

'My husband's mother was a local, Livia. She was proud of their ancient name. A sense of history and continuity in a changing world makes us what we are. That is why I am determined to keep this house, no matter what.'

It was just as well Rissa truly believed in what she was saying. The scornful look on Livia's face could leave her in no doubt about the housekeeper's feelings on the matter.

With Livia's help, Rissa sorted her luggage into those items she would be keeping, the ones that could be given away to the charity shop, and designer pieces to be resold at a good price. Rissa had always been careful with her possessions, and her clothes were immaculate. The most expensive items were invariably those that had been worn only once, or sometimes not at all. Luigi had bought her many designer pieces, but his taste had been for the skimpy and revealing. He had not been a man to put up with any objections, so Rissa had persuaded him to invest in several silk jackets for her to wear over the strapless tops and cutaway evening gowns.

Pleased with the amount they had achieved, Rissa looked at her Rolex. It was not yet ten a.m. Her heart leapt as she realised there was time to go exploring in the grounds before the sun rose too high.

Antonio watched her hurry down the wide stone steps at the back of the *palazzo*, noting that her turned ankle looked as good as new. He had already been to see Mazzini, and knew which way the wind was blowing. The agent had been suspicious of Antonio's self-appointment as the Contessa's right-hand man, and the officious little man had insisted on ringing her to check. From the way he had spoken to the Contessa over the phone, Antonio guessed there was more to Mazzini's interest in the girl's welfare than mere business.

Antonio saw and heard everything, but said little. It suited him to keep Rissa guessing about his own domestic arrangements. He had a good car, and commuting from Florence would be no problem. Working on the *palazzo* would be a pleasure, not a grind, and he intended to arrive early and leave late each day. This would give him plenty of time for roaming the grounds unobserved.

He'd discovered that the Tiziano estate had plenty of possibilities. Close study of the place showed it to be a rare treasure. The girl must be aware of its value, too, or she would have sold it. Antonio knew that Mazzini was also keen to get his hands on the *palazzo*. If Rissa would not sell, then there was only one way either man could take legal possession of the estate. Antonio smiled. They must both be considering similar tactics. It was a method particularly enjoyed by Italians, although men the world over would kill for the chance to get lucky in property by seducing such a prize.

He laughed silently as he studied Rissa from his vantage point on top of the estate's crumbling bell tower. She would never think of looking up, so he was able to watch her picking her way gingerly through the scrub and tumbled stones. A perfect example of her type, he thought cynically. Who else would dress in close-fitting white jeans and a pale lemon tee shirt for a jungle expedition?

He wondered idly what it would be like to take her to bed. Over the years he had enjoyed women from every social strand, but they had all shared one desire—a wedding ring, marrying them to Antonio's fortune. Their problem was that

Antonio had no illusions about the venal, grasping ways of women. He had seen many other rich men fall under the spell of beautiful girls. The affairs always followed a predictable pattern. Once the ring was securely on a girl's finger, she would develop a serious addiction to spending. It might begin honestly enough, on designer labels or prestigious parties, but it was never long before the muscle-bound personal trainer moved in, and cocaine replaced the *petit fours*.

Antonio had managed to avoid the honey traps of these 'legal whores', as he called them. To turn the tables and pass himself off as nothing more than a builder, eager for a rich woman's favour, appealed to his sense of humour.

He would be enjoying the Contessa while planting worries in her mind about the *palazzo*. He had not been able to regain it by offering a good price, so he would have to use psychology. A young, attractive widow, alone in a foreign land, would be desperate for someone to lean on—especially when she heard of the Tiziano Curse. His smile widened. If she *were* superstitious, she would be out of the place like a shot. If not, she would still quiver and appeal to him with wide-eyed innocence. He could sense it. The way she had looked at his half-naked body told him everything.

His feral instinct had been to take her there and then, tumbling the neatly laid table in their shared urgency. If the housekeeper had not been there he probably would have done, he thought wolfishly. But then his smile faded. The only way to bring it back was to remember the way the girl's body had responded to him so seductively each time their paths crossed.

Dark sickles of swifts screamed over the derelict olive groves. They made Rissa look up sharply. She was wondering if the birds would disappear south for the winter, like English ones did, when a slight movement caught her eye. On top of the *campanile* a silhouette stood out against the hard blue sky. Rissa recognised it immediately.

'Antonio! What are you doing up there? It can't be safe!'

'It is safe enough, Contessa,' he called back. Dodging out of sight, he reappeared a few moments later at the open door of the old tower. 'Although I do not recommend that you enter until a few running repairs have been carried out.'

'Is that what you were doing—checking it out?' Approaching cautiously, she glanced up at the crumbling stonework, but Antonio's body kept attracting her gaze like a magnet. He was wearing a plain white tee shirt, which made the healthy colour of his skin glow even more desirably. His jeans were old, but well fitting, and speckled with paint of several different colours. Hands on hips, he watched her draw closer. It was a stance that made Rissa's mouth go dry.

'I went to see your man Mazzini earlier this morning, Contessa. You should be aware that he resents your presence here.'

'Rubbish! Why would he say such a thing?'

'Because he wants this house for himself?'

'He advised me not to accept the offer made by that AMI company, Antonio. If he had wanted to get rid of me, he would have made more fuss when I confirmed I wasn't going to sell to anyone.'

Antonio's dark eyes were watchful as he calculated what he should try next. He wanted to plant doubts in her mind, but there was a fine line between the scary and the unbelievable. After a pause, he clicked his fingers with apparent inspiration.

'He must have been thinking of that old Monte Piccolo saying, Contessa!'

'What old saying?'

'That the village will fall if the Tiziano estate goes out of the family.'

'That's ridiculous,' Rissa said, but something behind his laughter made her add, 'Isn't it? I expect it's a story made up to fool credulous locals—like the myth about the Tower of London needing its ravens if the English monarchy is to continue.'

'Ah, you have seen through us, Contessa.' Antonio's voice was low with amusement. 'Of course that is it! We locals were particularly lucky in the nineteen-forties, when a great earthquake happened at the precise moment the owners were removed from Tiziano. It was a complete coincidence, of course, but one which gave the old threat a whole new lease of life.'

His words brought Rissa up short. 'Earthquake? Do we get earthquakes here?'

'Yes, *we* do.' He emphasised her isolation heavily. 'Although they rarely happen. However, there was one time, when the eccentric bachelor Count Angelo had abandoned the place to go on a barefoot pilgrimage to Rome. The village was shaken to such an extent that every building except the church and *palazzo* was razed to the ground.'

Rissa gasped, but Antonio merely shrugged. 'Wooden houses are as easily destroyed as they are rebuilt. Nevertheless, leaving the *palazzo* without a Tiziano might not be worth the risk, if you believe in such things.'

'Oh, no!' Rissa's eyes widened in alarm as a terrible thought struck her. 'I'm only a Tiziano by marriage! Does that count?'

'Who knows?' Antonio grinned. 'In any case, that old wives' tale is probably no more true than the Tiziano Curse.'

This was too much. Rissa hoped he was making it up, but she had to know. She had been avoiding eye contact with him because of the effect it had on her, but she steeled herself to ignore his melting milk chocolate gaze and keep to the matter in hand. 'Signor Mazzini never mentioned any curse.' She managed to convey some suspicion.

Although he was unfazed, it was Antonio's turn to avoid meeting her worried gaze.

'He wouldn't. He wants you safely settled in here so that he can marry you and complete his master plan—a Tiziano in the *palazzo*, and him as master of the village. That is where this so-called curse is supposed to come into play. It is said that any faithless wife living here will attract the dogs of doom.'

Rissa did not know what to say. It sounded ridiculous. Antonio was looking as though he had no time for such old stories, but there was often some sort of historical basis for these things...

'I suppose you will feel happier among my *credulous* people if you have a man in charge, Contessa.' He threw more words at her like poison darts.

'Wait a minute.' Rissa narrowed her eyes. 'There's a great hall in there, lined with grim portraits of warriors and re-doubtable women. They all managed to survive here. I've been looking at the dates. Most of them lived into old age—with the exception of some of the angry-looking young men,' she added thoughtfully.

It was Antonio's turn to frown, but before he could question her Rissa supplied an answer.

'All those other members of Luigi's family braved the curse, so I shall have to manage it, too. You've said you'll work here while the place is being restored, Antonio. If you're so worried about my welfare, why not live here, in the site office? There's plenty of room. You could be here 24/7.'

Antonio threw his hands up in despair. 'That is a horrible phrase! You would give a stranger like me such licence? Just because I have told you I am good at my job, Contessa? And you call *us* credulous.'

'I am beginning to hate that word.' Rissa pursed her lips. 'Of course I wouldn't act on anything you said without—'

'Stop.' He held up his hand, silencing her. 'I have already arranged everything with Signor Mazzini. All my professional qualifications are to be couriered to him, as necessary—although I think I impressed him sufficiently by force of personality alone. But you should not take everyone at face value, Contessa. Tell me, did Luigi Alfere ever let you out on your own?'

'No, as it happens.'

'The man must have had at least a grain of sense, then.'

Temporarily lost for words, Rissa stared down at her red sandals, which were covered in dust.

'Can we start work now?' She looked up at him apprehensively.

'When you are so clearly ready for business?' he mocked. 'For instance, where is your measuring tape, your notebook and pens?'

Rissa was ahead of him there. With a flourish she pulled all the necessary bits and pieces from her back pockets. Her cheeks were burning, but this time it was not only the effect of pulsing female hormones. How *dared* this man approve of the way Luigi had kept her a virtual prisoner? A cage was a cage, even when it was gilded with twenty-four-carat gold.

'I mean business, Antonio,' she said firmly. 'Perhaps we ought to get to work before the ancestors catch up with us.'

Turning on her heel, she stalked off. Antonio took a moment to admire her curvaceous walkaway. That was before she threw a mischievous look over her shoulder at him.

'Come on!'

Antonio knew then that he should have trusted his instincts at their first meeting. He ought to have thrown her onto that bed, accepting the invitation flaunted by the fullness of those beautiful breasts. Her dark, dilated pupils and parted lips told him she would not have resisted, even if his mouth had followed his fingertips in exploring and enjoying every centimetre of her.

He grimaced. She is no different from any other woman, he reminded himself, and I know what they are like.

If his real identity were revealed to her she would have only one reaction to that sort of treatment: gimme, gimme, gimme—money, trinkets, and expense accounts…it was the way of the world.

Antonio shook himself and strode after the Contessa, his mind almost on the job in hand. No woman was worth all this agonising. Property was the only thing that mattered. Land and his family's heritage must be his only interest.

It took the sight of Antonio plunging through a tangle of olives and vines to put his high-handed attitude out of Rissa's head. More than once she caught herself gasping as a vision danced in her mind of Antonio's thrusting arrogance being turned on her, of him taking her there on the dry dusty ground, or pressing her up against one of the ancient oak trees as his hands pushed aside her flimsy clothing and—

She put one hand to her brow, dizzy with an image of his sensual power and complete domination.

'The sun is too much for you, Contessa?'

'No—no, not at all, thank you, Antonio. I'm finding all the facts and figures you are firing at me a bit hard to visualise, that's all,' she improvised, fanning herself with her notebook.

'Come—sit over here in the shade while I check the condition of this terrace wall,' he ordered. His plan was beginning to work rather better than he had imagined. OK, so he couldn't seem to frighten the girl with folk tales, but something else was definitely happening. If he could convince her that restoring the *palazzo* would be a mammoth project after all, that might scare her away. She would be more interested in choosing colour schemes for the interior than in organising essentials such as ground works and utilities.

Relieved that Antonio seemed to be engrossed in his work, Rissa began concentrating on her own calculations. Luigi might not have wanted her to go on and take up a career in marketing, but she could still use the things she had learned on her course. She had been streets ahead of her contemporaries at university, but had always brushed aside their praise with embarrassment. In contrast, her talent for spotting opportunities could be given full expression here. The hardest part would be convincing Signor Mazzini and Antonio that her plans could work.

She moved restlessly. Even the thought of Antonio's name could have a startling effect. The slightest pressure of jeans and tee shirt on the curves of her body now made her feel entirely feminine. She felt as though she was powerless before the heat of his raw sensuality. It was madness. She no longer needed him to stand before her to obtain this effect—simply the sound of him crashing through the undergrowth like a wild animal sent pulses of desire through the most intimate parts of her body. She had never felt like this before—not even in the first heady days of Luigi's courtship.

When Antonio returned to her side, the taunting smile on his lips almost stopped her noticing that his tee shirt was damp from pushing through wet foliage. It was clinging closely to him, and once again it was almost, but not quite, transparent. It showed off every contour of his body, the white fabric emphasising the smooth firmness of his bare arms. Rissa felt her face growing hotter by the moment. She began searching for a clean page in her notebook. Flustered, she dropped it, and her pen—the Mont Blanc Luigi had given her on their first date—rolled away towards a crack in the old stonework.

Rissa dived for it at exactly the same moment Antonio darted forward. They collided as the pen disappeared into the crevice. Rissa clutched at Antonio for support, but the collision and the sudden nearness of him was too much. The air was forced from her lungs. As she gasped, she drew in all the fresh, warm fragrance of him. Skin against skin, she felt the firmness of his muscles gliding beneath her fingers. The texture of him made the fine cotton of his shirt feel coarse in comparison.

'Well, Contessa, that was close!' Low and confiding, his voice caressed the small space between them.

'What do you mean? I've lost my pen, and it was a present from my late husband—'

'I didn't mean that. I meant this.'

He looked down at her fingers, which had closed convulsively on his arm. Rissa let go, as though his body was as inflammable as hers.

'You don't need to restrain yourself with me, Contessa. Feel free to let yourself go.'

Rissa scrambled to her feet and backed away.

'I—I don't know what you mean…' she began, desperately trying to stop her mind dwelling on what it would be like to feel him returning her touch, to stop imagining his naked flesh pressed against hers in that dance as old as time—

'Oh, but I think you do.' In one smooth movement Antonio stripped off his damp tee shirt and tucked it into his belt. His eyes were laughing as he moved softly towards her. 'You have lost a treasured memento of your husband. After so recent a bereavement, no one could blame you for breaking down at such a loss.'

Antonio's *double entendre* had been deliberate—a test to see if she really was as bad as all the other women of her class. He watched her expression change, and his smile became one of triumph. He had proved to himself that she was no different from the working girls on the streets of his home town, trading their bodies for the fleeting advantage of money. At least Neapolitan whores were honest in their dealings. *This* girl had married a man who had given himself airs for nothing more than the meaningless advantage of a title. Surely, he thought, if she had loved Luigi Alfere in the way a wife should, there would have been tears, or at least some expression of grief. Instead, she looked embarrassed and ashamed.

Antonio's expression hardened. Instead of thinking about her late husband, she had been thinking about *him*. At the same time, Antonio had been imagining her willing body entwined with his as they tasted each other's arousal…

With a great effort of will he turned away from temptation and went to pull a metal bar from a long abandoned pile of scaffolding poles. Using it to prise apart the flagstones and retrieve her pen would distract him from the magnet of her body.

The problem was that this girl was altogether too desirable. Antonio planned to get her house. It was nothing more than another of his business ventures, he told himself, and no woman could be allowed to distract him from his goal. Desire was wayward, and he had no time for that—or a sitting tenant.

When Antonio had pulled her pen from its hiding place, Rissa accepted it graciously. Then she suggested they should go back to the kitchen and start on some paperwork. Livia had already told her she would be busy there all day. Rissa could not think of a better passion-killer than the respectable Italian matron bustling about while she and Antonio worked on plans—and she certainly needed a passion-killer.

Rissa had hoped her nights at the *palazzo* would be better now that she had a proper room. It was not to be. That night she spent restless hours going over what Antonio had told her about the Curse of Tiziano. At least she was no longer alone in the house. Livia and Fabio the cat had moved back into their lair next to the kitchen. At first the old lady had been aghast at the thought of Rissa sleeping in one of the abandoned rooms. Then the deliveries had begun. First Antonio had hired men from the village to lug a comfortable new bed up to Rissa's suite. Then a convoy carrying the rented site office had arrived, bringing with it portable heaters and dehumidifiers. Satisfied that the Contessa would be catered for, whatever the weather might throw at them, Livia had agreed to move back into her old room.

Antonio had expected Rissa to want the gardens and estate to look 'pretty' as soon as possible. Instead, he'd had to hide his surprise when she'd told him to concentrate his entire workforce on the house. His expression had become unreadable as she'd stressed the urgent need to get two suites habitable as soon as possible. It had only been when Rissa had explained her priorities that his inscrutable expression had slipped—if only for a moment. One apartment would be for her aunt and uncle, the other would be proper staff accommodation for Livia.

'I can manage in these rooms for now,' she'd told him as they stood in the middle of her bare but now clean dressing room. 'As long as all the plumbing and electrics have been renewed by the time my family come and live here.'

The fleeting astonishment in his eyes had made her laugh at the time. Those eyes took on more meaning in the long, lonely hours of darkness. Thinking of Antonio each night was a dangerous occupation. His eyes were always full of such a liquid longing that they haunted Rissa more effectively than talk of any curse. She could imagine him whispering to her through the night, trapping her in the intensity of his gaze while she was helpless beneath the firm, experienced touch of his fingers…

She leapt out of bed. This was ridiculous! Snapping on the light, she pulled on her robe, tying its belt tightly around her slender waist. What was the least sexy thing she could think about? A hot drink, of course…and all those ranks of intense family portraits hanging around the great hall downstairs.

Rissa had been a mousy little thing until her adoptive parents had persuaded her to go to university. It had only really been on her trip to America after her studies that she'd begun to learn that the world was not such a frightening place after all, and that most people were much less alarming than they at first appeared.

Luigi Alfere-Tiziano had fallen into that category, she

thought as she crept around the kitchen, trying to find her precious imported teabags without disturbing Livia. Rissa had been dazzled by Luigi's good looks and charm long before she'd learned that he was rich and titled. In fact, it was the Alfere-Tiziano fortune that had come between them. Luigi's wild extravagance had always made Rissa nervous. As things turned out, she had been right to worry. Her husband's wealth had given him the privilege of endless credit and many servants, most of whom he had treated like dirt.

Rissa sat down on an oaken settle drawn up beside the enormous fireplace. The grate was empty and cold, but there must be plenty of dead, dry wood lying around the estate. She could not wait to see some glittering action in the hearth. Until then, she had to rely on her imagination to provide a roaring fire, crackling away in front of her. Snuggling down, she wrapped her fingers around her steaming mug of tea.

She gazed up at the portraits on the opposite wall. They looked rather better in harsh electric light. Daylight cast more shadows, making their faces seem particularly angular and severe. Something had already struck Rissa as odd about those pictures. Although the many different faces resembled each other, all sharing the same large, dark eyes and aristocratic features, none of the Tiziano family looked remotely like Luigi. Now she came to look around the room, something else was puzzling, too. The huge, ceremonial coat of arms that almost filled the chimney breast. She could not work out the motto, but it definitely included the word 'Michaeli'. Rissa had never heard either Luigi or his mother use it, and it made her wonder why. Luigi's family had been so grand, she was surprised they hadn't quoted their motto at every opportunity.

Rissa thought she could guess the reason why they'd kept

quiet about it. The Alfere-Tizianos had been so autocratic that they'd rarely stooped to acknowledge females. 'Michaeli' was probably the surname of some poor, unsuspecting girl like her, drafted in 'to widen the gene pool', as Luigi had used to put it. Rissa could imagine that once the Tiziano family had laid claim to her possessions and got their precious male heir, she would have been pushed into the background.

Rissa hoped the girl had been luckier than she had. At least a child would have been some consolation for Luigi. He had been eaten up with disappointment, and she had felt so guilty. Then again, she shuddered, pity the poor baby afflicted with a couple like *them* as its parents. Luigi and Rissa had found coping with the paparazzi hard enough. Photos of their child would have filled the glossy magazines, especially when it cried or took fright or otherwise did not behave according to the strict code of the Alfere-Tiziano family.

Two days without sleep began to catch up on Rissa. Her eyelids became heavy. Only the hard oak bench kept her awake. At last she stood up and set off for bed. She took one last look around at the 'rogues gallery' before switching off the lights.

All those faces *were* oddly familiar. If only she could think why…

Sunlight was streaming through the windows of her room when she opened her eyes next morning. Alarmed that it must be late, Rissa sat up. Then she realised something else beside the sunshine had woken her. There was a lot of movement going on downstairs in the kitchen. She went to investigate, and found Livia mopping the floor while Fabio the cat stared out truculently from a refuge in the chimney corner.

'*Scusi, signora.* I was about to bring you a cup of coffee when I tripped over Fabio and almost fell, dropping the cup as I did so.'

'Don't worry about it.' Rissa waved the housekeeper's apology aside. 'Are *you* all right? That is the main thing,' she said with relief, when Livia nodded. 'I never normally sleep so late, so you did me a favour by waking me.'

'No, I didn't, Contessa. I have bad news. I was coming to tell you that I must make an extra visit to the village, so you will be alone here for a while. There was a power cut in the early hours of the morning, so no bread was ready when I first went to the shops.'

'It's on again now, though, isn't it?' Rissa indicated the bare lightbulb, suspended above the kitchen table by a long length of fraying flex.

'Oh, yes, *signora.* I was going to set off as soon as I had taken you your coffee.'

'No—I'll go instead, Livia. I need some exercise to clear my head after waking up in such a hurry,' Rissa volunteered quickly.

She was also glad of an excuse to do some exploring, and possibly meet her neighbours. After a quick shower, she dressed in a tiny striped top and some hip-hugging jeans.

It was a ten-minute walk down into the village. There were no signs that the thunderstorm earlier in the week had ever happened. Rissa's sandals kicked up little puffs of dust as she walked down the track that was all that remained of the *palazzo*'s great drive. Now greenery pressed in on every side as nature tried to reclaim the land. Swifts screamed high in the sky, not low overhead as they did when rain was on the way.

Rissa hesitated when she reached the big gates that opened out into the village square. She was not so confident that she could step straight out into the street. Straightening her top, she sleeked down her hair with nervous hands and cleared her throat. If anyone spoke to her, she did not want to reply with a squeak.

Opening the door a fraction, she was about to take an exploratory peep when she remembered Luigi's scorn at her nervousness. *That is not the way a true Alfere-Tiziano behaves,* he would have said.

That was enough to stiffen her resolve. Taking a deep breath, she plunged straight out into the world beyond the estate.

Monte Piccolo's village square was full of people discussing the recent power cut, and stocking up in case there should be another one. They were all so absorbed that no one took any notice of Rissa. She did not mind. She was happy to slip through the throng almost unnoticed, apart from an occasional watchful nod. Returning the smiles, she moved easily between the crowds.

It was market day, and Rissa toured all the stalls. She chose brown speckled eggs from one great pannier lined with straw, a loaf of bread, and a flat pad of focaccia. She was heading for a stall advertising fresh local fruit and vegetables when she caught sight of Antonio. Her urge to call out to him was stifled when she saw that he was absorbed in animated conversation— with a woman. An extremely beautiful young woman at that.

Rissa took refuge beside the striped side screen of the nearest stall and watched the couple out of the corner of her eye. They were only a few metres away. Rissa could not make out what they were saying, but she did not need to. The impassioned rise and fall of the girl's voice and Antonio's low reassurance sounded suspicious enough. When Rissa plucked up enough courage to glance at them directly, the seductive smile on Antonio's lips as he ran an appreciative hand down the arm of his companion told her this was much more than a simple chat!

Her cheeks burning, Rissa looked away to concentrate on her purchases.

She picked out half a dozen huge beefsteak tomatoes and a selection of salads, then took a chance and looked back at the alcove where Antonio and his 'friend' had been standing. It was deserted. Perhaps he had swept the girl off for a more intimate assignation?

Rissa hardened her heart and told herself that she did not care. It did not stop an invisible hand from clutching at her heart and squeezing tears into the corners of her eyes. Then the unthinkable happened—she heard the low music of Antonio's laughter close at hand. She had to look. Glancing in the direction of the stall she had just left, Rissa saw him. The girl had disappeared, and he was leaning over the colourful display of fruit and vegetables to tease a giggling toddler held in the arms of the stallholder.

He did not seem to have noticed her. Rissa wondered whether or not to go up and speak to him, but he was sharing a joke with one of the locals. It seemed rude to interrupt when he was having a conversation with one of his countrymen. She hesitated, wondering if he would turn and acknowledge her. Then she was suddenly struck by a frightening thought. Suppose he was telling the villagers what he really thought about her? His silky treatment of the unknown girl had shown Rissa that she was not the only one to benefit from his easy manner. What if he was a rat who enticed all women with the same deadly charm, then laughed about it afterwards?

She did not wait to find out. Clutching her purchases, she melted into the crowd before Antonio could look round.

# CHAPTER FOUR

'Where are you living?' Rissa asked Antonio later that day. They were discussing plans for the refurbishment over Livia's tomato and basil salad.

'Not far away. Over there.' He broke off a piece of focaccia and used it to gesture in the general direction of the Arno.

'I thought you were going to be living in the site office?'

He nodded. 'I might, but at the moment men are trooping in and out all the time. I value my privacy. Projects soon take on a life of their own, and it will become quieter, but for now I prefer to keep myself removed from my workforce.'

Rissa put her head on one side. 'But not the locals?'

'That is the beauty of living in anonymous lodgings.' He ignored the lilt of curiosity in her voice, concentrating instead upon his meal. 'I prefer to rent rooms where no one knows me. That way it is easy enough to dip in and out of company as and when I please. It can be impossible to escape from other people when you live amongst them permanently.'

'You are so right,' Rissa agreed with feeling. 'Mind you, I need a designer dress shop urgently. The faster I can get into Florence at the moment, the better.'

Antonio fixed her with the indulgent smile she had seen him play over the unknown girl earlier that morning.

'Ah…the beautiful Contessa does not need to gild herself on my account. I find her irresistible enough as it is,' he murmured, and then cursed himself silently. The girl was smiling at the touch of his flirtation, but he had intended to make her do all the running. He was pretty sure she must have seen him with Donna that morning. Now she would think he was nothing more than a gigolo, and that was not his intention at all. He wanted credibility.

Rissa was rebuking herself too. Antonio's flattery made her light-headed, despite confirming what she'd already suspected about his true nature. But then, she had been sensible all her life, and where had it got her? She was alone and lonely in a foreign country, without enough money to get back to England, and saddled with a house that would be eating money until she could think of some way of making a living out of it. The only reckless thing she had ever done in her life was to accept Luigi's offer of dinner, five long years ago, and look where *that* had led!

She knew she must be sensible and quash Antonio's attentions straight away, but that was her mind talking. Her body was growing increasingly rebellious. Antonio was clearly the kind of man who would come on to any woman, Rissa told herself. She knew that his type would run a mile from any sort of commitment—unless, like Luigi, they were under pressure to produce a legitimate heir. She knew it was wrong, knew she'd get hurt, but she couldn't deny the intensity of her attraction to him.

'I'm glad you approve of my appearance,' she said, before common sense could stop her. Then she blushed and looked down at her plate, shocked by her own words.

Antonio stopped and gazed at her. After her fine speech about keeping the old Alfere traditions alive, he had begun to have second thoughts about her. Perhaps she might be the first titled woman he had known to break the mould, but, no, she was exactly the same as all the rest. The self-styled Contessa Alfere-Tiziano was no snow maiden, but a red-hot sure thing. That blush could not deny it, he marvelled as he watched the hard points of her nipples rise to thrust against the thin cotton of her blouse. She was aroused, and so, Antonio had to acknowledge, was he.

Rissa was burning with a mixture of guilt and desire. I have got to get back on track before things get out of hand, she realised. If I don't, Livia might return to find us making unusual use of her kitchen table!

She could think of only one way to cool her passion, and that was by speaking out. 'I should not let your pretty little friend down in the village hear you talking like that, Antonio.'

It certainly brought him up short. There had been a smoky, after-dark quality to her voice, which turned his desire for her into a pounding ache. His body fought against common sense. Antonio had proved to himself yet again that the Contessa was the worst example of her type, picking up social inferiors for fun. By rights, he should have nothing to do with her beyond his work on the *palazzo*. Donna had told him that the girl had cast her spell on Mazzini. The land agent had been using Donna as arm-candy for months now, but Antonio knew *that* wouldn't stop a woman like the Contessa moving in to squeeze a rich old suitor until his pips squeaked. Antonio had seen it all too often. No wonder Donna was looking to him for sympathy now.

Rissa took a deep breath. There was nothing for it but to

soften the truth with some cautious talk. 'I need the security of knowing I've always got plenty to fall back on, Antonio. Selling off some of my designer clothes should bring in good money. If this project is to get off the ground, I don't want it to be tied down by cash-flow problems.'

Rissa felt the savage heat of her passion almost instantly transformed into burning shame. Thinking about the sad state of her bank balance always concentrated her mind, and it had worked as well as ever. She could only hope that Antonio did not guess the real reason why she was forced to sell her clothes.

'Hmm.' Antonio picked up his pen and did a few calculations on the pad beside him. Then he sat back in his seat. 'I cannot pretend that this will be a cheap, easy project. The *palazzo* is going to take a great deal of money, Contessa. It is not merely the cost of supplies. There is also the matter of paying the workforce. And the services of Signor Mazzini are expensive, I suppose, especially when he has a high-maintenance mistress like Donna to support. She is the creature you saw me with in the market,' he added, in an off-hand manner.

'That is why I must realise some of my assets, Antonio.'

'At least I am working for free.'

'I haven't forgotten, and I'm very grateful,' Rissa said firmly.

'Mind you, I could always become your own, personal, tax-deductible expense—' he laughed wryly, but Rissa stopped him with a horrified gasp as Livia bustled into the room.

'No—no—I am sure that won't be necessary!' she said hurriedly, never quite certain when he was serious and when he might be joking.

'Do not worry, Contessa. For the greater glory of a place like the Palazzo Tiziano, I am glad to work for nothing,' he said with a knowing smile.

\* \* \*

During her marriage, Rissa had become used to living in luxury. It had been a false paradise, but a very comfortable one. Abandoned in a Manhattan duplex, she had been brought out only for the grandest social occasions, spells in the Hamptons, or trips on the Alfere-Tiziano yacht. She had experienced gracious living, but her time had been dictated by the social calendar.

Things would be very different at the Palazzo Tiziano, Rissa realised as she stepped out onto the upper terrace next day. Antonio had gone into town to organise electricians and plumbers, but even when the utilities had been sorted out Rissa knew the house would still look stark and sad. There would be precious little comfort for her beyond her own suite.

Thinking of her bedroom instantly conjured up Antonio's image again, so Rissa quickly concentrated on making another circuit of the estate. An idea had been forming in her mind ever since she had caught part of Antonio's conversation with the old stallholder yesterday morning in the market. When she had asked him about it, Antonio had been only too willing to give her more details.

It turned out that the market gardener's only son had a good office job in Florence, and had no intention of carrying on his family's tradition of working on the land. The elderly stallholder wanted to retire, and would have to close the stall down. The fruit and vegetables were so popular with Livia and other villagers that Rissa knew its loss would be significant. Italians loved fresh, homegrown food, and although Rissa had no money for creature comforts at the Palazzo Tiziano, she had lots of land. She knew from tours with Antonio that her estate already grew pine nuts, almonds, figs, grapes and apricots. Sadly, fallen fruits enjoyed only by insects surrounded the untended trees and bushes.

As she walked carefully around her property now she could see more possibilities. Wild strawberries grew in cracks between paving stones. If they could manage in such poor places, how much better would they grow in a proper plot of good rich soil? Large, saleable berries from cultivated plants were sure to find a ready market in the village. Rissa worked her way towards the far boundary of her estate, where the old *campanile* stood like a pointing finger. *It is a beautiful building*, she realised, stopping to admire the vine-covered tower. Although it was clearly not in good condition, Antonio had been to the top without coming to any harm. All the dangerous areas around the place were marked off with striped tape and cones now—that had been one of his first jobs. The campanile had no warnings, so it could not be in *that* bad a state. Surely she could take a quick look inside?

*The idea of having a fling with Antonio has opened my mind to all sorts of risky things.* Rissa smiled as she walked up to the wooden door. She had already decided that the tower would be an ideal setting for a café, with views out over the grounds. Her adoptive parents only had window boxes back in England, but they looked on a trip to their local garden centre as a special outing. If they could have tea and cakes while they were out, that counted as a real treat. Rissa knew that by appealing to the villagers' enjoyment of coffee and chatting, as well as their desire for good fresh produce, she might provide herself with an income.

Reaching the *campanile*'s door, she paused and looked around. There was no one about. She picked up the great iron ring that served as a handle and immediately caught the tang of lubricant. The door was dry, and cracked with age, but its handle turned smoothly enough. Pushing it open, she peered into the shadowy interior.

Rissa had expected rubble, dead leaves, and perhaps some pigeon feathers. To her surprise, the spacious interior was clean and tidy. A notebook, clipboard, pen and large surveyor's tape measure lay on a far windowsill. Someone was already hard at work somewhere.

'Antonio?' she called, making her way to the staircase that must lead up to the bell tower. There was no reply. Gingerly starting up the steps, she put her hand to the wooden banister, which creaked menacingly. Rissa felt unsafe. She was about to retrace her steps and creep back out into the grounds when a sudden clatter made her jump. Grabbing for the stair rail, she felt it dissolve into powder beneath her hands and lost her balance. With a scream, she fell crashing to the ground.

Firm, authoritative hands were running over her body. Rissa tried to rouse herself, but her head was pounding and her throat was dry with dust. She was powerless. There was nothing she could do but lie still in the half-light and submit to a fingertip examination of each of her limbs in turn.

'Antonio!' she managed at last.

'Shh. You have had a nasty fall, Contessa. Do not move until I have checked thoroughly to make sure you are OK. Do you make a habit of tumbling to the feet of every man you meet?'

There was a low chuckle behind his voice, but it was his hands that concerned her. They moved with practised ease over her body. His slow, measured movements were almost a caress as they glided across her skin. In the silence, Rissa closed her eyes again. As Antonio's examination ran across her ribcage an involuntary gasp escaped from her lips.

'Was that painful?'

He bent so close that the stimulating male tang of him was almost a taste on her tongue. Her body began to respond, making her catch her breath again.

'You are in pain?' His voice was almost a purr, as though he expected her to make the most of the situation.

'No—ouch! Well, only from this lump on my head,' she winced.

'Let me see.'

Sliding his hands beneath her shoulders, he drew her gently into a sitting position. His face was now only millimetres away from hers.

'Look into my eyes, Contessa.'

It was hypnotism. Rissa was trapped in the deep, dark depths of those brown eyes. With a little gasp her lips parted, and she moistened them with the tip of her tongue, already imagining that she could feel the pressure of him taking possession of her mouth. Her fingers clenched convulsively and she found that she was gripping his arm. With a shock, she sprang back to reality. What a position to be in! Blushing, she scrambled away from him, desperate to hide her humiliation.

As he stood up, Antonio too had something to conceal.

'There cannot be much wrong with you if you can move like that!' He forced a chuckle, but his voice was low with testosterone. The fact was that Rissa was having a disturbing effect on him.

His plan had been to get his house back, with or without seducing her—it had not mattered much to him either way. This was to have been an emotionless business venture, completely free from the entanglement of feelings. Antonio could deal with basic sex. That gave him no problems at all. It was this sudden urgency of real desire, ravening need, which grew and consumed him with a fire of longing the type of which he had never known before. When he had felt her pliant body responding to his touch, he had been almost overwhelmed with the urge to take her right there, to move his body even closer to hers than he was to his own, to—

She slipped past him and was gone. Brushing dust from the knees of his jeans, Antonio followed her out of the building and into the sunlight.

'If that place is unsafe it should have a sign on the door.' Rissa rubbed the bruise on her head as they walked round to begin surveying the outside of the main building.

'It was perfectly safe until you decided to go exploring, Contessa. Most of the ground floor is good enough to use as extra storage space for supplies. It is *not* suitable for casual visitors.' He finished sternly. 'Now, if you stand on the bottom rung of this ladder, I shall go up and investigate the state of the upper facings of the house.'

'It was the clatter you made dropping this wretched thing that made me lose my balance,' Rissa said as she watched him advancing up the steps towards a clear blue sky.

'If you had not been poking around in a place that I had already told you was not totally safe, Contessa, your guilty conscience would not have made you jump like a frightened rabbit.'

'It seems such a waste of a good building. One day it ought to be made into extra living space.'

'I hope you are not suggesting that it should become another holiday home?' he said gruffly. 'Property and rental prices in the village are astronomical because of them. Young people cannot marry easily, because houses are so expensive here. When wed, they often start life together by living with their parents. No developer could be bothered to build cheap homes in Monte Piccolo. There is little work here, so it is executive houses and holiday apartments that make all the money. The only hope for young people today is to move away from pretty villages like this.'

'I might be able to help with some of that, at least,' Rissa said. 'The *palazzo* can provide jobs. Could you make sure you employ as many people from the village as possible, Antonio? It would at least give them some chance of making money without leaving home.'

'OK, but only if you are prepared to give proper contracts of employment and legal rates of pay. There must be no under-the-table deals for cash. I will not trade on their desperation,' he warned.

'It will all be arranged properly, through Signor Mazzini.'

Antonio shrugged. 'That won't please him. He prefers to employ his friends from town. If I choose the workers, Mazzini won't have any control over them. Are you willing to upset your gentleman friend like that, Contessa?'

'Signor Mazzini is not my "gentleman friend", as you put it. In any case, I thought you said that woman you were talking to in the market place was his girlfriend?'

'They have a casual arrangement, Contessa. Are you jealous?' Antonio came down the ladder and snapped his pencil back into its holder on top of his clipboard. 'Although this will take your mind off romance—it looks as though the Palazzo Tiziano needs a whole new roof. That will not come cheap. You should be more concerned about that than with other people's love-lives.'

Rissa shook her head in bewilderment. 'It needs a new roof? Signor Mazzini didn't say anything about that!'

'He did not have to, Contessa. You were inheriting the old place, not buying it.'

'How much is it likely to cost, exactly?'

She was looking worried. Antonio raised his eyebrows. Trying to scare her out of the house with old wives' tales had not worked. Perhaps this different set of thumbscrews might do the trick. Rich women liked to spend on luxuries, not property maintenance. Sticking his hands in his pockets, he rocked back on his heels, pursing his lips. He studied the façade of the once grand house for a long time before replying.

'Hmm. The new work must match what it replaces. Flashings and coving and ridge tiles must be cast and cut to match the original work. Master craftsmen will need to be employed, and maintained on site for as long as it takes. We are talking about a great deal of money, Contessa.'

'How much?' Rissa probed nervously.

'That is impossible to pin down, but big money, certainly.' She heaved a huge sigh.

Antonio tore his gaze away from the beautiful old house and regarded her keenly. 'Look—may I speak frankly, Contessa?'

'You might as well. Whatever you say cannot possibly make my situation any worse, can it?' she muttered.

His mouth almost twitched into a grin. 'In my opinion, the old place is not worth your while. You don't have to put yourself through all this stress, Contessa. Why don't you sell up and go back to your people in England?'

Rissa folded her arms, hugging herself against the chill draught of financial disaster. 'You *know* why, Antonio. You have said as much yourself. A rich developer would snap this place up at a fraction of its historical and real value. One of them was sniffing around within days of my husband's accident. There are wolves everywhere! They would either knock the *palazzo* down completely, or make it into expensive flats. Whatever they did, these beautiful grounds would be lost for ever under acres of concrete, parking spaces and the designer homes you yourself were so scornful about not long ago.'

She was turning his own words back on him. Antonio considered them. What she had said was true enough, but he knew there must be some deeper reasoning behind it. Women always liked to keep men guessing. It was the way they worked—they preferred to keep their prey off-balance. There would be some other motive for the Contessa wanting to keep the Palazzo Tiziano.

Antonio led the way around to the back of the house. He was deep in thought. His company, AMI Holdings, had made such generous offers for the whole estate that anyone in their right mind would have taken the money and blessed their luck. His people back in Cardiff, and the staff of Mazzini's office in Florence, had all agreed that the Contessa would be mad to turn it down. Then Mazzini himself had stepped in to block the first offer. The Contessa had refused the increased figure. She seemed to prefer scraping a bare living here rather than cutting her losses and heading back home.

Antonio had to know if there really was anything between her and Enrico Mazzini. Secure in the knowledge that no unattached woman could resist him, he decided to put her to the test.

The house had been developed over the centuries. Additions to one end of its main building had created a private, sunny area, sheltered on three sides, but open to the south.

'This would be perfect for sunbathing,' he said, treading down the dry grass that had been left to grow untended for years.

'And the weather is exactly right for it today, too.' Rissa joined him in padding the greenery down into a soft bed.

'Then be my guest, Contessa!'

Rissa laughed. 'I'd have to go back into the house and fetch some lotion. Then the moment would be gone. I would find too many jobs to do before I could get out here again!'

'Then let me fetch some for you. This spot is completely secluded, and the men are all working on the other side of the house. You can strip off and stretch out in privacy.' He was looking at her so innocently that Rissa was struck with sudden devilment.

'All right—I shall! There is a bottle on top of the cabinet in the kitchen, Antonio.' She put a hand to one strap of her sundress, but stopped when she saw that he was still watching.

He took the hint and walked off with a smile. A pleasure delayed would be double the fun. In seconds he had retrieved the sun lotion, but did not go straight back outside. Instead he took the stairs two at a time and went into Rissa's suite. It overlooked the sheltered quadrangle, giving Antonio his own private view of the grass below.

The girl must have lost her nerve. She had not stripped off, but was lying face down on the grass in her sundress. All her most interesting features were still hidden from Antonio, but despite that he felt himself rising to the challenge. Her smooth, slender limbs and the gentle curve of her back were meant for his caress. He turned away from the window and strode off to put his fantasies into action.

Stealthy as a panther, he padded across the grass, taking care that his shadow did not disturb her. Even so, she sensed his arrival and began to raise herself on one elbow. It was too late. Silhouetted against the sun, he was pouring sun tan lotion into the palm of one hand.

'Lie down,' he commanded. It was not a voice to be questioned. Rissa heard him snap the bottle closed and tensed. He noticed.

'This is no good. You must relax to get all the benefit of this sun, Contessa.'

'Yes, but I'm not altogether sure that this is—'

The firm strokes of Antonio's hands running over her shoulders stifled any objections.

His lips twitched with the hint of a smile. 'Contessa, explain to me how you are supposed to apply this stuff all on your own!'

Rissa felt him take long sweeping strokes up her neck and down her arms. She knew he must be kneeling astride her, but he was taking care that no part of his body touched hers apart from his swirling, massaging hands. Suddenly his movements stopped. She expected to hear the bottle being opened again. Instead, the halter neck of her sundress was unfastened. She gasped as it fell away, leaving her back completely exposed.

'As soon as I leave you will wriggle out of it, so why take the risk of leaving the skin beneath your straps unprotected?' His fingers spread a slick of lotion over her shoulderblades.

Rissa closed her eyes, revelling in the half-forgotten feeling of a man's hands running over her body. She knew she should call a halt, but part of her—something buried deep inside—made her want him to continue, even to risk going further...

He did not. Instead, she heard him pour out more cream. This time he moved back and began oiling her calves. When he progressed beneath the hem of her dress, Rissa gave a deep, heartfelt sigh.

'That is good, isn't it?' Antonio was enjoying himself hugely. The contrast between his rough workman's palms and her soft skin gave him a delicious foretaste of pleasures to come.

'Mmm.'

He flattened his hands against her thighs, making swimming movements that went up and around, up and around, higher and higher, until the tips of his fingers brushed beneath the elastic of her panties. The intrusion met with no resistance, so as smoothly as ever Antonio continued, each circuit taking him a little further into the forbidden zone. When those tactics brought his palms fully into contact with her bare behind, he could resist no longer. His smooth strokes changed to a cupping, squeezing motion.

'No!' she warned him firmly, but not before he had heard a little moan wander between her parted lips.

'Why? Because you do not like it?'

She liked it very much, but in this situation honesty would be her downfall. To put a stop to it would confirm what Luigi had always thought about her, but then *he* had never made her body respond as Antonio did. Rissa tried to dodge the issue.

'It isn't that.'

'What is it, then? Don't tell me you are afraid of what people might think? That is the worst reason of all, at any time and in any place.' Antonio leaned forward until his breath caressed her shoulder. 'The *palazzo* is empty. None of the workers has my permission to come around to this part of the building, and my word is law.' With the last word he kissed the delicate skin beneath her ear.

The touch of his lips released a shiver of anticipation that coursed through her body. Reality slipped away. Rissa melted beneath his hands as they ran along the length of her body, still slick with lotion. Squirming beneath him, she twisted like a seal, desperate to escape but equally desperate for him to continue stroking her body. The strange new feeling suddenly threw a switch in Rissa's head. *I can't do this*, she thought. *If I go any further Antonio will find out. He will discover the horrible truth about me and I couldn't bear it.*

'Stop!' A coiled spring of fear and desperation, she hit him a glancing blow. He leapt away, equally horrified. Clutching at her dress, Rissa crouched in the grass like a fawn at bay. Antonio blacked out the sun. As he approached she saw that his dark eyes were turbulent, and his hands were balled into fists.

'I—I don't want this, Antonio. I never intended you to go as far as you did.'

His stare was cruel with disbelief. She could not meet it, and shut her eyes against her shame and his fury. When he spoke, his voice was low and dangerous.

'No. That is a lie. You were as willing as I was, Contessa. But then the truth kicked in. You got cold feet. You began to think that your Signor Mazzini might dump you if he thought you had been playing around with your staff.'

His first few words were true enough, but the rest was a lie. Rissa agonised to herself. There was no way she could tell Antonio the true reason why she had called a halt. The fact was that, despite her marriage, she was still inexperienced in the ways of love. A man like Antonio would be sure to take advantage of that.

'No, Antonio—Mazzini means nothing to me. And as for the rest…you've got it all wrong…' Her voice faded as she saw the cynicism in his smile.

'I don't think so, Contessa. Your idea is to keep me sweet, and then perhaps I'll help you out still further by arranging some favourable cash terms for the building materials you need. Isn't that the way you are thinking?'

Rissa's dealings with Mazzini had shown her that the black economy worked in the same way the world over. He always quoted two figures for any transaction—one for cash, and one to go through the books. Rissa insisted on paying the correct amount for everything. Mazzini kept suggesting that everyone had his or her price, but she had been unwilling to believe it. Now here was Antonio, expecting her to be wise in all the ways of fiddling expenses and manipulating her workforce.

'This has nothing to do with any of that,' she muttered, but he had already made up his mind.

'Of course it does. A rich woman without a man is never satisfied. Then along comes wealthy old Mazzini. I am sure you can wind him around your little finger. You need to get the *palazzo* up and running, but you haven't yet managed to get your hands on his credit card. My offer to work for nothing must have seemed like a gift from the gods! In your world, Contessa, nobody does anything for nothing. Perhaps you were feeling a little guilty, eh? You were expecting a poor peasant like me to be overawed by the attentions of the lady of the manor. When I proved to be more than equal to the task, you pulled back.' He was looking down on her with undisguised contempt.

Rissa was in agony. She already knew what it was like to have her self-esteem trampled underfoot. Luigi's unspoken disappointment in her had tortured Rissa often enough. But that was nothing compared to the pain Antonio was inflicting on her now. Humiliation was burning in her face and forming an insoluble lump in her throat. A moment ago she had almost lost control beneath his hands, exposing herself in a way that she had never risked before. To learn that her reaction had fulfilled some kind of terrible expectation in him was a thousand times worse than all the old taunts put together.

'You don't understand, Antonio! I'm not like that!' she burst out when the pain became unendurable. He gave a mirthless laugh.

'So I imagined it—you *didn't* make the first move? I think you did, Contessa. I felt your body come to life beneath my hands. And when I responded in kind, I found you were as hot and willing as any woman I have ever known—'

'No!' Instinctively Rissa responded with all the pain of wounded pride, but he was quicker. With the speed of a striking snake he grabbed her wrist before her hand could connect with his cheek again.

'When the truth hurts, try to silence it, eh?' He grinned, his fingers biting into the thin skin of her inner arm. 'That is the way women like you work, isn't it?'

Rissa looked at him, horrified. He laughed.

'No, you might have pushed me to the edge, Contessa, but unlike some men I have no intention of pressing my advantage.'

'Then let go of me!' She managed to stop her voice rising to a scream, but it was a struggle. His grip was relentless and his eyes poured darkness into her. 'Any meeting I may have with Signor Mazzini is only for the good of the Palazzo Tiziano. You have no right to suggest anything else!'

She had to swallow hard to stop tears of panic and inner pain from rising up and choking her, but she was not about to break down in front of him. 'My first and only thoughts are always to do the best for this house.'

'Don't give me that! Your sort are always quick to play the old honour card.'

'And what exactly *is* my "sort"?'

'You are a typical member of the monied classes, Contessa. When they are down on their luck, they are always quick to hitch a ride on the lifeboat of new money. You had a fine meal ticket in the shape of Luigi Alfere. When you lost that, it was time to find another. Along comes the portly, vain Signor Mazzini, and you are set up for life again. Well, congratulations—you could hardly have made a better choice. The man is old and unfit—with any luck you won't have to suffer his attentions for too long before you wear him out. Then you'll move on to some other rich provider—anything to stop you having to fend for yourself. You are a leaner, Contessa. You lean on people to get what you want, always relying on someone else to come up with the goods.'

'No! I won't listen to this!' Growing hysteria lent Rissa the strength to rip her arm from his grasp and turn her back on him as she did up her sundress. 'You know nothing about my circumstances. Nobody—especially not a man who comes across like an over-sexed dinosaur when it comes to women— speaks to me like that. Especially on my own land!' she announced. But he was already striding away around the corner of the house.

Rissa was as taut as a bowstring all the way to her room, listening for the sound of Antonio in case he decided to seek her out again. It never came. Only when she had retreated behind locked doors did she collapse onto the edge of her new bed and bury her face in her hands. How could Antonio be so utterly wrong about her—especially when she had been so right about him? On that first dark night she had sensed instantly that he was all man. Why, then, had *he* misjudged *her* so badly? She had always fallen outside the circle of well-to-do women who ran the social life of Manhattan. That didn't stop her recognising the picture Antonio had painted of idle privilege. But she was different—wasn't she?

She knew how those women would have reacted to that kind of treatment from a man like Antonio. He would have been thrown off the premises without a reference. Rissa would have done the same. But three things stopped her. One—Antonio galvanised everyone into action as soon as they became involved in the *palazzo* project. They were only a few days into the work, but things were already happening on a grand scale. Two—he was working for no wages. At least, that had been the arrangement when they'd last spoken civilly about the matter. And last—but in Rissa's mind most importantly of all—he had taught her a vital lesson. Her body was not the lifeless thing of marble that marriage to Luigi had led her to believe.

She had thought the fault was on her side, but now she was beginning to wonder. Given the right stimulation, she could respond like the most hot-blooded, passionate of women, and Antonio had reacted accordingly. Every time she looked at him, she was playing with fire. Giving in to temptation was only a touch away. *Well, I shan't be burning my fingers,* she told herself. *Antonio has done me a favour by destroying any fantasies I may have had about him. His reality is too painful. I won't be going there again,* she thought, still burning with humiliation when she remembered how he saw her. He had said that she was a woman on the make, no different from any other. It was such a painful jibe that tears of outrage sprang to her eyes. Rissa rubbed them away in fury. She had thought her defences against the world were so good that no one—especially no man—would ever be able to breach them.

Antonio was the only one who had come close to breaking down her resolve. She vowed then and there that he must never again come so close to discovering her painful secret.

# CHAPTER FIVE

RISSA knelt outside the great front doors of the Palazzo Tiziano, her radio playing by her side. She was weeding, shaded from the heat by a broad-brimmed straw hat. Every crevice around the big old house was green with weeds. She might not be able to re-tile a roof or use an angle grinder, but she could at least work to make the place look a bit more presentable.

In the days since Antonio had compared her to the idle women of his acquaintance, she had found a million things to do. They all involved keeping her head down, as far away from him as possible. She had been working from morning until night to stop her mind dwelling on what had happened.

It was now almost midday, and Rissa had been on her hands and knees since five o'clock that morning. She had made so many trips to empty her pail of weeds that she had lost count. The work was hard. Only the memory of Antonio's taunts that day about the lazy society she had left behind kept her going. Rissa was determined to show him that she was totally unlike those other women. Besides, if she took a back seat and did nothing towards restoring the Palazzo Tiziano, she really would be in Antonio's debt. She hated the thought of obligation like that. It was bad enough to know that the *palazzo* was such a drain on her rapidly vanishing finances.

She sat back on her heels and looked up at the fine, creamy stonework of the building's façade. Blank windows gazed out over the rolling Tuscan countryside. Rissa bit her lip. Curtains behind all that flawed glass would cheer the place up instantly, but no money could be spared for luxuries like that. Then she had an idea. A few old rose bushes were still clinging to life in the wilderness of the estate. Their willowy growth could spare armfuls of flowers for the house.

Brushing gritty soil off her hands, Rissa stood up. She looked down proudly at what she had achieved. A large area of the courtyard was now looking neat and presentable. She was overdue a break in which to do something nicer. Fetching some scissors from the kitchen, she set off, and within ten minutes had filled her weeding bucket with wands of sweet-smelling flowers. As well as roses, she had found sprays of myrtle, rosemary and arbutus, to make a special arrangement for her bedside. There was no point in living in such splendour if she could not enjoy it indoors as well as out.

As she carried her prizes around the corner of the house, she walked straight into Antonio. He must be the only man who can make overalls and a hard hat look sexy, she thought, and blushed.

He looked pointedly at her container of flowers. 'Where have you been? Livia wants to serve lunch. There are plenty more jobs around here that are more important than picking flowers.'

'I have spent all morning on my hands and knees clearing the terrace!' Rissa bridled indignantly.

'I know. But, as I say, if you want to make yourself useful, there are more urgent tasks that need tackling first.'

'The front of this house is pretty important to me. And, as I am sure you would be the first to point out, Antonio, I am totally unskilled labour.' Rissa stood with one hand on her hip, daring Antonio to contradict her.

'I know, so I have thought of a job that even you can do, Contessa. All the exterior paintwork needs to be stripped off the ground floor of the main house. That will be your task this afternoon, once you have had your food. The sun will be away from the front of the building by then. Have you ever used a blowtorch?' He grinned, knowing he was right to be scornful. This delicate little Contessa might dabble with cosmetic touches, like weeding or flower arranging, but when it came down to real work she would be sure to disappear without a trace.

'No, I haven't—but if you could spare some time to teach me, I could learn.'

This was not the reply Antonio had expected, but he rallied instantly. 'You'll have to be careful not to crack the glass, Contessa. Perhaps if I tell you that it costs twelve euros to replace each of those small panes, it will inspire you not to break any.'

It did, but Rissa was not about to let Antonio think his instructions had intimidated her.

She did not hurry her lunch. Then she arranged displays of flowers in several of the downstairs windows at the front of the building before strolling off to find her instructor.

'My employees will not be impressed if you use all their containers for foliage, Contessa,' Antonio said, as he filled a workman's trug with a blowtorch and scrapers.

'I only used a couple of their buckets. There were some old vases in a cupboard,' she countered, shivering at the thought of all the cobwebs that had been hidden away in there as well. 'Now—what about all this desperately important work you want me to do?'

Antonio was wary of underestimating Rissa a second time. He took great care to teach her exactly how he wanted the work done.

'You are a quick study,' he said at last, when he could no longer fight against giving the compliment.

'There is no need to sound so grudging.'

'I am a busy man, Contessa. I don't have time for point-less chit-chat.'

'Then don't feel you have to waste any more of your valuable time on me,' she said lightly, peeling a long curl of aged paint off a windowframe with the satisfaction of someone who had found a new vocation in life.

Antonio wasn't about to march off straight away. He had not obeyed any woman since he was fifteen, and he was not about to start now. Strolling away in his own good time, he found himself listening, waiting for her to call him back. When she did not, he went to find comfort in checking up on how things were going back at the headquarters of AMI Holdings.

Reaching the site office, he pulled off his overalls. Then he straightened his shirt and brushed down his jeans before taking his place at the desk. Switching on his laptop, he checked the share prices. Careful growth and continual mo-nitoring meant the market was smiling on AMI Holdings. That was good. His staff would all be in line for another windfall payment at Christmas. Antonio fired off the e-mails that would eventually cascade down through his thousands of workers and sub-contractors. He had interests across Europe and the United States, yet despite his international business,

Antonio was very much a hands-on employer. When his own fortunes rose, he wanted everyone to share in them.

When he had finished on the computer, Antonio allowed himself the luxury of a hot *macciato*. This was one of the perks of his deception. Pulling rank as site manager actually gave him the chance to savour drinks—proper drinks—from beginning to end. When he was working outside, coffee after instant coffee had to be parked and abandoned. If the cups were eventually rediscovered, there was always a thick layer of plaster or dust on the surface of his drink, so Antonio had become used to going thirsty. Today would be different. He had managed to speak with the girl again, after that setback over the sunbathing, so he deserved a reward.

Some of his newer staff might have found it strange that Antonio Michaeli-Isola chose to spend his annual leave working unpaid at the Palazzo Tiziano, but then their boss was an unusual man. He rarely took time off work for any reason, much less holiday. There had been real trouble in his early life, until a teacher at his school had tried to find out the reason behind his truancy.

Old Dini had discovered that Antonio was out earning money when he should have been in the classroom. The boy had felt he had to do something to support his widowed mother and aged grandmother. Antonio's talent for working with his hands had been put to good use. Anyone in the area who had needed jobs done quickly and well had called for him. When his teacher had learned about this, he had persuaded the school's vocational department to hone Antonio's skills.

The boy had repaid all the trust put in him. By the age of nineteen he had earned enough to buy his first derelict property. This had been sold on to a young local couple for an affordable price, though Antonio had still made a good profit on the deal. And now, however high he might fly, he never forgot what it was like to be at a disadvantage. That was why he liked to go back to labouring now and again. Working with his own hands instead of merely issuing orders was Antonio's idea of a good time. To be restoring the Palazzo Tiziano made it a double pleasure. Not only could he take pride in what was being achieved, he knew that sooner or later the place would be his.

He owed it to his ancestors to care for their home. They had lived and loved here since Roman times, certainly, and perhaps even right back to the Etruscans. On the other hand, Antonio felt he owed nothing at all to those pampered upstarts the Alfere family. They had merely got lucky. It was, Antonio supposed, what they called the fortunes of war. He did not intend to be on the losing side *this* time.

As for the Contessa… He thought for a moment, gazing into the middle distance with half-closed eyes. Taking her would be sweet revenge. It would be no more than those treacherous Alferes deserved. There would be a more personal bonus, too. Not only would Antonio be avenging his family's honour, it would serve the Contessa right for leading him on. He was looking forward to enjoying her and righting wrongs at the same time. His workmen always paused to admire the girl as she passed, and that really annoyed him. Not only was she distracting them, it stirred an unexpected mixture of possessiveness and an instinct within Antonio that was disturbingly close to the animal. This did not sit easily with his finer feelings. It aroused him to know that the girl he needed to bed to secure the greatest prize of all—his *palazzo*—was the object of other men's desires. Yet the whole master and mistress thing left a nasty taste in his mouth.

The trouble was, that girl was a thief. She had married into this house, obtaining it under false pretences. Now she showed every sign of wanting to hang on to the place. He sipped his coffee, frowning. She was a burglar of emotions, inspiring a powerful cocktail of feelings within Antonio. Plenty of women could arouse him physically, but the Contessa Alfere-Tiziano also managed to rouse him to anger and seduce him at the same time.

No other woman had ever affected him like this before, and it made him uneasy.

Rissa felt herself fizzing with anticipation as she approached the site office door. She had survived one conversation today with Antonio, but now she was approaching his lair. Confidence in the work she had done for him was making her bold. Gingerly, she tapped on the door. A loud order to 'come in' made her hesitate. It was only for a fraction of a second, but that was too long for Antonio. He pulled the door open to confront his visitor. Dressed in well-cut jeans and a white linen shirt, he was one of those men who showed his style even on a working day.

'Where is your hard hat?' He pointed to a nearby sign. It was one of many dotted all around the busy building site that the estate had become.

'I left it on the front doorstep while I walked over here from the house. It is too hot to wear that thing when I am not working.'

His dark brows contracted. 'It is never too hot to obey the rules of Health and Safety.'

Her face compressed with anger. She spun around on her heel, ready to march off again.

'Wait!' He caught her by the arm.

'I was going back to fetch it.' Rissa glared at his restraining hand. Instantly he let her go. 'I only came over to see if you wanted to inspect the work I have done.'

'This isn't technical college, Contessa. At school, the teacher gives you ten out of ten for decent work. Out here, in the real world, you must take responsibility for yourself. If you are satisfied, then so am I. This is currently your house. I am merely here to make sure things run smoothly and to schedule. *If* I am allowed to get on without interruptions, of course,' he added dryly.

Rissa was about to reply in kind. Then she realised his attention had been snatched away by something else. Turning around, she saw Donna, the dark-haired young woman from the market.

The newcomer was picking her way across the courtyard. Even from a distance she looked wonderful. A white off-the-shoulder lacy top was cut short to show off a strip of flat, bronzed stomach above a pair of hip-hugging Capri pants. A large pair of sunglasses was pushed up on top of her head, holding back a riot of purplish-red curls. As she drew closer, Rissa realised that the stranger's mass of hair had the dry, straw-like texture caused by constant over-processing.

Antonio did not seem to mind. His attention was straying lower down, to where a pair of strangely immobile breasts bulged over the low neckline of Donna's *broderie anglaise* top.

'Antonio—I'm *sooo* glad you are here! I cannot imagine how I would have felt to have struggled all the way up here and then found the place empty!'

Rissa bit back the retort that Antonio was only one of dozens working at the *palazzo*, but it hardly seemed necessary. Donna was ignoring her totally, and had eyes only for Antonio.

'Enrico is having a dinner party this evening. Why don't you join us?'

Antonio smiled briefly. 'I assume your invitation also extends to my client the Contessa, Donna?'

The woman turned a pair of pale blue eyes on Rissa. Twinkling with laughter, she shot a look that dared her to accept.

'Actually, I'm rather busy tonight.' Rissa smiled graciously. As far as she was concerned, stripping paint sounded much more fun than spending hours watching Donna make sheep's eyes at Antonio.

'In which case I would be delighted to accept.' Antonio gave the messenger such a knowing look that it made Rissa blush. Donna merely winked archly and turned on her heel.

'We'll see you at around nine, then, Antonio. *Ciao!*'

'*Ciao,*' he repeated, raising his hand in farewell. For some moments his eyes were fastened on Donna's well-upholstered rear end as it undulated down the drive.

'Your friend might have found it easier on her stilettos to use the telephone,' Rissa observed.

'Yes—although it would not have been such a pleasurable experience. For either of us.' Antonio gave one of his eloquent smiles.

*I certainly didn't enjoy it,* Rissa fumed as she walked from the site office back to her work on the house. A hard knot of pain was tangling her emotions, confusing her. Antonio was an overbearing misogynist. If that was the kind of man Donna wanted, then she was welcome to him. *I don't need that sort of conflict in my life,* Rissa told herself.

But, if that was the case, why did the sight of Antonio exchanging glances with Donna affect her so much?

Antonio never needed much sleep. Next morning, he was strolling through the grounds of the *palazzo* before the sun had pushed clear of the furthest line of hills. Pencil-thin cypresses were still nothing more than black shapes pointing skywards as he approached the front of his beautiful *palazzo*. He stopped a few metres short of the façade to study its new appearance. The growing daylight was no longer reflecting off ancient white paintwork. All the exposed wood on the ground floor now looked as though it had been ravaged by fire.

Heart in his mouth, Antonio went forward to inspect any damage more closely. There was none. The girl had been careful enough, he admitted grudgingly to himself as he fingered all the mouldings and the *palazzo*'s great double doors.

It really was a beautiful building, set off by ideal surroundings, Antonio thought, casting a critical eye over the cobbled forecourt. The Contessa had done a good job there as well. She had shown vision on their first tours around the gardens, too. The mousy little English girl was displaying hidden depths and talents.

He approached one of the tall windows. Leaning forward, he cupped one hand against the glass to see into the room beyond. Rissa had filled a Lalique vase with roses and put it on a French-polished side table. Antonio noticed that she had placed a tablemat beneath the crystal. That would certainly stop water or the base of her flower arrangement marking what he suspected was a Louis XVI piece. His inspection continued. In her urge to improve the *palazzo*, she must have washed away inches of dust from this room alone. It was one of the best-preserved areas in the whole complex, and she was trying to show it to advantage.

The high walls and carved ceiling had all been cleaned, making the room look even more airy and spacious. It was empty, apart from her flower arrangement and a dustpan and brush standing beside the huge marble fireplace. Antonio began to feel uneasy again. It would not be long before his men were being borrowed to carry out silly, female-inspired tasks like black-leading grates or sanding the floorboards— which looked good enough to take the treatment and then remain on display without carpets, he noted in passing.

Stepping back from the window, Antonio prowled around the rest of the ground floor. Livia was not due to start work for more than an hour, and he suspected that Rissa would not be surfacing at any time soon. She must have toiled long into the evening to achieve so much paint-stripping, he thought with wry amusement. It had probably been an attempt to work off all that sexual frustration.

Eventually, he went over to the site office, let himself in and switched on his laptop. The business side of his brain watched the display of international financial news, but the analytical part of his mind was elsewhere. It was employed in a much more complex problem. The image he had been sold of Larissa Alfere-Tiziano, as the press called her, was that of an airhead who'd got lucky. On that basis, *his* people had made *her* people good offers for the *palazzo*. Antonio's first jolt had been her refusal to sell. Then his confidence had taken a blow when she had not been scared away from the place by either its condition or his tales. If he could neither buy nor frighten her out of this house that was rightfully his, there was surely only one route left. But that business with the suntan lotion had put a dent in those plans, too.

What was wrong with the woman? She had been hot for him, then suddenly the barricades had gone up so fast it was a wonder he hadn't lost his fingers—or something closer to the action! Antonio stroked his chin thoughtfully. She was a woman alone, and had been clearly tempted by the thought of sex with no strings. But when it had come to actually doing it…something had gone wrong. Antonio knew she had the potential to be as much of a sexual being as he was. He had felt it in her response. Her dark, sensuous eyes had been all for him, and that generous mouth had been silently asking to be kissed. Yet she had pulled back at the last moment…

He grimaced at the memory of Enrico Mazzini's dinner party the previous evening. Donna could do with taking some lessons in restraint from the English Contessa. Concealed by the long flowing tablecloth, Donna's prehensile toes had been groping about in Antonio's lap from *antipasti* to *grappa*.

The meal had been a test for him in more ways than one. Mazzini had been barely able to conceal his fury at the unexpected guest. The land agent had kept telling everyone that Donna had made a mistake and invited Antonio instead of the Contessa Alfere-Tiziano. And he had referred to Antonio as 'our friend the workman' all evening. Antonio did not care. Donna obviously hadn't told Mazzini that she had invited his great rival in the contest for possession of the Palazzo Tiziano, and the thought of Mazzini's annoyance amused Antonio. He smiled to himself. It took one to know one, and in Enrico Mazzini Antonio recognised another man of determination. Mazzini wanted to get his hands on the *palazzo*. It had been obvious from the start of the dinner party that the invitation Donna had been so keen to deliver had been intended only for the Contessa.

No doubt her ladyship would have felt more at home there than I did among the posing, pouting glitterati, Antonio thought. A shadow crossed his features. None of the people he had met at that party knew what it was like to do any real, physical work. He had been able to tell from the pinkly perfect state of their hands. Everything had been handed to them on plates since birth. None of them had really *earned* their living.

Shocked, Antonio found that his hands were clenching into fists as he stared unseeing at the computer screen. Nobody should be in turmoil over such a minor thing, should they? He switched off the machine, but found himself thinking of Rissa again, and the way she had leapt back from his touch. It had worked on him like a bucket of iced water. *If that is the way she wants it, then that is the way it will stay,* he thought bitterly.

Pushing back his chair, he got up to fix himself the first coffee of the day. As he did so, he noticed a rectangle of paper standing out clearly against the dingy industrial carpeting of the site office. It must have been pushed under his door outside of working hours. That was not in itself unusual, as there was no letterbox. Opening the door had pushed the item back, so he had not seen it when entering. Strolling over, Antonio picked up what turned out to be a good-quality envelope, addressed to him. Slitting it open, he saw that it was a list of suggestions for improvement to the *palazzo*, written in neat, well-formed handwriting and signed by the Contessa. She must have delivered it the night before.

What Antonio read in her letter raised his eyebrows as well as his spirits. She wanted to make the estate a commercial paying concern. Antonio was violently opposed to the thought of people traipsing around his property, but he had to admit that her ideas were imaginative. She wanted to involve the local people in decisions made about the future of the house. That showed naïveté—planners and their regulations were the things she had to worry about. The girl might have a fancy title, but it was becoming clear to Antonio that she was not afraid to use either her head or her hands.

Her letter also contained rough plans to develop the many outbuildings as craft workshops, or offices for small businesses. She was even suggesting that one building could be set up as a cyber café. Antonio had doubts about these ideas. Monte Piccolo was not the first call for a holiday destination. The market for dream-catchers, handmade soap or other niche products would be small in summer and probably non-existent in the winter. A computer drop-in centre was only slightly more reasonable, although there was still a problem. People hated going on foot for any distance these days, and the estate building she had earmarked for the project was a good half-mile walk uphill from the village. Visitors would want to come by car, equalling chaos—especially in wet weather. It would also require a lot more additional parking space.

Rissa's third idea made him laugh out loud. She wanted to open an English-style café and plant centre in the grounds of the *palazzo*. Antonio had spent a lot of time in Britain. The food there seemed to be either fried or floury. Sometimes it managed to be both at the same time. He could not see his fellow Italians going for that sort of thing. As for a garden centre—his people were self-reliant and hard-working. If they wanted plants, they took cuttings or sowed seeds. Swapping between neighbours, friends and family was the rule here, rather than the exception. No one would come here to *buy* plants!

The letter's final suggestion wiped the smile from Antonio's face. Rissa had noticed the richness of wildlife in the Piccolo valley, and no one could fail to be impressed by the beauty of the surroundings. The Contessa wanted to turn the grounds of the Palazzo Tiziano into a proper nature reserve. People would be drawn from the towns to experience local wildlife at first hand. There would be observation hides, bird-feeding stations, nest boxes and a whole list of other wildlife-friendly ideas.

This sounded dangerously close to Antonio's own dream of a place close to nature, where he could escape from his hectic life as a billionaire property developer. The estate had already started to work some kind of magic on him in the time that he had been working there. Why shouldn't it do the same for other people? Because this is *my* house, he reminded himself sharply, and I do not intend to have members of the general public wandering about as though they own the place. It is bad enough having to suffer that cuckoo of a Contessa, he thought darkly.

He read the letter again from beginning to end. Despite her grand ideas, there was a hint of uncertainty hiding behind the Contessa's words. She must be desperate for approval. This gave Antonio an illicit thrill of anticipation. Beneath that icy exterior she really must be a nervous little mouse. Why else would she be seeking advice on such major steps from a virtual stranger?

He folded the letter and tapped it thoughtfully against his even white teeth. She might have held out against his temptations so far, but this letter displayed all the signs of a woman in a tight spot. First there had been her idea of selling her clothes. Now she was planning all sorts of schemes. It sounded as though the Contessa needed money, and wanted to use the *palazzo* to help her get it. This was despite the fact that she had no contacts in the village and knew virtually no one. She was reduced to asking him—a man whom her land agent regularly dismissed as nothing more than a workman—for advice. Donna had also warned him that Mazzini was telling the English girl that her site manager was not to be trusted.

Antonio's smile broadened. Any woman who was *this* desperate for support must fall to him eventually. He would be ready to take possession of both her and his birthright when it happened. It might take time, but Antonio had plenty of that. He had the money she clearly lacked, too. The only cloud on his horizon was the growing idea that he might have to let her goad him all the way into marriage. Still, it was a sacrifice he was willing to make. Once he had drawn her in with sex and money, cutting off her supplies of both would soon see the Contessa heading for the divorce courts. When that happened, Antonio would be ready for her. His lawyers were the best in every field, and they would have history on their side. It would be the time when certain cats would be let out of certain bags.

Antonio was looking forward to watching the fall of the house of Alfere, and the idea of a sweet triumph over that beautiful girl gave him still more reason to smile.

His plan could not possibly fail.

# CHAPTER SIX

RISSA had been so fired up by her work on the house's exterior that she'd hardly slept that night. After falling into a doze just before dawn, she'd woken with a start. She had been dreaming about footsteps outside her window. Waiting in the half-light, she listened for long moments. All was silent. The thought of being some practical help around the site made her get up, rather than linger too long in bed. Washing and dressing in lukewarm water from the old and criminally unlagged hot water tank, she went downstairs and got busy in the kitchen.

Within a couple of hours the air was rich with the fragrance of baking. Rissa had produced trays full of English teatime treats. When the kitchen door latch clicked, she called out without looking up.

'Oops! Sorry, Livia. I was going to get all this washing up done before you arrived.'

'It isn't Livia. It's me.'

Rissa jumped at Antonio's low, harmonious voice. She whirled around, instantly on her guard, but he had been distracted. Every horizontal surface around the kitchen was lined with the cakes and savouries she had been making, and he was inspecting them minutely.

'I thought I would try out a few things, Antonio... Although you won't have been to the site office yet this morning, so you won't know what they are for.'

'On the contrary, Contessa, I was probably in there before you awoke. I know exactly what all this is about.'

'Oh, really?' Rissa suspected a trap.

'Yes, and I should warn you that your idea is unlikely to be popular in Italy, where we know how real food tastes. May I try one of these things you have made?'

He raised an eyebrow, indicating a tiny individual meringue sandwiched with *crème pâtisserie*. Rissa nodded, and he put it straight into his mouth.

'This is not English food as I remember it, Contessa,' he said thoughtfully. 'Your sexual frustration has clearly been worked through in several useful ways.'

'My *what*?' Stunned, Rissa flapped her teatowel in agitation.

'You know what I mean.' Finishing his cake, Antonio's fingers hovered between a tray of cheese scones and one of cherry muffins. 'When we were together the other day, you got cold feet at the last minute—for whatever reason. It has left you boiling with energy, which has been looking to find an outlet. That is why the paintwork at the front of the house has been so expertly stripped—because you have not got as far as any other sort of stripping for a while. As for these cakes—well, it is bound to be some kind of frustrated fertility rite, don't you think?'

'I resent that!'

'Why? Because it is true?'

'You have got a mighty high opinion of yourself, Signor Isola. What makes you think I don't have high standards in every job I attempt?'

'Because I know women.'

'Not this one, you don't.'

'You are going to hand out all this largesse to my work-force, to make them love you even more than they do now.' Antonio had initially chosen a cherry muffin, but as he finished the last morsel he frowned and decided to give in to temptation. Leaning over the cooling trays again, he lifted up a cheese scone.

'I don't need anyone to love me, thank you very much,' Rissa said. But Antonio noticed her expression. He was alert immediately.

'You may not need any mental stimulation, Contessa, but physically you certainly desire it. You wanted me the other day. Confess it.'

'I have no intention of confessing anything, to you or anyone else, Antonio. Now, if you would excuse me, I must get this room cleared up before Livia arrives.'

Draping the teatowel over her shoulder, she turned to put the kettle on to boil for more hot water. She did not hear him go, but some strange instinct told her when he had left the room.

'I don't care what anyone says, *signora*. You are doing a good job here.' Livia said later as she sampled the cakes Rissa had made.

'Are you hinting that somebody is unhappy with my plans?'

Livia gave an uncomfortable smile. 'This place means a great deal to Signor Isola.'

'Yes, but he is only the site manager here. It is going to be *my* home,' Rissa said firmly.

'Only because your husband's family came by the *palazzo* illegally—' The housekeeper stopped as a shadow fell across the kitchen threshold. It was Antonio, returning from the building site.

'I came back to see if you would be available for work today, Contessa.'

His silky words were directed at Rissa, but his eyes were black arrows pinning Livia to her seat.

Rissa took her time in finishing one of the cherry muffins. Licking her fingers with dainty relish, she made him wait for her reply.

'Actually, I wanted to continue cleaning the main reception room—for part of today, at least.' She planned to wipe down the picture frames and dust the canvases of all those supercilious ancestors. That would give Antonio a start. If he thinks his distant forebears had some quarrel with the Alfere-Tiziano family, let him tell them direct to their regal faces, she thought.

'Very well, Contessa.' He started to stroll away, calling back over his shoulder, 'But if you should be at a loose end, come and find me. There are plenty of useful things that you can do.'

Rissa had a few last-minute worries about trying out her cooking on the workmen, but it had to be done. They were exactly the type of people she wanted to attract to the estate. There were plenty of them about, replacing the roof and working on the wiring, so she had a captive audience.

Antonio had strict rules about his men going off-site during working hours. Rissa guessed that his teams of workers might appreciate a break at mid-morning. Their arrogant site manager was so scrupulous about workers' rights that he could hardly complain. The sun was relentless, and the sky was as hard and blue as Lapis Lazuli. It was only proper to offer them all some cake and homemade lemonade in those conditions.

She dressed carefully. Men were men the world over, but Italian men came with a special reputation. Antonio had proved that to her already. She pulled on a soft, stretchy top in pale pink, with long sleeves and a discreet scooped neckline. To play up the demure image, she added a floaty silk skirt and a pair of impractically strappy sandals. These are exactly the type Donna would choose, she thought darkly, then rebuked herself for being catty.

Each working day, Antonio had coffee in his site office at eleven o'clock precisely. It was the time when he attended to paperwork and made urgent phone calls. Rissa knew he would be out of circulation then for an hour or so, and it would give her time to do some market research.

Armed with a tray of delicacies, she set off around the building site. The workmen always looked at her when she passed, but until now it had only been covert glances. Now she was approaching them directly, with something to offer, their expressions were more openly admiring.

'Here you are, gentlemen. This is a little break for you. I'm sure Signor Isola wouldn't deny you a taste of some good old-fashioned English food.'

'Lemonade?' one of them questioned. 'Do they know what real fruit is like in England?' The whole gang laughed at that.

'You would be surprised, *signor*. I have been able to pick some herbs from the *palazzo* gardens for the cheese pastries, and there are fresh wild strawberries in the tarts,' Rissa told them with a smile.

She set down the tray and withdrew a short distance. It was not because she wanted to keep apart from them for social reasons, but because their appreciative expressions were not all directed towards the food. The way they looked at her made her feel uncomfortable.

The men were quick to clear their plates. They had been brought up to love good food that had been freshly prepared, whether it was simple peasant fare or choice local dishes. Soon they were expressing their approval to each other over empty plates and glasses.

Rissa felt a surge of pride. It was another boost to her self-esteem, which had been pretty well squashed from the time she had married Luigi. In his world, women were supposed to do nothing but look beautiful and provide sons. He would have laughed out loud if Rissa had suggested she might be able to make her own living. *But this is what I was born to do*, Rissa thought with sudden realisation. She was relishing the satisfied comments of her customers, and smiled when one of them stacked up the tray with empty crockery and brought it over to where she was standing.

'That was delightful,' he said carefully, in his best English. 'May I carry this back into the house for you, Contessa?'

'Thank you, but I can manage,' Rissa replied with equal politeness. She recognised the look in his eyes and knew it would be safer to distance herself from him, and the faster the better.

'*Si*—yes—but couldn't you find some other use for me…inside, eh?'

He left no doubt about what he meant. Rissa felt sick. Were all men like this, seeing her only in terms of sex? Or was it somehow her fault? Did she give off all the wrong signals?

That was what Luigi had told her. The words he had used on their honeymoon stabbed through her yet again. Over the years she had tried to please him, but nothing had worked. Her love for him had never faltered, but for some reason everything had always been reduced to blame and guilt.

A new nightmare suddenly replaced her old one. The workman was moving in closer to her. She could feel his breath against her skin. Whirling away from him, she stopped dead. Antonio was standing in the open door of the site office.

That is typical of an Englishwoman abroad, he thought fiercely. But the feeling that boiled through his veins was resentment rather than disdain. The sensation annoyed him. Why had she got under his skin in such a way? He strode out into the courtyard, ordering the men back to work.

His instinct was to send Carlo straight down the road without a reference, but that would solve nothing. Not when Rissa herself had behaved in such a manner.

'Get back to work with the others,' he growled at Carlo. The workman shrank beneath Antonio's glare and dissolved into the background. 'Contessa—what does it say about your judgement when you allow things like that to happen?'

Now that Antonio had saved her from the wolf, Rissa managed to rally. Instead of muttering an apology, she faced up to him. 'The men were helping me test the recipes I intend to sell at the café here.'

The girl really did have spirit; there was no doubt about that. *She'll need it*, Antonio thought. And determination too, if she is going to work as hard as I had to.

'How can you be so careless—appearing in public wearing such clothes?'

'What?' Rissa looked at him, mystified. Antonio clicked his tongue.

'That thin skirt is quite transparent in the sunlight. Your legs were the first things I noticed when I appeared at the door of the site office. I dare say that was what stirred up Carlo and the others.'

His words worked better than he had anticipated. With a horrified gasp, Rissa blushed the colour of a Tuscany rose.

'I must go and change!'

'I'll take the tray.' Antonio grasped it as Rissa dashed back into the house. He followed, but not before surveying the work of his staff. He did not want his workmen to think that the sight of Carlo trying to get lucky had aroused anything more than an employer's rage at working time wasted. Antonio chose not to think too hard about what feelings the little scene had really sparked in him.

When he got inside the house, the kitchen was deserted. He could hear Livia, busy upstairs with the new vacuum, so he dumped the refreshment tray on the table and went in search of Rissa.

The door to her suite was closed, and all was silent. Being so close to a pretty girl's bedroom usually triggered an instinct in Antonio to dive in and possess. But after what had happened the last time he had been tempted by her, he was not so sure that those feelings could be trusted. After wrestling with his conscience, he raised his fist and banged on her door.

In one movement Rissa threw it open and bounced out.

'Antonio! What are you doing here?'

Her hands were behind her, and he heard the unmistakable click of a key turning in the lock. That was a pretty clear message. Lifting both hands in a soothing gesture, he took a step back.

'This is not what you might imagine, Contessa. I came to bring you a warning. A friendly note of caution.'

Rissa looked up into his steady dark eyes. There was no trace of fire in them now. Instead they were limpid with concern—*although it makes him even more desirable,* Rissa thought with a pang. *He really is very good-looking…*

'I am concerned only for your welfare, Contessa.'

*And charming with it.* Rissa felt herself wavering. No man had been so caring towards her for years. It made her appreciate her vulnerability. She wondered, not for the first time, what it would be like to have Antonio's protection surrounding her.

'A woman in your position must take great care of her reputation, Contessa. It reflects upon the dignity of this ancient house.' His gaze travelled appreciatively down the length of her body. 'Thank goodness you have seen sense and changed your skirt. That wisp of silk made you look like a tart,' he finished firmly.

'How dare you?' Rissa gasped, snapping out of her reverie at once. Before she could get into her stride, she was interrupted.

'Cooee—Antonio?' a thin voice trilled. 'The men said you were in here, so I came on up—'

It was Donna. Her tinkling tones advanced up the stairs in the most annoying way.

'This place needs a really good clean,' she said disdainfully. Her nose wrinkled as she inspected her fingertips, which she had just trailed up the banister rail.

'I am so sorry, Donna, but this is a private house. It isn't geared up for visitors.' Rissa smiled sweetly, before turning on her heel and walking off with purpose. She was not about to retreat into her own suite, so she headed for the sound of Livia's vacuuming. Opening the appropriate door, she left Donna and Antonio to their own devices.

Livia switched off the suction as soon as she saw Rissa.

'Ah—you have been speaking with Signor Antonio again.'

'How could you possibly know that, Livia?'

'Oh, because you have roses in your cheeks, *signora*.' The old lady chuckled.

'If I do, it is only because he makes me so angry.'

'He is not so bad. All Antonio needs is a wife to mellow him. A good local girl, to keep him in the valley and feed him up.'

'I don't think a plaster saint could mellow that man.' Rissa sighed. She went over to the dusty window—only to be rewarded by the sight of Antonio squiring Donna to a smart blue cabriolet. One of his hands was patting the small of her back in a gesture that should have been merely polite. Rissa read far more into it.

Good riddance to our unwanted guest, Rissa thought firmly, but something Livia had said triggered an unusual resentment within her. Donna was a local girl. And Antonio had shown himself to be a traditional Italian man. She might not be able to deny his powerful sexual attraction, but his attitude towards her was acting as a great contraceptive.

*It isn't as though I have to care what he thinks of me,* she thought fiercely. *He doesn't have any finer feelings to offend, and I'm never likely to get entangled with him emotionally.* That image made her pause for a minute, and she had to concentrate hard on the pain he had given her by touching Donna in full view, out there on the terrace. Why did she get such a pang when she saw them together? Was it envy, that they were obviously an item when she was so isolated? Or did the green-eyed monster have something to do with it, too? Rissa was not sure that she wanted to know the answer.

She spent the rest of the day throwing herself into the task of cleaning all the old family portraits. Antonio might be scornful, but she found a strange reassurance from knowing that she was now part of a long line of survivors—even if they were only her relatives by marriage.

It was mid-afternoon before she stood back in the centre of the salon to admire her handiwork. The paintings would need professional restoration as soon as she could afford it, but for the moment a soft duster had worked wonders. One picture of an imposing man on horseback had come up particularly well. She flicked a last speck of dust from his nameplate. Then her heart leapt as she heard a familiar masterful tread on the cobblestones outside. She did not have to look out of the window to know that Antonio was coming into the house.

Rissa had not trusted herself to watch Donna drive away earlier. If Antonio had accepted a lift from the woman then, why was he striding back in here now?

She resented the fact that Antonio spoke so directly to her femininity. Her heart was fluttering and her mouth was dry even before he came into the room. And all this after he had been so critical of her dress sense! When she'd been living in Manhattan, Rissa had heard other wives at the gym say that sex with their staff was the best sort—it was without strings. Then again, they hadn't been involved with Antonio. Those women always held the whip hand with their lovers—sometimes literally. If the guy caused trouble, or began getting above himself, he got the sack. Rissa knew she could never play that card with Antonio. She was relying on him too much.

For most of the time she could almost convince herself that she needed him as her site manager more than she needed his body. When he strode into her salon now, she was not so sure.

'Contessa—you need to come with me and OK the detailed plans for the outbuildings,' he announced sharply.

'I'm surprised you haven't done that yourself,' she said as he held the door open for her to pass through.

'I designed the layout, so you should have at least some say in the final decision.'

'After the way you criticised me this morning, Antonio, I thought you would set more store by your mysterious friend Donna's opinion.' Rissa's cheeks stung again at the memory of their confrontation.

'There is no mystery about Donna—none at all,' he said as they left the main house.

As they rounded a corner Rissa stopped dead. A gleaming red Ferrari Scaglietti crouched outside the site office, as though on guard.

'Good grief! You aren't employing men who can afford something like that, are you?'

'It certainly isn't coming out of your budget, Contessa. She's mine.' Antonio walked forward and ran a hand over the car's bonnet. It was as sleek and shiny as a cherry. Inspecting the scarlet surface, he pulled down the cuff of his shirt and repeated the caress, to remove any traces his naked palm might have left behind.

'You work in construction, yet you drive a car like that?'

'Doing things like *this* allows me to afford trinkets like *that*. You could call it a perk of my profession,' he said, without once taking his eyes off the Ferrari.

Rissa circled this touching love scene to reach the door of his office. 'I'll just check the plans while you two are busy out here, shall I?'

'I shall be there in a second. Then, when we have finished

in the office, I must go into Florence. Would you like a lift? You said a while ago that you were desperate for designer dress shops.'

'That is only because I have a lot of things to sell.' She stared at the gleaming red sportscar. 'There won't be room to pack a single dress box in that thing, let alone transport your building supplies.'

Antonio clicked his tongue. *'That thing!'* he muttered under his breath, then tore himself away from his car to unlock the office for her. 'There is a waiting list for passenger space in my car, Contessa. Though exceptions can always be made…'

'I must sell my dresses to get enough money to pay for all this.' She nodded towards the plans as Antonio indicated where she should sign.

'Then you are serious about getting rid of your things? It is not a joke?' he probed as they left the office again.

'I have never been more serious about anything in my life—except this house. And the two things are one, really. The Palazzo Tiziano needs money, and I don't think I'll ever have enough. What I *do* have are a few beautiful assets.'

Hands on hips, Antonio stood for long minutes savouring some of those assets as she studied his car.

'OK,' he said at length, 'Pack up everything you want to take into town and I shall find transport for it. But first I must put away my car.'

'You can leave it there, if you like.'

Antonio looked at her as though she had suggested exposing a baby.

'You must be joking! She is going straight back under cover.'

'Where do you keep it?'

'In the building that houses the old olive press.'

'I didn't know I had—' Rissa began, and then the penny dropped. 'Ah—the only stone building around here with a lock that actually works! I've never been able to get inside that place.'

'That is because I have the only key.' Antonio patted the pocket of his jeans.

'So—I am supposed to live in a house whose doors can be unfastened with twigs, while your car is locked away safe and secure?'

He looked at her narrowly. 'The Palazzo Tiziano has seen many people come and go, but it has never entertained a Ferrari.' He eased his driver's door open in a heat-haze of testosterone.

Rissa carried on towards the house, pointedly ignoring him as he coaxed the Scaglietti into a graceful arc and drove off in a gentle hiss of gravel.

He arrived back at the main door of the *palazzo* a short time later, this time driving an ordinary white van. Rissa raised her eyebrows as she handed him the first dress box.

'*You'll* be driving a workman's vehicle?'

'Why not? I am a workman.'

Rissa added more shallow boxes to the growing pile in his arms. He stowed them all securely in the back of the van, then returned to open the passenger door for her.

'Wouldn't you rather I drove this thing, Antonio?'

'This is not a time for English driving—or for English speaking, either. We shall speak in Italian all the way to Florence, Contessa. Only when I am convinced you can bargain fluently will I let you do business there alone.'

Obediently Rissa climbed up into the cab, accidentally giving Antonio a good view of her legs. In celebration he crashed through the gearbox as the van buffeted and veered along the *palazzo*'s potholed drive.

Rissa did not have time to question his high-handed attitude. He began firing questions at her in Italian, making her do sums and calculations while he dodged the traffic and sped along the A1. Rissa was glad to reach the edge of the city's pedestrian zone, where Antonio stopped, reversed, and slotted into a tiny parking space in one movement and at a speed that made her queasy.

'What is the matter, Contessa? You have gone pale all of a sudden. If you are worried about haggling in the shops, don't worry. I shall be doing the business for you.'

'Didn't I do well enough on the way here? Livia says my Italian is getting better all the time.'

'You were…' Antonio searched for a word '…adequate, Contessa. But you are not a poker player, that I can tell. I shall do all the talking, and I will make far more money than you ever could. It will be like lifting cherries out of pannetone, believe me.'

'Are you sure?'

He clapped a hand to the van's steering wheel and leaned over to her confidentially.

'Do you think I paid full price for my beautiful car? No.' He grinned and got out of the driver's seat. 'That is why you will let me do all the talking, Contessa.'

Two hours later, Antonio seized Rissa by the elbow and steered her rapidly out of their last appointment.

'Fifty thousand euros!' She gasped as they reached the pavement.

Antonio immediately put a finger to her lips. 'Not in front of the street people, Contessa.'

'That's about…' She calculated frantically, but wasn't up to the task. 'Well, enough to keep the *palazzo* going for a while and pay some back to my aunt and uncle too.'

'You are in debt elsewhere?'

'I owe them, yes.'

'How much?'

'I don't want to talk about it. That's a debt of honour. Surely as an Italian you can understand that?'

Antonio regarded her minutely. Honour was not something he had expected to find in a girl who had married into the Alfere family. He liked to think he was a good judge of character, but it was slowly dawning on him that he might have been too quick in judging her. The suspicion that he might be wrong about something began to grow. Antonio never apologised, because as a rule he never made mistakes. This was unknown territory to him. Clearing his throat, he started off down the street in the direction of the Duomo.

'Let me buy you a drink in celebration, Contessa.'

'Oh, no, I can't let you do that. Not after you've earned me so much money.'

'You haven't got it all in your hands yet,' he warned.

'In which case, let's pick up some bits and pieces and have a picnic on the way home.'

He did not seem impressed, but they walked on for a few more metres before he put his feelings into words.

'Do you know what I could really eat right now? A big, thick bacon sandwich, smothered in tomato ketchup. That is *real* food after a hard day's work.'

Rissa sighed. 'I know how you feel. It's the sort of rubbishy comfort eating that really hits the spot once in a while. What a shame Florence is too sophisticated for that kind of thing.

I can't remember the last time I had one of those,' she finished, with real longing.

'I can,' Antonio said darkly. 'My good friend Ricardo works at the Excelsior. He always keeps a ready supply of ex-pat treats. Some of the English and American visitors there don't like what they call "foreign food".'

'That's tourists for you.' Rissa sighed, feeling very much a tourist herself as Antonio turned away to make a phone call.

Twenty minutes later they were ushered into a suite of rooms that looked like heaven and were perfumed with vases of fresh flowers.

'We can't do this!' Rissa hissed, when Antonio had closed the door behind his heavily tipped friend Ricardo.

'Why not? I happen to know the guy who is staying here very well. He won't mind, and it beats a picnic.'

He lifted a silver lid. It revealed a pile of sliced white bread, overflowing with grilled bacon. Red ketchup had been set out in two white china ramekin dishes complete with silver spoons. There was only one thing missing.

'Oh, no—they haven't brought you any coffee, Antonio.'

'I was in the mood for the full English experience.' He picked up the teapot and filled the two cups that had been provided.

'This is bizarre!' Rissa said as they enjoyed their meal. 'Do you have any other friends in high places, Antonio?'

'I have one or two. Anything Signor Mazzini can do, Contessa, I can do better. You can be sure of that.'

It was such a frank statement that Rissa had to comment. 'You really don't like that man, do you?'

'He does not have the interests of the Palazzo Tiziano at heart, Contessa.'

'And I suppose you do?'

'You should not have to ask that question.'

'No,' she replied, lost in thought. 'Sometimes I think you are more interested in the house and estate than you are in me—I mean, in my wishes,' she corrected herself hurriedly. But Antonio was not about to let the moment pass.

'The Palazzo Tiziano and its estate is part of my family's heritage. As for you…you are an extremely beautiful woman, Contessa. When the dress shop staff were inspecting your dresses, I could not help but wonder what you looked like in each one. Which was your favourite?'

'The full-length black velvet,' she said, without hesitation.

'The strapless one?'

Rissa nodded, as a pearly droplet of butter escaped from her final sandwich and ran down the side of her hand. She put down her bread and started to reach for a paper napkin, but Antonio stopped her. Catching her wrist, he raised it to his lips. Before she knew it, Antonio was tracing the course of the butter with the tip of his tongue.

She immediately snatched her hand away. 'No, don't do that. I don't like it.'

'Yes, you do. You are an extremely sensual woman, Contessa. I could feel it the other day. Making love on the Tiziano grass in the open air may not be your thing—although in my opinion you don't know what you're missing—but there can be no excuses today, Larissa. With the exception of my friend Ricardo, no one in the world knows that we are here.' Taking her hand again, he kissed each finger. All the time he was watching her, watching her with those bitter chocolate eyes.

'I can't,' she pleaded, hoping he could not guess how true that was.

Antonio smiled. 'Of course you can. And you will. It is my wish, Larissa, and your desire.' His voice was a hiss that trickled all the way down her spine.

'No—no, really. It isn't my desire. I don't have any feelings like that. For you,' she added quickly. 'I mean, my husband was the only man that ever—er, well, you know…'

He stopped, suspicious of her motives. 'I know…what?'

'Luigi was my first…' She hesitated, not knowing what to say. *Lover* was not the right word. His frustration and her inexperience had put paid to all that. She had always loved him, right up to the end, but it had never been enough. 'He was my first…partner,' she said eventually.

'But surely you are not saying he was your last? I may have misjudged you in some things, Larissa. And for that I should apologise. However, there is no mistaking the need we have for one another. We want each other. Do not deny it.'

He was speaking about the deep desires that were shaking her body as though they were just another biological process. Rissa could hardly believe she could be so attracted to a man who attached no more importance to her love than Luigi had done. Her husband had seen producing an heir with her as his contribution to continuing the Alfere family line. To Antonio, sex was clearly nothing more than an item ripe for crossing off his 'to do' list. Were all men obsessed only with the end result?

'You are forgetting one important thing, Antonio.' She tried to inject some strength into her voice. 'I don't want you.'

'Look me in the eyes and say that.'

Rissa opened her mouth to deny him again, but there was no time. He leant forward and stole a savage, all-consuming kiss. At that moment all her self-control collapsed. In twenty hot, pounding seconds Rissa became his. She tried to struggle, but when he pulled away his eyes were dark with a fierce desire. She knew it mirrored her own. With a faint primal cry she surrendered, digging her fingers into the sliding muscles of his shoulders as he bent to possess her mouth again. His hands slid down to knead her in the same way he had massaged her naked flesh when she had been lying on the grass. Now she could feel the reaction it caused in him. He was grinding her against a firm ridge that was pushing masterfully against the front of his jeans.

Antonio was exultant. Her instant reaction was perfect proof. She wanted him. In the same way she had needed him to take her on the grass, filling her until the heat of their passion reached meltdown and this desire exploded, blotting out all thoughts of the past.

Reaching for him, she found his erection, straining to be freed from the petty restriction of clothing. In an agony of desire Rissa threw back her head, gasping wordless sounds that told him all he wanted to know. His lips found her throat, his fingers pulled at her shirt. As it fell away he circled her nipple with his thumb, teasing it into a point. Then his mouth followed, moving over her bra. Finally releasing her breast from its confection of silk and lace, he began suckling hungrily like a—

Rissa jerked backwards out of his grasp.

'No. I can't!'

'That isn't what it felt like to me.' Antonio fought to catch his breath. This was not supposed to happen. After that business with the sunbathing, when she had as good as proved herself already spoken for, he had intended to keep things light. The trouble was, the nearness of her always had such an effect on him. One touch was all it took to blow away his best intentions and sacrifice his self-control.

'This is not a good idea, Antonio,' she said shakily.

'Of course it is,' he snapped. 'We want each other, and this is the perfect opportunity.'

'That is why it is wrong. I should never have agreed to be alone here with you.'

Frustrated and confused, Antonio had no option but to release her. They had been so hot for each other. What had happened to change it?

The question tormented him all through their painfully silent drive home. Only one thing was certain in his mind. Antonio had never been defeated by a challenge before, and this damned well wasn't going to be a first. He was going to have the Contessa Larissa Alfere, however long it took.

He could wait.

# CHAPTER SEVEN

RISSA tried to avoid Antonio altogether after that, but it was impossible. Next day he approached her in the garden, on the pretext of bringing a drink from Livia.

'You said that you owe your parents money, Contessa?'

Rissa put down her tools and brushed off her hands. She had been helping to rake out the stones of the *palazzo*'s structure, ready for the workmen to start repointing. It was a dirty, boring job, but it needed to be done. Rissa reasoned that if it was something she could manage, it freed up a member of Antonio's skilled team to do more valuable work.

She bit her lip, gazing out across the countryside. Her excitement at selling those dresses should not have goaded her into letting that little detail slip.

'I went too far, Antonio. I said something I now regret.'

'It aroused my suspicions. I have seen too much of life to believe the best in people. You must either be very duty bound or very guilty to still be supporting your parents at your age. Which is it?'

'It isn't either of those things. I simply owe them a great deal.' She bent over to dust down the knees of her jeans. It should have told him she was unwilling to continue the conversation, but as she straightened Antonio handed her a glass of lemonade. That killed any hope of escaping into the house. He had stopped her from using the need to fetch a drink as an excuse.

'You have borrowed a lot of money from your parents?' That idea had caught his attention.

'N-no. That's wrong on both counts. They are not my parents; I'm adopted. They have been so generous over the years, because I was everything to them. Now it is time to pay them back.' She took a long drink to hide her discomfort.

'Ah. Then it *is* guilt that drives you?'

'No, not at all!' She reddened and looked away.

Antonio felt as though he had been cheated. Why wouldn't she open up to him? Women were usually only too anxious to talk, trying to ensnare him in their plans. Why was this one so different? More importantly, why did he find himself so bothered about her evasiveness? Because I am concerned at having such a secretive person living in my ancestral home, he told himself. It is nothing more than that. His mind kept on working at the problem as she sipped her drink and tried to ignore him. Antonio did not know which annoyed him more.

'Ah…I know what it is, Contessa,' he said at last. 'You went all out to make an advantageous marriage to a spectacularly wealthy man so that you could siphon off his money in their direction to assuage your guilt—'

'Certainly not!' she flared with annoyance.

Antonio was a seasoned interviewer. He knew that silence was often a more successful tool than interrogation. Sure enough, as he waited, Rissa could not stand his continued scrutiny.

'Luigi had more to worry about than my parents. I tried my best never to trouble him with their concerns,' she recalled sadly.

Antonio congratulated himself. He had succeeded in

business because he was a shrewd judge of character. He knew when somebody was putting up a barrier, and he was as skilled at demolishing defences as he was in building houses. Larissa Alfere might give the impression of a marsh-mallow, but she had constructed a solid centre to protect something deep within her. He was determined to chip away at it to reach the kernel of her truth.

'You were ashamed of the poverty of your upbringing and tried to keep the two halves of your life hidden from one another?'

'How dare you?'

Antonio raised his hands. 'It is something to which I can relate—believe me, Contessa. I did not mean to offend you.'

She had bridled at his explanation, and he expected her to either storm off or change the subject. She did neither.

'Since you seem determined to find out the truth, Antonio, my husband was a proud man who despised need or weakness in others. He expected everyone to be a winner. That is why it hit him so hard when there were parts of his life that were…not so successful. He had enough to worry about, without me pestering him. I had to develop my own methods for helping Aunt Jane and Uncle George.'

'You poor little thing!' Antonio mocked, but stopped when she levelled a fiery glare at him.

'You cannot imagine how hard it is to know that the people you love are suffering.'

'I do know,' he murmured, but Rissa was still burning with the memory of it all.

'I was so desperate to help them I had to become devious. I persuaded Luigi that some of my expenses had to be paid in cash. You know how popular the black economy is. People like hairdressers, florists and personal trainers often prefer to be paid off the books, rather than by cheque or direct debit. It is a regular thing in the City.'

'And among builders,' he said tersely, recalling their earlier conversation.

'I always did things properly. But because I'd heard other women talking about what they got up to, I knew how money could be found to help my aunt and uncle. By saving up small amounts of cash at a time there would be no paper trail, and Luigi would not trace what I was doing with his—I mean, my money.'

Antonio gave a silent whistle. 'How long did you manage to keep it up?'

'My husband never found out.' Rissa shook her head slowly, remembering how terrible it had made her feel. 'He enjoyed the idea of working the black economy by giving me cash. Nothing infuriated him more than paying tax, so he loved to think that the Revenue was losing out.'

'Didn't he notice that you were cutting corners?'

Rissa gave a brittle laugh. 'No one needs their hair done every day, or their flower arrangements replaced according to each change of outfit. As for the Filipino body-shaper—one whole floor of our Manhattan apartment block was given over to gym equipment and pools. I was quite capable of exercising on my own. Walking around town and using the subway saved money, and kept me fit, too.'

Antonio's brow creased in a frown. 'I have never known a woman who would willingly give up any of the advantages she could extract from a man.'

'You've obviously been hanging around with the wrong sort of girl,' Rissa said casually, thinking of Donna. 'I managed well enough—although if I had known the sort of debts Luigi was going to leave I would have squirrelled away a lot more money to cover them.'

'Are all Manhattan wives engaged in this type of racket?'

'I have no idea. I didn't exactly fit into their set, so they were never keen on sharing anything more than idle pleasantries with me. Everything I learned came from accidentally overhearing their chatter. Some of them have extremely loud voices.'

Antonio was miles away, thinking of her free-flowing auburn hair rippling in the breeze as she jogged through Central Park.

'They snubbed you?'

She lowered her lashes and avoided looking at him. 'It didn't matter. I have always been a bit of a loner.'

Antonio felt a surge of distaste at the thought of what she must have endured. He had seen the lifted and Botoxed features of rich women harden still further when one of their circle did anything out of the ordinary. Their jealousy must have been poisonous when they'd been faced with this natural little beauty, he thought with a pang of protectiveness. How could anyone treat her like that?

'Is that why you were happy to come to the Palazzo Tiziano?'

Rissa took another long, slow drink of lemonade. Then she handed him the glass, with her thanks. Realising that he was not going to learn any more, Antonio watched her turn back to the unforgiving stones and set to work again.

Rissa tried to hide her pain by bending over the task in hand. Antonio had stirred so many agonising memories within her. Her first meeting with Luigi had swept her away on a tide of adoration. Money had been the last thing on her mind then. Obviously the fact that Luigi dressed so well had struck her from the moment their eyes had met across the diner, but it had never been an issue between them. A far darker spectre had come to haunt their relationship.

Things had come to a head when he had travelled with her to inner-city London and visited her adoptive parents at home. Luigi had been polite, but distant for the whole afternoon. Rissa had accepted that, as the Silverdale family's circumstances were so different from his own. But the explosion had come as they'd been talked through the fourth album of Rissa's baby pictures. Luigi had stormed out of the house. Rissa had followed him, frantic, and from that moment their relationship had changed. There had been no need to pretend any more.

The one thing that the whole of their world had been waiting for, from the old Contessa to all the occupants of the Keir Hardy Buildings, was not going to happen. It was a release for Rissa, but not her husband. His pride and the weight of family expectation had crushed the life from him. The man Rissa had loved had begun to disappear behind a haze of cigarette smoke and alcohol fumes. She'd persuaded him to seek help, hoping the setback would be temporary, but Luigi had been too immersed in his own unhappiness.

Despite their troubles, Rissa had never stopped loving him. The suspicion that it was her fault had always shadowed the back of her mind. Perhaps she had not been attractive enough, or eager enough. Sex had never been spoken about at home while she was growing up. She had been an innocent when she'd married Luigi, and had learned little from him. All Rissa knew about sex had been picked up from gossip around the gym, so she had had no answers to their problems. She had convinced herself she must be frigid, but the way her body and mind reacted to Antonio was now making her wonder. She wanted him, but she was scared. If at the last moment something went wrong, he would discover what Luigi must have known all along—that she could not please a man. Despite the turbulence of her need, Rissa could not bear to lay herself open to such heartache again.

She was so wrapped up in herself that she scratched her probe blindly between the stones, lost in thought. She had known nothing but love and care from her adoptive parents. To deny them the grandchild they craved had been an added cruelty. They would have doted on a baby. Rissa wondered wistfully if she would ever be lucky enough to give them what they wanted. This was a hard, cruel world in which to bring up a child.

They said that when poverty came through the door love went out of the window, but money brought its problems, too. Rissa was being careful with the windfall her dress sale had brought, and was keeping an even closer eye than usual on the *palazzo* project's cash flow. This had led her to become suspicious of Mazzini, her land agent. One of Antonio's suppliers had written to her directly, asking why a payment of ten thousand euros had been blocked by order of Enrico Mazzini. Rissa had tried ringing her agent's office, but had been told he would not be in until that afternoon. Uneasily, Rissa had made arrangements to pay the supplier direct. Antonio had confirmed to her that the order had been delivered, on time and in full, so there had been no alternative.

Her spirits were sinking with doubt. Mazzini was always so dismissive of Antonio and his advice. Yet the workmen and supplies that Mazzini recommended were far more expensive than those used by Antonio. She had discovered in a round-about way that Mazzini's friends and relatives controlled several of the dearer suppliers. Rissa might not know much about the building trade, but cronyism did not seem a good reason for her to be spending more money.

Antonio could tell she was troubled. He'd touched a raw nerve. The way she had suddenly shut down suggested it. The Alfere marriage might not have been as perfect as the glossy magazines always said, he thought wryly.

He felt moved to reach out to her, to salve whatever wounds that toad Alfere might have inflicted. Then he brought himself up short. That was in the past—a distant time unknown to him. She was a grown woman now, and one that he fully intended to have.

'I can't concentrate on this with you standing over me like a thundercloud, Antonio. I'm going inside to try and contact Signor Mazzini again.'

'Larissa!'

His tone made her drop her hand-fork in shock. She blinked up at him.

'I know that events in the hotel inflamed you as much as they affected me.'

Colour began to creep up from her breasts to her face.

'That is not something I wish to rekindle, Antonio. I should never have agreed to go into that suite alone with you. It was...an oversight.' She could not look at him directly. He could feel the tension preparing her body for flight, and eased his tone.

'Don't forget that for a few precious moments, Contessa, we enjoyed ourselves. There was clearly something happening between us. As a red-blooded male, it is not a feeling I am willing to deny. Where would be the harm in it?' His voice was low and caressing now. 'We are both free agents. As sensible adults there can be no recriminations when neither of us have any strings or commitments.'

*No commitments.* The words fizzed through Rissa's already overheated mind. She knew he had a point. What would it matter? A pulse began to drum in her ears. It was true that she had vowed never to become emotionally entangled with a man again. And Luigi and Antonio were so similar in some ways, with their direct masculinity. She was wary of giving her heart, only to see it trampled again. On the other hand, if there was no danger of important feelings being involved...

Other women did it. She had heard them in the hairdressers or the gym, discussing their latest sexual adventures. Satisfying their baser instincts never seemed to worry them. On the contrary, casual sex without any messy, emotional baggage was often the only thing that kept those sad, meaningless women functioning.

'Love is one complication that I don't need in my life at the moment,' she announced briskly. There could be no honey without the comeback of a thousand bee stings—she had learned that from her life with Luigi.

Antonio shrugged. 'Who needs love? I am talking about sex, Contessa—not so pure, but simple. You want me, Larissa. Admit it.'

Rissa had to make two attempts before the word emerged. 'Perhaps.'

He chuckled. It was a deep, provocative sound.

'I knew you would agree eventually.'

'I suppose a man like you can spot all the signs?'

'Experience counts for a great deal,' he allowed. 'Although I pick and choose my conquests with care. Are you as choosy, Contessa?'

The question stung her, and she jumped as though it was a physical shock.

'I—I think I should still be in official mourning for the Count. That is not the sort of question you should be asking me.'

'But it *will* be OK for me to take you to bed?' Antonio supplied evenly.

Rissa twisted her hands together. There was so much that was alien and scary about all this, but Antonio had been such a help and support to her. He had worked out what needed to be done around the *palazzo*, hired the workforce, and was pushing ahead with the restoration at speed. The class divide meant nothing to her—after all, she was probably from lower stock than he was—but the gossip columns would go into overdrive if they got hold of a 'Contessa and her site manager' story.

'A woman in my position has to be extremely careful, Antonio.'

'You are thinking of "Kiss and Sell"?' His eyes were checking out all those places he burned to touch, but his mind was clear. They might kiss, but the only one selling anything would be her. And it would be the Palazzo Tiziano that would be changing hands, not money.

'It's no good wasting time talking like this, Antonio. I—I really must go and arrange a meeting with Signor Mazzini.'

His eyes ignited at the mention of the other man's name, and the expression in them almost melted the last of Rissa's reservations.

'Why? I have everything under perfect control here.'

'Yes, but I need to make sure things keep on running as smoothly as they have been doing so far.'

'This would not be an excuse to escape from me, would it?'

'What on earth do you mean?'

'It isn't an attempt to preserve your dignity? Are you afraid I might be about to take you here and now?'

Rissa knew it was time to put her foot down.

'No. It is merely the fact that daytime is for working, while the night—' She faltered.

'Oh, you are surely not going to allow yourself to be tied down to that boring old tradition, are you, Contessa? If you want me, it cannot be constrained by some socially acceptable timetable.'

'What are you suggesting, Antonio? You won't take any wages—' She gave him a wary look and he picked up on it.

'That is true. And I have no need to become your male prostitute. Unless the thought appeals to you, of course,' he finished smoothly.

Despite his casual reply, Rissa realised he had been stung by any suggestion that he would want to be paid for the privilege. Clearly he enjoyed coming on like a wolf, and wanted to be in control.

'It doesn't,' she said quickly.

'You don't need to be so defensive, my lady. Plenty of women enjoy the chance to do a little dominating.'

His voice was arousing her, caressing each word before he let it fall into her breathless silence. She longed to submit to his seductive technique, to the powerful play of those muscles beneath the smooth warmth of his skin, the fragrance of his masculinity and the power of his personality...

Rissa felt a tremor ripple through the very core of her femininity and gasped aloud. She was lost.

'This time it would be for you, Contessa. You can—' Antonio stopped, sensing that someone was approaching. One of the roofing contractors was heading in their direction for a consultation.

Antonio stepped away from her to sort the matter out,

giving Rissa time to catch her breath. Her whole body was on fire. His words alone could make her respond like this, and she shivered at the thought of what might lie in store for her.

'The men will be finishing for the day in about half an hour. That gives you time to go and deal with Signor Mazzini.'

Rissa nodded. She could not speak. Antonio had brushed every sensible thought from her head. He had played on her sensitivities and she felt stripped naked beneath his acquisitive eyes. She had revealed more to him in these few days than she had to anyone else. Now her emotions were quivering with—what? Was it apprehension—or might it even be excitement? She could hardly dare to admit it. At least satisfying her desperate need for him would get this madness out of both their systems.

Antonio watched her pick up her hand-fork again and walk back into the house. Not for the first time she had surprised him. He had expected this to be a simple, bloodless matter of convincing a woman she would give him anything he wanted. He had had no problems achieving this aim in the past. But this was different. No woman had made him hunger as Larissa Alfere did. No other woman had shown such potential to catch fire beneath his hands. It had trembled through her, from that river of russet hair right down through those long, long legs. He savoured that picture of her and—

Rissa could feel him watching her, and had to make a determined effort to stride rather than scuttle back into the *palazzo*. As soon as she had learned the rules of love according to Luigi, she had encased herself in a protective shell. Antonio had been working away at her until she was powerless to resist. How had he managed it? More importantly, what would happen now?

* * *

Livia already had their meal waiting on the kitchen table. Rissa had taken her place and was cutting into her courgette bruschetta before Antonio strolled in. Eating his meals in the kitchen was one of Antonio's few concessions to being in charge.

'Ah—Signor Antonio—someone called Marian rang you, from Cardiff.'

'Cardiff?' Rissa said, with a quick look at Antonio.

'Yes—that is what I said.' Livia fussed in the pocket of her apron. Pulling out a crumpled piece of paper, she smoothed out the creases and read it carefully.

'She says that as you were in charge of providing the new hospital wing, it is only right that you are the one who opens it. She would like to know if you would be free for their official ceremony on the twenty-seventh? Apparently your personal number has been unobtainable recently.'

He did not look pleased. Sitting down at the table, he helped himself to some cold roasted peppers.

'It sounds as though you will have to manage without me for a few days, Contessa.'

'You don't sound very keen.'

'Unlike the great and good of London and New York, I hate publicity.'

'Perhaps if you check your schedule, you could find an excuse not to go?' Rissa frowned. The huge wall chart over in the temporary building was covered with his careful script and various colour-coded labels. It had the status of a holy relic among his workforce.

'Everything stops for Marian,' he said succinctly, pouring out glasses of iced mineral water for all three of them.

Rissa wondered what he meant. The adoring look Livia was giving the unsuspecting Antonio made her think that this

Marian might have let the housekeeper into more secrets than she was revealing.

'Is it all right if I leave early today to take Fabio to the vet, Contessa? Signor Antonio said it would be OK, but I wanted to check with you first.'

I'm sure he did, Rissa thought, brought back to reality. It was hopeless to try and remember if Antonio had mentioned anything to her about the matter. He had bewitched her completely with all his talk of pleasure. Rissa could not even recall if they had really arranged an assignation—whether he had put the words into her mind, or if he had suggested it aloud.

'Of course, Livia,' Rissa said, without looking up from her meal. It was on the tip of her tongue to tell the housekeeper not to bother with the washing up, but any hint that she might be keen to get Livia out of the way would only give Antonio the impression that she was desperate for him. *But then, isn't that the case?* Rissa thought as Antonio suddenly pushed aside his meal and stood up.

'If you are ready to go now, Livia, I will walk you down to the village. I'm sure it won't hurt the Contessa to do her own washing up for once.'

'Oh, but *signora—signor*—I would not want to put you to any trouble!' Livia said, already taking off her apron and flipping it into the washing machine.

'There's no problem. I need the exercise.' Without looking at Rissa, he swung away from the table and held the kitchen door open for Livia.

Rissa's appetite evaporated instantly. She had been keyed-up for him to make another move on her as soon as Livia disappeared. Now her passion was reaching fever-pitch, he had gone.

# CHAPTER EIGHT

FOR the first time since moving in on the estate, Antonio began making a point of avoiding Rissa. After all his taunts about the way she kept getting cold feet, he was now beginning to wonder whether sex with her—emotionless or otherwise—was such a good idea. The more he learned about her, the more he realised this was not going to be a simple conquest.

He concentrated on his work, moving between the various groups of builders with ease. This meant he was always busy.

Rissa tried to convince herself she was glad he now distanced himself from her. He was always tied up, discussing things or talking on the telephone.

She had caught enough snippets of his conversations over the weeks to know that he had several other building projects in progress, both in Italy and Great Britain. She had misjudged him. He was no rootless part-timer, but a true businessman, with fingers in plenty of pies. There were lots of calls on him, and she was becoming increasingly curious about his private life. When Antonio had left to attend the hospital opening in Wales, Rissa had wondered if he travelled there with company. She hadn't seen Donna from the time he'd left until the day he returned.

Mazzini had certainly acted as though he was a free agent while Antonio was away. Rissa had had to refuse invitations from him on an almost daily basis. Her fingers had been burned early on, when, in her naïveté, she had accepted a formal invitation to take a working lunch in Florence. Rissa had been too nervous to eat much. She had stuck to a simple salad and mineral water, despite Mazzini's encouragement. That had been just as well, for she'd discovered later that Mazzini's own generous helpings had been charged to her account with the land agency. It had been a harsh lesson, and Rissa had been wary of mixing business with pleasure ever since.

Her attitude had done nothing to dampen Mazzini's enthusiasm, and he'd called into the *palazzo* every afternoon in Antonio's absence. Rissa had made it clear that she did not expect all these visits to show up on the accounts. Mazzini had claimed to be hurt at the very suggestion, spreading his plump pink hands wide in a gesture of innocence. His smile had almost convinced Rissa, but she was still cautious. She was keeping a close eye on her finances. She had separated her own private funds from the *palazzo* accounts, and knew exactly how much she could afford to spend. An extravagant agent was not an allowable expense. She had enough of those already.

Antonio's trip to Cardiff had been a success, although it did not feel like it. He'd called into the offices of AMI Holdings. They were missing him, but everything was humming along almost as usual. Attending the hospital open day, he'd accepted praise from the staff whose new wing bore his name, but it had not been enough. Something was missing from his life.

He started for home, still trying to pin the feeling down. As he crested the last hill above the *palazzo*, he felt sure that his first sight of home would fill the void. It didn't. He continued his journey hopefully, but still felt faintly cheated as he nosed his Ferrari into a parking space directly outside the house. Getting out of the car he gazed around, uncertain what he was looking for. Suddenly a movement made him look up. Rissa was standing at a window, waving to him. He waved back, and then went straight up the steps into the house.

Abandoned on the gravel, his Scaglietti waited patiently for him to remember that he had left her unlocked.

The guest suite was nearly finished. Rissa could hardly contain her excitement, as it meant her step-parents would soon be able to come and live with her. They had ventured out of England only once before, to attend Rissa's wedding, and she was determined this trip would be even better. She had learned from Antonio. Failing to plan meant you were planning to fail, he always said. So she telephoned one of Luigi's old friends. He lived in London, and was the editor of an upmarket lifestyle magazine. The offer of an exclusive photo-shoot when the *palazzo* was complete proved to be irresistible. He agreed to accompany the Silverdales on their forthcoming journey to Monte Piccolo.

Privately, Rissa wondered how much the chance to make up to a supposedly rich widow had persuaded him. Luigi had always been insanely jealous of the man's interest in her, although the Count had managed to hide his envy at the time. Freddie Tyler was far too influential to be upset, and now Rissa intended to use that influence for her own ends.

When Freddie saw the potential contained in her beautiful home, he would be sure to give it a good write-up. Publicity should attract holidaymakers to the area, which was already trying to publicise itself now that locals could take pride in 'their' *palazzo*, and visitors would help the economy of Monte Piccolo, as well as Rissa's finances. The gardens were producing well, and she had designed a website to advertise everything. Her early training in marketing had taught her to be ready to take advantage when and where she could. Lucky breaks came to those who planned ahead.

As the date of completion drew nearer, Livia decided to get into character. She bought herself some severe black dresses, and took to wearing a collection of keys at her waist like a dignified châtelaine.

'I shall need a full list of Mr and Mrs Silverdale's likes and dislikes, *signora*, together with those of Mr Tyler, well in advance of their arrival,' the housekeeper announced in her new ultra-efficient manner.

'Of course, Livia. But you don't need to make any distinction between them. Every guest is going to be treated like royalty here. I shall just be so glad to see some friendly faces—besides yours, of course,' she added with a smile. Livia had thawed out quickly once she had realised that Rissa was not brain-dead, like most of the women who had been attracted to the Alfere family in the past.

In her original list of suggestions for Antonio, Rissa had said she wanted to produce as much food at the *palazzo* as possible. To her surprise, mountains had been moved and miracles had been worked. It had happened. Antonio had mobilised his troops. They had spent one precious afternoon of perfect weather clearing, levelling and grading an area where Rissa could make a garden. She had added seeds and water, which had sprung into life as if by magic. And, one morning each week, Livia had been taking grapes, lemons, salad bunches and other vegetables down to sell at the market. The money only trickled in, but the effect it was having on Rissa's self-confidence was out of all proportion to the small amount of cash the estate was earning. She could look forward to having her own money again.

A few euros spent at the market on plants and seeds had produced an almost instant effect. The reverse had happened with the *palazzo*. Rissa had poured money in, and things had looked more and more desperate. Now, all of a sudden, the house blossomed. With the *palazzo* structurally sound, and part of the garden a thing to be proud of rather than a wilderness, Rissa decided to throw a party for the locals. The people in the village were her future customers, and her enterprise could only grow with their help. She had heard from Livia that the people of Monte Piccolo were curious to know exactly what was going on inside 'the big house'. Some of them had even been peering in through gaps in the stonework of the estate wall when they thought no one was looking. Now was a good time for her to hold an open house. It would keep people interested, and with luck it would give them something to look forward to.

Entertaining at home was an exciting new idea for Rissa. Her step-parents never invited people to their house because they were ashamed of their relative poverty. Luigi had always hated having people in any of his homes. He'd preferred it to be just the two of them—and the old Contessa.

Rissa could not wait to fill her new house with sound and laughter. It was empty and echoing at the moment. With no soft furnishings or carpets in place yet, it seemed the ideal opportunity for welcoming anyone who wanted to come. There was also another reason for her generosity. Since arriving at the *palazzo*, Rissa had spent most of her time wearing old clothes. She was either working in the garden or sorting through abandoned rooms. Before Luigi's death she had felt faintly embarrassed by the designer clothes he bought for her at every opportunity. Now, for once, she could not wait for an opportunity to dress up again.

Slipping away to the room where the last of her expensive clothes were stored, Rissa spent some time marvelling at the remnants of the extravagant lifestyle that had once been hers. Beautiful gowns, bias-cut to show off her slender figure, reminded her of dinner parties that had continued until daybreak. There were elegant suits for attending the races in Kentucky, tea dresses worn to Washington receptions, and silken peignoirs designed for wearing at home when doing not very much at all. Hers had been a life of privilege and inertia. Compared to the hard work and worry of her time at the *palazzo*, Rissa now realised she had been living a half-life until arriving in Italy. She had been vegetating, when she might have been experiencing real life. Despite everything, this was *fun*.

Her party was planned to coincide with the afternoon's *passeggiata*. Rissa hoped that people would follow the signs set up at the estate gates, leading them through to the grounds beyond. Their curiosity would be rewarded on the terrace in front of the house. Rissa had borrowed some tables and covered them with lace curtaining rescued from inside. These had washed up a treat, and been bleached by the sun. There was lemonade made with the estate's own fruit, wine from a local supplier, and free samples of the type of food she was hoping to sell in the *palazzo* café.

When all the arrangements were well under way, Rissa

showered and changed. It was a novelty to have water spraying from the showerhead in her new luxury bathroom rather than from some accidental leak about the place. She spent a long time luxuriating, but luckily it never took her long to get ready. A touch of lipstick and a suspicion of face powder was enough, given the healthy glow that outdoor living was giving her.

She had already chosen what she would wear: a white linen skirt, teamed with a sleeveless navy top sprinkled with polka dots. It was too hot for the matching jacket, so she left that behind on its hanger. Scooping her thick, dark hair into a clip, she added a thin gold bracelet and matching necklace. Then she spritzed on the last of her Chanel, and went out to meet her public.

The building team had already gathered, almost unrecognisable in shirts and trousers. They usually strolled about in shorts, stripped to the waist. Now they stood about in uncomfortable groups. Antonio was the only one who looked at ease. He was wearing a light-coloured linen suit, teamed with a cotton shirt open at the neck, giving a hint of body hair. This illicit glimpse of his smooth brown skin aroused Rissa more than his fully bare chest might have done. It was the allure of the half-hidden, and she had to fight the temptation to feast her eyes on him openly.

It worried her that in five years of marriage Luigi had never been able to ignite half the feelings within her that she could get from simply looking at Antonio. Merely to walk past him made her pulse pound, and she found herself inhaling deeply so that she could catch the clean, male scent of him.

She was scared. Her body was reacting in ways she had never known before. It was taut with expectation today. Parties were when things happened, weren't they? What if Antonio took her aside and tempted her again? With one murmured request he could undo her resolve not to give in—that was all it would take. If he wanted her then she was his. No question. There would be no denying him this time. Her body was seeing to that.

And who was Rissa to deny herself? She had been a good, loyal wife, despite all her troubles. That torture had ended with Luigi's death. Now she was free, why shouldn't she indulge herself for once?

Anticipation added a champagne fizz of excitement to her already heightened senses. There were so many questions still whirling around in her head. If she slept with Antonio, would she hate herself for giving in to temptation, or look on it as one of life's great experiences? Perhaps once would not be enough? Glancing at him covertly, Rissa knew it would not. She had given her heart once and seen it battered. Could she bear to go through that again?

But she might be running ahead of herself. Surely Antonio Isola could have any woman he wanted? The look in Donna's eyes each time they met made that clear enough. His drive and ambition on behalf of the Palazzo Tiziano must surely be mirrored in his intimate life. He was all male, and would take every opportunity to prove it. If he wanted to bed Rissa, surely he would have thrust aside her doubts and taken advantage of her before now?

The thought of his touch on her body brought a fierce glow, but it was a pleasure that might never be tasted.

Rissa moved through her guests in a dream. She smiled her thanks at their appreciation and exchanged a few words here and there. All the time she kept her face turned away from where she knew Antonio to be. She was scared he could read her thoughts, and she knew her eyes would betray her innermost feelings. She did not want his probing intelligence working out how vulnerable she felt in the face of his charm. When all was said and done, the careful weighing up of advantages and disadvantages counted for nothing when matched against her raw, pulsating need for him. One word, one look from him, and Rissa knew she would be in his arms and in his bed, making all her fantasies reality.

Antonio paced around the party like a caged lion. He was restless with desire, and resented it. The Contessa Larissa Alfere-Tiziano was supposed to have been a minor diversion on the road to acquiring his *palazzo*, but something had happened. Somewhere along the line, simple physical desire for her had been overtaken by a real need. Antonio knew all about satisfying plain, old-fashioned lust. That was a game for the flippant and shallow. What he was experiencing now craved a deeper satisfaction, an eternal pleasure. His body ached with it.

Seeing Rissa drifting through her flocks of admirers, seemingly oblivious to the effect she was having on them, seized his insides and screwed them up. The women watched her easy, understated elegance and style. The men appreciated that too, but in less subtle ways. Rissa seemed to rise above it all, treating the appreciative looks with a gentle innocence.

He wondered what the audience would do if he gave in to temptation and grabbed her right now. He would kiss her until that coolly aristocratic body melted in his arms and responded with the hot passion he had kindled in her before and could not wait to taste again.

* * *

The entertainment was not all one-way. Although the locals had come to inspect their new neighbour, and see what she was doing to the old place, Rissa was learning too. Elderly people—some of whom had worked at the *palazzo* in the old days—were keen to share their memories. Mothers, grateful for somewhere new to push their buggies, fed grapes and lemonade to toddlers in the shade of the fig trees. Middle-aged couples came to poke around the gardens. But Rissa was disappointed that there were no youngsters at her party.

There were plenty of them hanging around street corners, in their counterfeit fashions and designer sunglasses, but the way young people were being priced out of Monte Piccolo was not their only problem. Teenagers who stayed in the area had nothing to do. And kids with time on their hands could lead to trouble. Rissa began to wonder about expansion plans even before her ideas for the *palazzo* were up and running. Perhaps Antonio would reconsider having one of the outbuildings made into a cyber café? He had already talked her into having the main house wired for multimedia and communications. She could not imagine that it would cost much more to run cables through to another building.

She risked glancing in his direction, and stiffened. Donna had appeared, and was talking to him with animated delight. Antonio smiled at her physical nudges, but glanced away often, to study the depths of his half-full glass of Chianti. *What are they talking about?* Rissa wondered as Donna lifted a ripe fig from one of the wicker fruit baskets set along the length of the tables. As the woman took a bite, rich juice spilled down her chin, making her laugh. It tickled Antonio's fancy, too, and as he joined in Donna raised her fruit to his laughing lips, kissing them with the sweet, unctuous flesh.

Savage, aching jealousy suddenly gripped Rissa. Burning, she turned away. *I must have been mad to think of trying to talk business with Antonio at a time like this,* she thought. *He is too busy making up to that—that woman.*

Rissa busied herself topping up the glasses of her many guests. Livia had been forbidden to wear her uniform, and was under instructions just to mingle and enjoy herself. When Rissa went looking for her housekeeper, she found her seated beneath a great spreading holm oak with a covey of other matrons. They were busy sizing up the guests.

'Thank the good Lord those builders came wearing clothes!' Livia announced as Rissa offered them all more *biscotti*. Her friends clucked indignantly.

'It is not right that a *contessa* should be subject to such sights—with the exception of one young man, maybe.' Someone in the coven chuckled. They were all looking at Rissa with such mischievous delight that she was immediately suspicious.

'What do you mean by that, ladies?'

'You must know, *signora*,' Livia explained. 'It has been a long time since a true Michaeli-Tiziano lived in this house. Make sure the place is not much older before the family line is secured, Contessa.'

Rissa looked at her housekeeper quizzically.

'Find yourself a nice young man and fill the place with *bambini* as quick as you can, Contessa.' A hook-nosed harridan wagged a finger at her. 'The old names must continue.'

'She *has* a nice young man. And not only that, he is a—'

'Livia! Is there any more wine?' Antonio's voice cut

through Rissa's astonished silence. He was bearing down on the group beneath the tree like a thundercloud.

'This is Livia's day off. Perhaps I could get you some?' Rissa said sweetly as the old ladies nudged each other and murmured together. They smiled, realising that Rissa was looking back at them. She could not help but think that there was something sinister about their talk—and Antonio's oh-so-convenient interruption.

'It isn't for me,' he said sharply. 'The general supply is running low.'

Rissa did not wait to see if Livia's friends would explain what they meant. She was more concerned to make sure her party was running smoothly.

'Ah, Antonio!' Donna arrived at his side again, to attach herself to his arm. 'Enrico keeps warning me that you are untrustworthy, but I guess I just like playing with fire.'

'Excuse me, Donna. I must circulate.'

The dark-eyed beauty flashed a savage look at Antonio as he interrupted her flirtation once again by striding off through the crowds. Her resentment turned to anger as she saw that he was threading his way through the guests with a purpose. He was heading to where Rissa stood, as dignified as any of the Tiziano family portraits.

Dusk was creeping up from the east, and Rissa was wondering how to wind things up tactfully. It had been a good party, and most people had already drifted away—but not Donna. Every time Rissa looked up, it seemed as though the woman was hanging on Antonio's every word. At one point Donna had even been hanging on to him physically.

Enrico Mazzini suddenly materialised at her side. He was

the last person Rissa wanted to see, but she pinned on a pleasant smile.

'I have just completed a tour of your house, Contessa. You are to be congratulated, both on your vision for the *palazzo* and your catering.'

Antonio was closing in on them. Every time he'd sought her out with his eyes today some other man had seemed to be claiming her, and this time it was his worst enemy. Yet again, he thought, Mazzini has her cornered.

'The Contessa and I have urgent business to discuss, Signor Mazzini.' Antonio's fingers closed around Rissa's elbow and he steered her deftly into a position where any man wishing to speak to her would have to get past him first.

Mazzini did not look happy. He looked even less delighted when Donna sashayed up to take possession of his arm.

Rissa smiled up at Antonio, trying to soften his expression.

'Today has been a great success, hasn't it?'

*No—success for me would have been ravishing you in your newly completed suite,* he thought. But what he said was, 'Isn't it time you brought things to a close, Larissa?'

It was exactly what Rissa had been thinking.

'How? I can't very well start clearing the tables. It would seem so…obvious.'

'Just stand on the front steps and say a few words.'

Rissa hesitated. Antonio was standing so close to her that she was enveloped by his shadow. She could feel the electric thrill that seemed to crackle from his dark eyes. If she dismissed everyone then he might go too, and that was not what she wanted.

'What is stopping you, Larissa? Is there something wrong? You cannot have disapproved of me rescuing you from Mazzini.'

Rissa was silent for a moment, looking down at her hands as she tried to form an answer.

'No…it's quite the reverse, Antonio. The truth is… Look, I haven't been able to get you out of my mind since the night we met, and…' Her voice died away. She gazed up at him expectantly.

It was the moment Antonio had been waiting for. 'Then go up there and get rid of all these people!' he growled, his voice low with intent.

Ducking past him, Rissa ran up the front steps of the *palazzo* and turned to face her remaining guests. She was on fire, and hoped everyone would think it was nothing more than nerves. She clapped her hands to get their attention.

'Thank you all for coming,' she announced, scanning the crowd. Although she was careful not to look in Antonio's direction, she could feel his eyes boring into her. 'I hope you have all enjoyed yourselves…'

Rissa's mind was racing as she said nice things about the builders' work and Livia's cooking, and then wished them all a good evening. A round of applause greeted the end of her speech—and one immovable Antonio, planted squarely between Rissa and her escape route into the house.

'You dark horse,' he murmured, his lips lifting into a grin. 'If only they knew why you were so keen to dismiss them.'

Rissa gathered all her courage and looked directly into his deep, delicious eyes. It had to be said. 'Before… anything happens, Antonio, there's something you should know about me.'

She paused. Behind them the guests were disappearing, like her conviction, into the dusk. Bats began to flicker around the twilit garden.

Over the years women had flattered Antonio into bed, deceived him into it, and used every other trick in the book. Now the great Contessa Larissa Alfere was trying to join in the game.

'No!' Antonio pulled himself up to his full, imposing height. 'I will accept no more excuses, no more words. It is time for me to take you,' he murmured.

In the distance they heard Livia call out a goodbye as she closed the estate gates behind the last guests. When the house-keeper went inside, they were left completely alone together in the garden. His lips parted in a smile of triumph, but Rissa needed to speak.

'The problem is that, despite Luigi, I'm still a virgin, Antonio.' She went on quickly, before he could laugh, 'I don't know if I can live up to your expectations. That first night— when I fell down the bank and you rescued me—you awakened my body in a way that my husband had never managed, not in five years of marriage. Since that moment I have ached for you, craved you. That is the truth...' Her words struggled out individually, each one waiting for his scorn.

Antonio watched her carefully. He was shocked by her revelation. It would have been the easiest thing in the world to say yes, but the fear in her eyes made him wary. He wanted to be sure she was ready.

Rissa was taut with anticipation. She had wanted to remain cool and impersonal. Instead she felt hot and flustered. She should have put things differently, but it was not the easiest thing in the world to say. Surely if Antonio had really been receptive to her he would not have held back for so long? Perhaps he had only been toying with her instincts? Perhaps he was keeping all his love for Donna...?

'And now you want to give yourself to me?' he said sternly.

Rissa felt herself redden with shame. 'Yes,' she nodded, head down. 'I *want* you, Antonio. And I need—' She stopped. 'What?'

'I need a child to carry on the Alfere name. Everyone says so—Livia, her friends—'

He cut her short with an explosion of disgust. 'You think I would be a pawn in a game like that? For goodness' sake, Larissa, you should adopt a child, if you feel so strongly.'

'No. Perhaps it was a stupid idea after all.' Rissa could hardly speak for regret. Now she was embarrassed. This wasn't going quite as she had wished.

'I don't see why not, if you are so keen to raise another little Alfere. The gossip columns will have a field-day if you take in a photogenic orphan. You could cement your position as Saint Larissa, the grieving widow.'

The mocking tone of his voice lit her reaction. 'I'm not interested in photo opportunities, Antonio. I need a child of my own. A child that only you can give me, because it is only you that I truly want!'

'In his soundbites, Luigi Alfere was always angling for pity because you were infertile,' Antonio retorted, remembering his research.

He had gone too far. 'That was never true.' Her eyes blazed with pain. 'It was the official line, put out for public consumption. I felt so sorry for him, I agreed to the story. My only fault was incompatibility. Somehow it never seemed to work between us. I always loved Luigi, but it was never enough,' she finished sadly.

'I see,' Antonio said slowly. 'But why me? How do you know I would make a fit father? You cannot simply sleep with anyone these days,' he mocked.

Rissa was out of her depth. 'You aren't anyone, Antonio. I have learned enough about you since you have been working here to know that you would be far too sensible to put your own health at risk. The care you take over your work has convinced me of that.'

He laughed, a rich, full-throated sound that made the crickets chuckle on the dusky bank below the terrace where they stood.

'How right you are, Contessa. I always take the greatest care of everything,' he murmured. 'And now, the time for talking is over.'

# CHAPTER NINE

His voice had been low with anticipation. A tremor flashed through Rissa's body, its turbulence focussed on the depths of her being. She could say nothing, but as Antonio pulled her into his arms a gasp escaped from her lips.

His hands roamed over her back, then his fingers dug into the smooth pleat of her hair and brought her face close to his. Without waiting for her to reply he kissed her, hard, until her head swam and she gripped ineffectually at his powerful shoulders.

'Antonio! Not here—what are you doing?'

'Isn't it obvious?' His eyes were flashing dangerously with lust. Kissing her again, he probed the soft willingness of her mouth with his tongue. Finding no resistance, his left hand moved to her shoulder, caressing its way around to cup her breast.

Rissa felt her body melt into warm syrup as Antonio's fingers worked their way beneath her top. He had the hands of an artisan, firm and assured. As they ran over her lacy, insubstantial bra she felt the fabric catch and dissolve, but she did not care. Pulling the restraining cups away, he freed the full magnificence of her breasts. For a second his kisses paused as he found the peak of her nipple with his thumb and fingertip, teasing it into wakefulness. Before her eyes closed, Rissa saw his face transported with desire, his lips slightly parted. Seconds later she felt his teeth grazing her neck, nipping at her earlobes in an orgy of sensuality. Tremors of excitement took a direct line from his kisses through her body.

With his right hand, Antonio was massaging her flank, kneading her soft flesh through the thin linen of her skirt, which rode up to give him free access to her bare skin. Rissa was so alight with longing that she became as conscious of his body as she was of her own. As he pulled her closer she felt the large, masculine ridge pushing against the front of his jeans. Instinct took over and she pressed against him, delighting in his sigh of anticipation. Rissa thought of all the occasions when she had wondered what it would be like to go all the way with him, and now here she was, experiencing every heady nuance of Antonio's boundless desire. Greatly daring, she slid one hand down to brush against him.

'Witch,' he growled. 'Go any further and I shall have to take you here in the garden—which I do not intend to do.' Suddenly she was lifted up into his arms. It took almost every grain of his self-control to wait, but he carried her through the echoing house and straight up to her suite. 'Your beautiful new bed is a far more fitting place.'

'Go on, then,' Rissa breathed. 'Take me now, Antonio. Please.'

To have her begging for release like this swept away the last of his restraint. She was torturing him—but two could play at that game, even at this late stage.

'If you are a virgin, how do I know you really mean it?' he taunted her, and was rewarded with a primal cry of desire. He smiled, silently adding that it would be his pleasure. Her clothes were flimsy, and fell aside at his touch. Pushing her back onto the soft insubstantiality of the duvet, Antonio ripped off his own shirt. Kneeling on the bed, he towered over her, bare-chested.

'So—how does my lady like it?'

'I—I don't know…I've never felt like this before,' Rissa heard herself say. It was as though she was living a dream—a fantasy. 'I never experienced anything like this with Luigi…'

Something snapped inside Antonio's head. That name… He never wanted to hear that name again—yet here it was, coming between him and his pleasure. Furious, he flipped Rissa over onto her front and pressed his body down full-length on top of hers.

'You will never speak that name again. Not even in the hottest moments of your passion. I will make you forget him—'

And Mazzini, he thought with a pang. She would have no thoughts of other men in her head when Antonio made love to her. He wanted to fill Rissa entirely—her senses, her mind and above all her body. She would be so full of him that there would be no room left for anyone or anything else. His powering need for her was engulfing him like a tidal wave and would not be denied.

He had to be the one who drove all others from her life. The rogue male within him was about to take exclusive possession of his woman. He paused minutely. What was that about *his* woman, all of a sudden? He'd had so many over the years. He had got the measure of them long ago. And yet…

'Forget who?' Rissa breathed huskily, her mind a heady mix of sensations. She reached back to touch the smooth plane of his muscular arm. It was the moment when she realised with a rush that she had a desperate need to gain fulfilment from his body. It was a want she had never experienced so violently before, and she tried to stifle the thought.

Antonio was looking at her curiously. The fire in her eyes as she looked back at him was a nice touch, accentuating the tigerish longing in her voice. She was an accomplished liar, if nothing else.

'So, you are ready to give yourself to me in order to continue the Alfere line?' His harsh words made her gasp.

'We aren't talking about that now,' Rissa pleaded. 'We're talking about wanting and needing. You want me. I need you.'

'The hired help?' Antonio queried.

'You know what you are worth, Antonio,' Rissa murmured.

He growled into her neck, burying his face in the fragrant flow of her hair.

She came alive at his touch. As he leaned over, pressing his chest against her spine and nuzzling the nape of her neck, all thoughts flew away. Only feelings were left. As their bodies moved together she became more and more receptive to his touch, until every centimetre of her skin was glowing. Twisting beneath him she ran her fingers through his hair, pulling his head down to nuzzle again at the sensitive peaks of her nipples. This time there could be no going back. When she cried out now it was in anticipation. Her senses were running wild.

As Antonio covered her breasts in kisses, the shadows criss-crossing the bedroom grew darker and the breeze from the garden running over her body was more deliciously perfumed than ever. Her bedlinen had never felt so crisp or cool. It was so quiet that she could hear Antonio's breathing change as he drank in the warm fragrance of her. Feeling the warm pressure of his erection against her thigh, Rissa moved to appreciate his body as much as he was enjoying hers.

'No.' He caught her hand before she could make intimate contact with him. 'Don't do that. I like to stay in control—as I am sure you already know.'

He slipped away from her then, but without losing body contact. Rissa was delirious with need. Muscles low down in her stomach were cramping with it. He felt the tightening and met pressure with pressure, sliding a finger between the delicate folds of her femininity and using tiny movements to coax the honey of her arousal. It was too much for Rissa. Arching her body, she opened like a flower, calling desperately for his love.

The moment had come. He responded by riding into her with smooth, easy thrusts. They surfed together through waves of mounting passion, engulfed in kisses and caresses that made them rulers of their own paradise.

Next morning, Antonio tried to counter pleasure with pain as he jogged along the still-dark road. How many women had he taken in the past? He tried to bring some cold common sense to the subject. For some reason his mind refused to compute. The hard fact was that none of those other conquests mattered any more. Rissa was different. She had been as stiff as a cypress. Now she was as sweet and warm as honey. She had changed.

It's not my problem, he told himself briskly. That attitude had levered him out of her arms before she woke, and sent him off on this five-kilometre run before sun-up. He put his head down and sprinted hard for another few hundred metres. The going was tough. It was all uphill, and by the time he reached the next crest his breath was coming in ragged gasps. Pausing, he regrouped his thoughts.

Work on the Palazzo Tiziano was complete. She would expect that to be the end of the matter—job done, so *ciao*, Antonio. That might be her arrangement—but it was not his. She had the house, but he still wanted it. This was not supposed be happening. He had intended to marry Rissa, get the house, then dispense with her. Now she had the house, and was going all-out to secure a family line of her own. Antonio knew it was time to act before *he* became the dispensable one...

This was a good vantage point for looking back down the valley. As he watched, a sliver of sun rose above the distant hillside. He could just make out the *palazzo*'s roof, shining in the first beams of dawn. Down there, the ancient woodwork would begin to click and creak as it expanded in the growing warmth. Fabio would be mewing to be let out of the back door. Coffee and *biscotti* would be perfuming the air as Livia started work. And Rissa would be waking soon, roused by the chirrup of sparrows prancing along all those ridged red tiles.

Taking a deep breath, Antonio started to jog back down the hill.

He had planned to take a quick shower in the ground floor wet room before surprising Rissa with breakfast in bed. Instead, she surprised him. He was still busy soaping down when the bathroom door opened and she walked in.

'Antonio?' Her voice was husky with desire.

He sighed. It was exactly as he had predicted. Virgins were like seal pups—lay a finger on either, and they would follow you everywhere. He remained aloof, but there was no hiding his physical response as she opened the shower door and stepped inside. Head down, meek as a geisha, she knelt in the water that had coursed down his body and kissed him. The thought of her small pink tongue tantalising him towards still more delights made him moan with pleasure. Leaning back against the tiled wall, he enjoyed the contrasting sensations of the cool needles of water and her warm, soft mouth. Adjusting the thermostat, he drew her up and pulled her into his arms. The shower was soaking them both, droplets beading his chest and her hair.

Filling his palm with citrus shower gel, he enrobed her head with bubbles, soaping her body until it glittered. Rivulets ran over her breasts and belly. He scooped them up and used the silken softness to slide his hands over her thighs and bottom. The dark triangle of curls hiding her femininity foamed beneath his fingers, and with a sob of excitement she pressed against his palm as he sought out her path of pleasure. He found that watching her abandonment and knowing that he could make it even better for her gave him almost as much of a kick as the anticipation of his own orgasm.

'You are a wicked, wanton girl,' he murmured into her hair. 'I have never known a woman so willing.'

She looked up at him, still hazy with desire, but with one part of her mind unable to believe what she had just heard.

'What did you say?'

He grinned. 'If I wasn't the seasoned lover that I am, you would wear me out. No lesser man could cope with your demands.'

'Do you mean that?'

'One so beautiful and arousing should not be let out of bed without a bodyguard. That is how serious I am.'

With a mew of delight she fell into his arms again. He responded by lifting her off her feet, taking her weight as she twined her legs around his waist and accepted his love again.

No, not love—*lust*, she tried to tell herself afterwards, when they had reached her bed again in a tangle of towels. This man was acting on nothing more than instinct. That was the arrangement.

Turning her head into the soft white pillow, she squeezed her eyes shut and tried not to cry.

# CHAPTER TEN

RISSA woke alone the next day. She had learned that Antonio was a light sleeper, and wondered if that was her influence. When he brought coffee and rolls for her breakfast, she had another reason to worry. His face was troubled, and he seemed distracted. The dream is over, she thought. Now the nightmare begins.

'Is there anything wrong, Antonio?'

'No. No, of course not,' he said abruptly. 'I need some fresh air, that is all.'

Rissa tried to keep her voice light. If he needed to escape, the last thing she wanted was to keep him trapped. 'Why don't you take your pride and joy out for a spin?'

'Why not? How soon can you be ready? I will fetch the Ferrari.'

'You want me to come too?'

His expression was enigmatic. 'Yes.'

They had to stop for petrol high above Monte Piccolo. Rissa got out of the car to stretch her legs. The breeze that always played through the hills lifted her thin cotton skirt as she studied the newspaper headlines on a display rack. Innocently, she was arousing the interest of several men drinking coffee in the shade of an ancient walnut tree. When she strolled over to lean against the stone wall separating the country road from a tumbling slope below, Antonio's eyes never left her.

'Come on. Let's get home.'

Rissa regarded him warily as he pulled out of the petrol station. It was odd that he seemed to think of the *palazzo* as his home, but then, she reasoned, he had been living and breathing the place for months.

Antonio was the last member of the building team left on site. Peace had descended after weeks of destruction, but it had been replaced for her by a secret sadness. Soon Antonio, like her first Italian summer and its swallows, would be gone.

'I am having second thoughts about our arrangement.'

Here it came. He was going to announce the end of their affair. Rissa dug her fingernails into her palms. She hid her hands in her lap so that he would not see. Following his past examples, she kept quiet, persuading him to speak by her silence.

'Our couplings should stop, Contessa.'

Still she said nothing. Antonio changed hands on the steering wheel. Staring at the road ahead, he whipped the Ferrari through a switchback of hairpin bends. Out of the corner of his eye he saw Rissa blanch and screw her fists into tiny balls, but still she did not fling herself on his mercy. Taking her to the edge of fear had not released her feelings into words.

'The only way you can begin the new Alfere dynasty is to find someone to love.'

'I thought I loved Luigi, but it never happened then.' *The difference is that I know I love you,* Rissa cried out silently to herself. *But that's the last thing you want to hear from a woman.*

'It will—one day.' Antonio tried to catch her eye, but her

head was bent. 'Come, Larissa—I have something for us back at the house. I have been saving it for just such an occasion.'

When she did not reply, he put his foot to the floor and drove.

Antonio's Ferrari was abandoned to cool down below the front terrace. He disappeared towards the kitchen while Rissa wandered slowly in through the *palazzo*'s great front doors.

'Vintage champagne, but only ordinary glasses from which to drink it,' he announced, when he had sought her out again. Removing the cork, he poured her a foaming measure.

'You drive a magnificent car, and now you present me with this? Your firm must think highly of you to pay you so well.'

'I am a perfectionist,' he said simply.

'Why don't we take a walk around the house now, and admire your handiwork?' Rissa suggested. 'It is Livia's day off, so we won't be disturbed.'

They went from room to room in near silence. Rissa was delighted with her completed home, but Antonio kept finding something to do. There were always window frames to be inspected or handles to be rubbed over with a cuff.

'It's as though you love this place as much as I do, Antonio.'

He gave a humourless laugh, his dark eyes guarded. 'It pleases me.'

'Then don't leave straight away,' she said impetuously. 'Stay a while longer.'

He did not answer, but took the bottle and refilled her glass. She accepted it with a smile and they continued their leisurely tour of the *palazzo*. It took a long time and the rest of the champagne to reach the ground floor again.

'And to think—this is my home.' Rissa gazed around the main salon in wonder.

Antonio knew his mind should have snapped *No, it's* my *home*. But for some reason—the champagne, the Indian summer, or the end of the project—it didn't. Instead, he took her glass and placed it on the table.

'Yes, but it is *my* creation, Contessa. A combined effort that should be celebrated.'

Her lips parted, and the telepathy developing between them meant that Antonio did not need to ask. They fell into each other's arms again, ready to feed the flames of their desire once more. Without waiting to strip off, Antonio lifted her onto the table. Rissa locked her ankles around his neck and, pushing their clothing aside he took her hard and fast, right there beneath the largest equestrian portrait.

'A fitting tribute, I think,' Antonio said breathlessly as he helped her down.

Rissa could not answer. Her feet might be on solid ground once more, but her body was still in orbit.

The furniture restorer who called later that morning was a typically handsome Italian in his forties. He had brought his young apprentice along, to get some public relations experience, but the lad was having difficulty concentrating. He was standing in the grandest country house he had ever seen, and being spoken to by a *contessa*—one who had great legs, too.

'Quite a few good pieces were lying around the house when I moved in,' Rissa was saying, but the restorer shook his head and looked doubtful.

'I am sorry to tell you that there is nothing of any great value among them, Contessa. You will wish to fill your house with period-correct antiques, of course—?'

'Good grief, no!' Rissa could hear euro signs clocking up at an alarming rate, then realised she might frighten the two men if she started pleading poverty. 'I won't be doing that to begin with, anyway. There is no point in replacing perfectly good furniture. It may have been in storage for some time, but once everything has been cleaned and re-upholstered it will be fine.' They were standing in the room Rissa hoped would one day become a library. Right now she could not justify buying a daily newspaper, let alone paying out money for books. For now, the large salon was filled only with sunlight and echoes.

'It is all in different styles,' the apprentice argued, when he could tear his gaze away from the inviting curve of Rissa's breasts.

'I've thought of that. If you could re-upholster it all in the same design and fabric, that would give the whole job lot unity. It isn't as though the furniture will be close enough to be compared. This big old barn of a place needs seats far and wide, scattered all over the place.'

The door opened and Antonio strode in. Rissa began to smile, but stopped as soon as she saw the look of determination on his face.

'Gentlemen, this is Antonio Isola, my—'

'I have come to collect you, Contessa. We have business to discuss—over a working lunch, I think. So if you would excuse us, gentlemen?'

Rissa smiled and clapped her hands together to draw her meeting to a close. 'Well! That sounds like an offer I can't refuse.'

'Why do you say that?' Antonio looked at her sharply. She had misjudged his mood again, and regretted it.

'It's just a saying. Now, gentlemen, I think we have finished here, so I will say goodbye and look forward to seeing some fabric samples in due course.' Rissa had to throw the last few words over her shoulder as Antonio hustled her out of the room.

'That wasn't very polite, Antonio!'

'It was not very polite of *them* to undress you with their eyes like that. It is good that I arrived to take you away from them.'

They never got as far as going out for lunch. Antonio put his proposition in terms more eloquent than any words. Their picnic tray lay abandoned, along with the trail of clothes they'd left scattered from the door of Rissa's room to the huge luxury of her bed.

Antonio was content to lie and watch her doze. Warm afternoon sunlight filtered through the curtains, which moved in a sigh of breeze from the fragrant garden. Rissa stirred, then paused. Thinking he was still asleep, she eased her way out from under his protective arm and went over to look out of the window. He was happy to admire the sleek line of her naked body from a distance, until she raised one hand and rubbed the back of her neck. In an instant he moved from the bed to her side.

'What is the matter, Larissa? Do you have a headache?'

She nodded.

'It must be lack of food. You should have your lunch—but first…' He replaced her hand with his own, running his thumbs from nape to hairline. The muscles there were taut with tension.

He worked to ease them as she gazed out across the private garden she had made below her room. That had been the place where Antonio had first touched her with intent. She had wasted a lot of time since then, but she was determined to make up for that now.

'Antonio…' she said at last. 'Despite all those brave things I said about carving a future here for myself, I…I'm beginning to feel that my emotions might be getting the better of me.'

For a second his fingers stopped their circling. Then he resumed the long slow strokes of his massage, trying to ease the tension that was growing in her neck despite his efforts. 'Are you trying to tell me something, Larissa?'

'It won't be something you want to hear.'

'Try me. I have heard it all in the past, believe me.'

'I know. That is why it is so difficult for me to open my heart to you now.'

He chuckled. 'You are talking about hearts? That is a bold move when speaking to one of your workforce.'

'That's the problem. You're the last one left at the *palazzo*, and I've come to depend on you. What happens when you've gone, and the next disaster comes around the corner? The truth is I don't have any money, Antonio.'

There. She had said it. If he was only after her money, that would surely put an end to everything. He said nothing. Gathering up her remaining courage, Rissa carried on. 'This place is going to have to be mortgaged to the hilt to settle the remaining costs. That's my only chance of getting any money until the Tiziano estate starts bringing in cash.'

'Money isn't everything.'

She heard the smile in his voice, but before she could reply he bent his head close to her ear and kissed the lobe with infinite gentleness.

Rissa turned to him in wonder. At that moment she thought their minds fused, working as one. It was the ultimate high—loving him with a clear conscience and no secrets between them.

He kissed her again, and again.

'If it wasn't for all my cash-flow problems I would ask you to stay here longer, but to expect you to live in poverty wouldn't be fair.' Rissa sighed. 'Oh, how I wish money could make itself.'

'Let it.' Antonio nuzzled across her cheek and began nibbling her ear. 'The best things in life, like making love, are free.'

Rissa was tempted, but her money troubles were like an elephant in the corner of the room. No matter how much she desired Antonio, the moment was lost. He could feel it, too.

'What is the matter, Larissa?'

'Nothing.'

'You are more tense now than when I began your massage,' he murmured. 'Don't tell me that money is going to come between us?'

'No—no, it isn't that, Antonio.' She slipped her fingers between his and squeezed his hand. 'The trouble is that I've got myself cornered into another awkward situation with Signor Mazzini, and I can't see a way out.'

It was Antonio's turn to stiffen. 'Is he still bothering you?'

'No! Not in the way you might think.'

'Then you are having trouble with his accounting?'

There was no point in denying it. Antonio was too clever.

'I think I may have been giving him too much freedom over the arrangements for this place. He's always resented your suppliers undercutting his contacts. A few weeks ago I refused to pay a bill for consignments you had not ordered. He merely settled the account on my behalf, and added the cost to the quarterly administration bill he sent me this week.'

'Have you ever signed anything to state that he could act in that way?'

'No—Luigi's solicitor in New York appointed him as my agent. *I* haven't signed anything.'

'This is outrageous. Have you made him promise that it will not happen again?'

'Yes. I have written to him saying that if he acts in that way a second time I shall find another agent, and I sent a copy of my letter to the solicitor in Manhattan.'

'But on this occasion you have settled his bill?'

Rissa nodded, and gulped at the memory of it. 'It has just about cleaned me out again. I don't even know if I can survive financially until the mortgage goes through on this place. It is that close. I am so worried. Every letter from the bank sends me further down the road to ruin.'

'That is what Mazzini is counting on. He has always been keen to get his feet under the table here. Don't worry, Larissa. There can be no more trouble with the bank. Now that the work here is finished, getting a mortgage to repay the last few bills and give you some working capital will be a formality. There are only cosmetic touches needed.'

A shudder ran through her body. Antonio's movements became more caressing.

'Do not worry, Larissa. We will manage.'

He bent and kissed her hair. Rissa closed her eyes, hardly able to believe what she was experiencing. Antonio had said 'we'. For the first time in years it felt as though she could relax in security. At last someone was in her corner. She would not have to fight alone. As he took her in his arms she flowed around him.

Antonio felt her body mould to his as he swept strokes over

the smooth flare of her naked hips. The supple joy of her created its own reaction in him. He felt the pressure coiling his stomach muscles as his hands found their own way up to her breasts, cupping gently. She responded by turning to him and accepting a long, lingering kiss. Lifting her into his arms, he carried her back to the bed. It was still tumbled from their last lovemaking. In that warm, soft haven he coaxed Rissa into whispering her desire. As she trembled in anticipation, his hand drifted over the delicate curls of her mound. Her legs parted in anticipation and she moaned, eager for his touch. His finger found the little bud of her clitoris and circled it, bringing her almost to the peak of excitement. She reached for him, delicately stroking his insistent maleness.

'Sometimes only a kiss will do,' he murmured huskily, moving out of reach of her fingertips. Rissa's sigh of disappointment morphed into a moan of pleasure as he spread the swollen lips of her sex gently, and kissed the rose-pink heart of her femininity. A million sparkles ran through her veins. In her innocence she had never dreamed anything could make her feel so wanton and wanted. She arched her body, desperate for him to drink in her pleasure. He moaned with growing desire, and the sound brought her to a new peak of excitement. As his tongue teased her, he reached up to dance his fingertips over her nipples, igniting a thousand more darts of tingling fire. As she reached the summit of delight he entered her.

Her body accepted him, the core of her being rippling with a pleasure that he echoed with low moans of fulfilment.

'Oh, why did it take me so long to surrender to you?' she breathed, encircled by Antonio's protective arms. 'You have made me the happiest woman in the world, Antonio. I am so very, very lucky.'

# CHAPTER ELEVEN

When Rissa woke next day she stretched out for Antonio, but he was not there. Glancing at the clock, she smiled. It was nearly eight o'clock. He would already be hard at work on his computer in the site office. Perhaps he might be persuaded to take coffee with her, among the flowers that were making such a pretty picture in her newly restored garden? It would distract him from lining up his next building job, too.

Despite everything, Antonio still kept an eye on his business. Rissa had a terrible fear that when he found something suitable he would be off again. He had already spoken in general terms about his office, although it had been in passing. Rissa had not bothered to question him about his usual work. That was not important. Only Antonio's presence in her home mattered to her. Anything that kept him here for a little while longer was worth trying.

She cleaned her teeth and showered, smiling again at the faint mark on her calf. Antonio's teeth had grazed her skin when she had driven him beyond endurance again during the night. She thought of how her lonely, unfulfilled marriage to Luigi had been put behind her. Antonio certainly had no complaints!

Already wondering happily what they would do today, she

felt her dreamy expression change as she caught sight of something. There was a sheaf of papers on the *chaise longue*. Antonio must have left them behind by accident. It was easy enough to do—when the door of the *en-suite* bathroom was open, it hid that corner of the room. Dressing quickly, she went over and picked them up. Antonio might need them. Love danced in her eyes at the knowledge that he would have been too considerate to come back and disturb her after the turbulent night they had enjoyed. Then she saw the engraved heading on each sheet of heavy, top-quality writing paper. The words *AMI Holdings* were burned in black across every white page.

That could mean only one thing. Antonio was a traitor. He was corresponding with the firm that had wanted to buy the Tiziano estate. The realisation swept away Rissa's scruples and she began to read. The first few letters made no sense. They referred to charitable donations, to properties and places outside of Italy. None mentioned the Palazzo Tiziano—and then she reached one typed letter about a bill for the suite at the Excelsior she had visited with Antonio. AMI Holdings had settled it in full. At the bottom of the letter Antonio's distinctive handwriting noted that the amount had been reimbursed from his private account. All the details were there: dates, times and, most damning of all, the full signature of Antonio Michaeli-Isola.

The man who had stolen her heart was in reality the driving force behind AMI Holdings. That company was her enemy. Fear of their grasping ways had made her determined to hang on to the Tiziano estate whatever happened, but she had not expected tactics like this. Antonio had infiltrated every part of her home and her being. It was the ultimate betrayal.

Things began to fall into place. She had thought herself

stupid for letting Mazzini pull the wool over her eyes, but Antonio had blinded her with a much more dangerous weapon—love. Would the man stop at nothing to get her out of her own home, just so that his firm could ruin the place? A horrible thought struck her. She went out to the nearest staircase and ran her hands over the restored newel post and banister. How did she know the work Antonio had supervised was up to standard? What would happen if the building inspectors arrived and told her everything would have to be ripped out again and redone?

She had no money left. Rissa had been relying on the bank mortgaging the *palazzo* within the next few days. She had been spending money she did not really have, but only in the belief that it was an investment in the future of this grand old house. Antonio Michaeli-Isola had known all this, and it made him more dangerous than any Tuscan serpent. At that moment Rissa did not care. She snatched up the papers that had fallen from her fingers, and marched off to confront the snake in his den.

The site office door smashed back with an impressive bang. Rissa stood in the open doorway and thrust the sheaf of papers at Antonio, who was seated behind his desk.

'You lied to me. All you are interested in is getting your hands on my house!'

There was no point in denying it. Antonio stood up. 'At the beginning, yes, I was. But things have changed, Larissa.' His words were confident and laced with authority.

'Stop! I don't want to hear. You played with my emotions. You patronised me at first, because you thought I would soon get fed up with the *palazzo* and you would be able to pick it up for a song. And when that didn't work...' Her voice was dangerously quiet and her dark eyes stung with tears. She let him fill in the rest for himself.

'If your mind has been working so busily, Larissa, then you should also be aware that when my agents made their first move I instructed them to offer far above the market price for the *palazzo*. It was only when you refused to sell that I took matters into my own hands.'

'And when I wouldn't roll over and abandon the place, you put on an act to seduce it out of me.' Her voice dropped to a trembling whisper. 'All those beautiful things you have been saying to me while we…when we… They were all lies!'

'They were never lies, Larissa.' He put out a hand to her, but she shook it off. 'Yes, at first I was completely focussed on the house. That was because I wanted to make sure all the work was finished to my own exacting standards. Then, as time went on—'

'And you discovered I wasn't going to be easy to dislodge, you started making up to me. That was unforgivable, Antonio. You don't want me—you never did. It is only Tiziano that interests you.' She shook her head in disbelief and wiped away her tears. 'Why are you so blinkered? I love this place— but it is only stones and mortar, after all. It is relationships that matter in life, not…*things*. Why can't you see that, Antonio?'

His dark eyes flashed. 'Life is not as simple as you imagine, Rissa. It is more complex.'

It was an echo of the protests she could remember making to him. 'No, it isn't. You have been using me for your own ends, Antonio. You've betrayed my feelings by pretending to care for me when all you wanted was this—my home!' She gestured at the estate outside his window, still with the papers in her hand.

'You are wrong, Rissa. My feelings for you and my need for Tiziano cannot be compared.'

'Don't give me that!' Rissa was in no mood to listen. 'I have been lulled along by the fantasy that you really cared for me, that your words meant something. To think—I was so taken in by you that I told you things about my marriage I have never spoken of before. I confided in you because I thought I could trust you.'

'Rissa!' He slammed his hand down on the table. 'When we became lovers it was in *spite* of what I knew of Luigi and his family, not because I was cast in the same mould—'

'Of course you are!' Rissa cut across his words with a hiss of fury. 'You are so alike it is untrue. I fell for Luigi before I knew he was rich. Once money came into the equation everything was spoiled. Now you have pulled the same trick on me. That hotel suite, the call from Cardiff, the car—I should have known you were not what you seemed. You were hiding your millions and pretending to be an honest worker until you could sweet-talk me out of the little I have left in life.'

'Yes. Yes, I was using you. But that was before I realised my true feelings ran deeper than I thought.' His dark, penetrating gaze almost overwhelmed her.

She stared at him for a long time. Then, gathering all her nerve, she faced him with the question that she knew would mean the end of everything.

'Prove it.'

Antonio was not a man for half-measures. He reached out and dragged her into his arms. Driving his fingers through her hair, he pressed her against his lips, kissing her so hard and for so long that the blood sang in her ears. When he let her go, they were both breathless.

'Marry me, Rissa,' he breathed.

She listened to her beating heart, and then came to an agonising decision. There was nothing left but to put him to a single, vital test. Deep down, Rissa knew there could only be one outcome. She would be left to count down the seconds until the moment when Antonio abandoned her. Tears filled her eyes, threatening to spill out and ruin everything before he had a chance to do it for her. Then, rising on tiptoe, she placed another kiss on his firm, cool lips.

'Yes, Antonio. Yes, I accept…'

*Now! Do it now!* a voice screamed in her head. Rissa hardened her heart, knowing she had to strike before his widening smile destroyed her nerve for ever.

'Yes, Antonio—let's get married and start all over again. I have already made arrangements to sell the Palazzo Tiziano. Everything was put in motion yesterday. What could be better for us than to make a brand-new beginning together, away from here?'

It happened exactly as she had known it would. His hands were already falling from her. A dark shadow fell across his eyes. A few seconds before, his lips had been soft with warmth. Now they were hardened into a dangerous line.

'Antonio?'

He was drawing away, already heading for the door. It took all Rissa's strength to let him go.

'You have sold my—*our* home. Where do you *think* I am going?'

As Antonio stormed out of the room. Rissa sank to the floor, sobbing as though her heart would break. Everything had happened exactly as she had convinced herself it would. Antonio had only been interested in the Palazzo Tiziano. He had lied to her. He had wanted her house, not her. As soon as the object of his single-minded desire had seemed no longer to be up for grabs, he had dropped her like flawed marble.

Tay Spender was enjoying himself. It was not often that a solicitor—even a Manhattan solicitor—could be certain of getting the better of a billionaire, but today he was acting under a client's instructions. The fact that his client was an extremely beautiful young woman with a still more impressive estate in Italy tipped the balance further in Rissa's favour.

'Let me get this clear in my mind, Mr Michaeli-Isola. You are asking me to ignore my client's express wishes or…you'll do *what*?' he challenged Antonio. 'Are you going to send your boys around, or sneak a horse's head into my bed? I think not.'

'Do not insult me, Mr Spender,' Antonio said in a dangerous voice. 'That is not the way I work. I came here with a perfectly reasonable request—'

'To block a private transaction made by a vulnerable woman merely on your whim? If you believe that to be reasonable, Mr Michaeli-Isola, I suggest you spend a little more time here in the Land of the Free. Sure, money talks in Manhattan, but it has to be a darned sight more polite about it. Good day to you, sir.'

The solicitor bent over the paperwork he had been studying before the tall, impressive intruder had burst into his office.

Antonio had been wound up with anticipation, but as Tay Spender peered at him one last time over his spectacles all the tension left his body. He left the solicitor's office and closed the door firmly behind him. He took the elevator, and walked out of the building with his head high. After all, as Rissa had said, there was more to life than bricks and mortar.

It was then that he realised he could live without the Palazzo Tiziano. It would be a wrench, but if his family had survived eviction then so could he. The only thing he could not live without was Rissa. It had torn him apart to leave her so suddenly, and now he was aching to return. She had not replied to his e-mails, or picked up any of his telephone messages. The sooner he was back in Monte Piccolo, the better. The longing for her was a physical pain inside him. Gradually, he realised, that need for Rissa had replaced all his old gnawing desire for revenge. This was something he had never before experienced in his whole life. This was—

Suddenly it hit Antonio in the solar plexus like a physical blow. He stopped, right there in the middle of the suffocating, streaming sidewalk in the centre of New York City.

This was—*love*.

Rissa stood at a window and watched the last contractor's van drive away from the house. Antonio's image swam in front of her tear-filled eyes. From the moment he'd dashed away she had been desperate to rush after him, to listen to his phone messages and open the mails he had sent, but she had resisted. She could not lay herself open to any more pain from his silver-tongued lies.

He had deceived his way into her heart, and then into her bed. Yet, despite everything, she still loved Antonio so much that it hurt. Only by cutting herself off from him entirely could she hope to heal the wounds that loving him had inflicted on her.

The next time Antonio's distinctive red Ferrari streamed up the drive, Rissa dodged out of sight. She had come to a decision and her bags were already packed. Sales at the market had been bringing in a reasonable amount of money, and she had been saving hard. There was just enough in her account now for a budget flight to England.

It won't be running away, she told herself as she picked up her passport from the new dressing table. I'm overdue a visit, and it won't be long before I'm back here again.

Despite her words, the look she cast around her room had the poignancy of a final farewell. Antonio would take an age to stow his beautiful surrogate child away in its garage. She had a few moments to dream of how things might have been.

When she slipped out of the rear entrance, she took care to remove his set of spare keys to the house from their hiding place beneath a loose cobblestone in the yard. Antonio Michaeli-Isola needn't think that her absence meant he could start lording it over the Tiziano estate. She meant to deny him that pleasure for ever.

She left Monte Piccolo in the same way she had arrived— by taxi. I might be abandoning the place, as the Alfere-Tiziano family did, she thought, but I have to go now, while I still have my pride. One more encounter with Antonio would be sure to rob me of even that, she consoled herself as her driver veered around a bend. Antonio and the Tiziano estate were lost to sight—but not to her heart.

## CHAPTER TWELVE

RISSA had lost track. The red-eye connection and the flight passed by in a haze, but she was starting to come to terms with her decision by the time she had worked her way across London. Reaching the Keir Hardy Buildings, she was disappointed that it no longer felt like home. The graffiti and the cars burned out on the windswept wastelands around the tower blocks had not changed, but she had.

It was only when Rissa knocked on the door of Flat 83 that things got back to something like normal. George and Jane Silverdale were thrilled to see her. Within minutes she was being spoiled with a cup of milky tea. It was lovely to be home. She could put all the loneliness behind her.

Luigi had become increasingly distant in the later years of their marriage, leaving Rissa isolated, and the old Contessa, Luigi's mother, had been strong and silent. Between their first meeting and her death, three years later, Laura Alfere had not spoken a single word to Rissa. Luigi's young wife had been ignored in a way that only the truly haughty could manage. The old Contessa had communicated with Rissa only through her servants. This had done little for Rissa's authority and absolutely nothing for her self-esteem. A woman who could behave in the way that Laura Alfere had was capable of anything. Lately Rissa had started to wonder if Antonio's dislike of the family might have been fuelled by more than his simple disdain for the ruling classes.

As soon as she could tactfully extract herself from being fussed over by her parents, she offered to go shopping down in the precinct to pick up a few things. They had insisted she should stay in her old room, rather than find a hotel, and Rissa was glad to do so. All the same, she did not want to impose on them any more than she could help. Despite her offers to pay for the extra shopping, they pressed cash on her, and a list of her favourite British comfort foods.

Rissa had another reason for wanting to escape. She would have to pass the local library to reach the grocer's store. From her earliest days it had been impossible for Rissa to walk by without going in, and today would be no different. On-line information might be able to give her a few more interesting facts about AMI Holdings. Rissa wanted real proof that Antonio was as bad as she imagined him to be. The image of his abandoned love was too painful to bear without an antidote.

Booking an on-line session was easy. By the time Rissa had done all the shopping, and chatted to a couple of old neighbours she had not seen since leaving for university, it was time to check in and settle down in front of the computer. She was absorbed in typing out 'AMI Holdings' in full when a shadow fell across her keyboard. With a smile she looked around, ready to tell the librarian that she was doing fine. Then she froze.

'Antonio!'

'Yes.' Unshaven, and hollow with lack of sleep, he towered

over her like an avenging angel. Rissa tried to stand, but there was no room to push back her chair. He was blocking her escape.

'I left Monte Piccolo without telling anyone where I was going. How did you find me?'

'I have my ways.'

His voice was low and resonant. Rissa tried to gauge his mood, but his face was giving nothing away. The situation must be as intolerable for him as it was for her—after all, she had called his bluff, hadn't she? The fact that he'd had the nerve to track her across Europe when she wanted to lick her wounds in private fired a new anger in Rissa. She narrowed her eyes and squared up to him.

'What you mean is that you have an international network of staff with spies everywhere. First I hear that you hunted down my solicitor, poor Mr Spender, and now you have turned on me.'

He looked down on her steadily. 'Apparently your parents are the only Silverdales in the telephone book.'

Rissa swelled with indignation and slapped her palms down onto the library desk. Half a dozen people looked around at the noise. 'I knew it! You did not even do it yourself. You paid someone to get onto my case,' she hissed in a whisper. 'Although that doesn't explain how you got here from Monte Piccolo so quickly. It took *me* the best part of a day!'

'I flew myself.'

Rissa scowled. 'I know you have money, Mr Isola. That means you can't impress me with the fact now.'

'It is a light aircraft owned by AMI Holdings. It isn't my personal property. What would a man like me do with a thing like that? And my full name is Michaeli-Isola, if you intend to be formal.'

Rissa gasped. 'Michaeli? No wonder your signature looked

familiar. That name appears all around my house.' She stared at him. He stared back.

'That is because the Alfere family took over the ancient estate of Michaeli-Tiziano.'

Everything began to fall into place. Rissa's eyes widened with growing realisation. 'That is why you want my house. That is why you worked for nothing. The Ferrari—that suite in the Excelsior—no wonder you could sell me that story about taking paid leave! The great mastermind behind AMI Holdings probably earns more in his sleep than a hundred ordinary people in a year.'

'Wealth means nothing.'

Rissa looked at the sun-browned, experienced hands that had worked so hard for her house. A tremor ran through her when she remembered that they had been adept at working on her, too. It took an effort to harden her heart to reply.

'You might use it to impress gullible women.'

'True—although I knew better than to try it on you, didn't I?'

They looked at each other for so long that the screensaver cut in on the library computer. Rissa jumped.

'I must finish here and get back home, Mr Michaeli-Isola.'

'What are you doing?'

Rissa knew there was nothing for it but honesty.

'I was trying to find out more about AMI Holdings and their future plans for the Palazzo Tiziano. If they are honest enough to show them on the web, that is.'

'Don't bother about me. It is my family home that is important.' He covered her mouse with his hand and clicked on the data bar. 'Have you tried the name Michaeli?'

'You did not give me a chance to try anything.'

She thought he had taken control of the machine to stop

her. Instead, he typed in the words 'Michaeli-Tiziano', then pushed the mouse back towards her hand. 'It will not make for happy reading.'

'Would you rather I didn't see it?'

'On the contrary—if I had been completely honest with you from the start, Larissa, none of this would have happened. I would have gone to the Italian authorities and had the *palazzo* requisitioned. The case for the restitution of my family is so strong there would have been no argument against me taking possession. I did not have to go to the trouble of offering to buy it from you, but bullying is not in my nature.'

Rissa made a small noise of disbelief. He silenced her with a look. 'Call it a whim, but at first I wanted to take the peaceful, easy way out. If I had gone in with all guns blazing from the start you would have hated me.' He shrugged. 'But that would have meant nothing to me—then.'

His eyes burned with passion now, and it was all for her. Rissa could not resist a gasp. She was held in the power of his gaze and could not turn away.

'How can you be so convinced that my house is yours, anyway?' Rissa's voice sounded faint and faraway. 'Luigi's family were so grand they owned all sorts of property. Any dispute over the ownership of Palazzo Tiziano must date back centuries. No one but the Alfere-Tiziano clan could have any call on it.' Rissa tried to stand up for herself, but her convictions were beginning to waver.

She thought back to Livia's hints. Antonio was totally convinced he was the rightful owner, but Luigi had been so proud of his ancient lineage. Surely there was no way Antonio could have any sort of a valid claim? Anyone in England who harboured a grudge from Civil War days, or who resented their ancestors losing out to William the Conqueror would have to be insane—it was all so long ago. Yet Antonio must be similarly mistaken, and he was the sanest person she had met.

She was watching him. Antonio was watching the screen. Rissa heard him click on a link. Slowly, gradually, she turned to see what was on display.

For long moments she read in silence, then looked at the black and white photograph reproduced on the web page before her. It had been taken on the front steps of her beloved new home. A tall, gaunt woman was clutching the arm of a fat man in a trilby hat and a double-breasted suit. Children in varying sizes surrounded the couple. Standing beside the family group were uniformed men.

Rissa tapped the screen. 'That woman is the image of my mother-in-law! Contessa Laura made the first three years of my marriage a misery. This snap must have been taken a long time ago—during the Second World War, maybe—but there's no doubt about the Alfere family resemblance.' She did not add the 'Tiziano' name this time. As she read the caption, she realised that the wrong done to Antonio's family was recent.

'"Signor Alfere and his wife accept the keys of the Palazzo Tiziano as a reward from a grateful nation,"' she read aloud. 'So that must be Laura's parents—Luigi's grandparents.'

'Your husband's family had mine convicted of helping the partisans, but my grandmother managed to escape and eventually ended up in Naples. She arrived there with nothing more than the clothes she stood up in, and had to make a completely new life for herself. She could never afford to return home, or take her case to the courts. Mind you, our old family curse had the last laugh. Your late mother-in-law was the only child out of that gaggle to survive.' He nodded towards the picture. 'My grandmother always listened out for news from home. The Alferes were so desperate to keep the fine old family name going, they made your husband's father adopt it as his own!'

Rissa was still trying to take it all in. 'And to think I wanted to do everything I could to keep their memory alive.' She shook her head sadly.

'My mother was born in Naples, and never liked to be reminded of what might have been. But I always loved to hear my grandmother's stories about Monte Piccolo. I became determined to regain my family's property. It was always one of those distant dreams that life never gives you the time or opportunity to grab. But when I read reports that the last Alfere was dead, I saw my chance.'

'Why didn't you tell me all this right at the start, Antonio? It hardly seems like a suitable case for "forgive and forget". Your family were evicted from the Palazzo Tiziano, and Luigi's family had no claim to it at all!' Rissa was outraged on behalf of the Michaeli family.

Antonio was holding his small crucifix between finger and thumb, running it up and down its fine silver chain. 'I was not about to speak ill of your husband. He was born long after all this happened, and so was I. Neither of us was in a position to take any moral high ground.'

Rissa was not so sure. 'No wonder Luigi's mother was so horrible to me.'

'Every family has its black sheep.'

'Not yours, I'll bet.'

Antonio almost managed to laugh. 'Do you remember the portrait of that horseman, hanging in the main salon at home?'

Rissa thought back to her dusting—and to their antics on the table below that picture. 'Count Lorenzo, you mean?'

'That's right. He is pointing to his hunting hounds in the distant landscape.'

Rissa frowned, remembering the grisly sight. 'It was hard to make it out under all those dingy layers of soot and varnish, until I climbed a ladder to dust it down. The dogs are tearing a deer to pieces.'

'That's right. Lorenzo is admiring them from horseback.' Antonio nodded.

'But he was so handsome…' Rissa looked at Antonio and scrutinised him carefully. 'Yes…there is quite a family resemblance, now I know that you two are related. I always had the feeling those portraits looked familiar. Thank goodness you don't go in for blood sports, Antonio. You don't, do you?' she added quickly. There was so much she still had to learn about him.

Antonio shook his head. 'In any case, that painting of Lorenzo is an allegory. His first wife had an affair, so he hunted her down with his dogs.'

Rissa recoiled in horror. 'Oh, the poor woman!'

'The Contessa Lucretzia had been an Alfere before her marriage. My grandmother told me all the family stories when I was a child. It was a real pleasure to walk around your house that first time, matching my memories to those portraits. Lucretzia must have been an ancestor of your husband's. If we can find a picture of her, you might be able to spot a family likeness between it and your Laura.' He began another computer search, but Rissa stopped him.

'Don't call her *my* Laura!' She grimaced. 'From this moment on, I don't want her, or Luigi, mentioned ever again.'

Antonio lifted his finger from the mouse button. 'Are you sure?'

Rissa looked down nervously. 'I have never been more convinced of anything in my life.'

Antonio knelt down before her, lifting her chin so her gaze met his.

'Then marry me, and I shall exorcise you totally, right down to the Alfere name.'

Rissa spoke slowly and carefully. 'It is my house you want. You desire the Palazzo Tiziano.'

His fingers gently brushed her cheek. Rissa trembled. *He is going to lie and say no, that's not true, it's me he loves and not the house,* she thought. *He is bound to say no.*

'Yes,' Antonio said, after what felt like an eternity. 'Yes, Larissa, I cannot deny it. From the moment I was old enough to know what great injustices my family had suffered at the hands of the Alferes, I have been determined to reclaim my house. I have always wanted the Palazzo Tiziano more than anything else in this life—until I met you.' His hands slid around her back and pulled her into the longest, most tender kiss she had ever enjoyed.

For a long, luscious time her mind went blank, but as he released her all the darkness flooded back. 'But you couldn't wait to get away from me—you dashed off the moment I told you I had made the decision to sell the estate!'

This was the acid test, but he did not hesitate. 'With hindsight, I can see that was wrong. It was a wrench to leave you then, but I thought I could stop the sale. I had to move fast to try and block any arrangements you had made.'

'You would have gone over my head?' Rissa was aghast.

'I have already said it was wrong. But my reasoning at the time was that we would need somewhere to live once we were married. My idea was that the estate was our perfect home—mine by right and inheritance, and ideal for you because you love the old place. I was unsuccessful in my bid, but it does not matter much.' He grimaced, but managed to add, 'I can live without the Palazzo Tiziano.'

Then his face warmed with a genuine smile of love. 'As long as I can spend the rest of my life with you, I can live anywhere. Although you must promise me one thing, Larissa.'

'Anything,' she breathed.

'I would ask you to delay the sale of your estate in Monte Piccolo until my mother has been able to visit. She has always insisted in living in the present, but I would like her to see the house where her mother and father were so happy, and where she should have been born. I was intending my eventual purchase of the *palazzo* to be a surprise for her,' he finished quickly.

'Antonio! You're *accepting* the fact that I'm going to sell? You would say goodbye to all those centuries of your family's tradition just for me?'

'Of course. Although I must be truthful—it will not be without a pang,' he conceded.

Rissa gazed into his eyes for a long time. If she was going to make a confession, now was the time. But her mind was already working on a grander plan. 'I am so sorry I jumped to the wrong conclusion, Antonio,' she said slowly, giving herself time to think. 'I should have trusted you. Can you ever forgive me for turning my back on you?'

'No apology is needed—only another reply to the question I asked you the last time we were alone together in the Palazzo Tiziano. Will you marry me, Larissa?'

'Oh, Antonio!' she breathed. 'It would make me the happiest woman in the world if I could become your wife—'

A sudden outbreak of applause made them both look round. All the other library visitors had been hanging on their every word.

With all the guile of a natural-born Michaeli-Tiziano, Rissa announced that as she was the official owner of the *palazzo* until midnight on their wedding day, the reception would be held there, on the terrace.

Years of respectable working class life rose up in George and Jane Silverdale—Rissa's adoptive parents. They worried that they would not have anything to wear, would not know how to get there, and finally that they could not speak a word of Italian. Rissa explained that Freddie, her acquaintance the magazine editor, would accompany them from England, and Antonio supplied another lifeline.

'My mother speaks English quite well. She will be able to talk enough for all of you, even when she isn't translating!' he said as they sat in the tiny best room of the Silverdales' flat, drinking tea and eating biscuits.

Jane Silverdale had found a packet of paper doilies somewhere and set the biscuits out on a plate. This made Rissa frown at her mother quizzically, as she was used to eating them straight from the packet. Distracted, Mrs Silverdale noticed her husband dunking a biscuit in his tea. As she opened her mouth to apologise for this slip, Antonio solemnly did exactly the same thing.

'It's the only way to eat them where I come from,' he said innocently to his frantic hostess, as Rissa tried not to laugh.

Antonio and Rissa had told everyone they wanted a small wedding. No one took any notice. The entire population of

Monte Piccolo filled the church. The world's press had to wait around outside. Once the ceremony was over, only invited guests got into the estate grounds—Livia and a scrum of the biggest locals she'd been able to recruit saw to that.

A perfect clear autumn day, with plenty of good local food and drink at the reception, meant the party went on until dark. Livia arranged for lanterns to be set up around the terrace as Rissa slipped away unnoticed. Antonio had disappeared a few moments earlier, after making a secret assignation with his new wife.

She walked slowly up the grand staircase towards their suite. Her fingers danced over the newly restored banister rail, but her mind was troubled. She could see Antonio's silhouette on the upper landing, but there was a dark cloud threatening to stifle their happiness. Reaching the top step, she ran to him through the long gallery, silk and lace whispering as she went.

'Antonio! Listen—there is something I must tell you—'

'You don't need to tell me anything—except how pleased you are to see this again.' He handed her a shallow cardboard box from one of the best dress shops in Florence.

Rissa put it on a side table and lifted the lid. Folded between layers of softest tissue lay the favourite gown she had sacrificed for the *palazzo*. 'My black velvet! Oh, Antonio— you bought it back for me!'

'I knew it would be the perfect present.' He smiled as she held the dress against herself and twirled around.

'It was a shame you didn't give me this straight after we cut the wedding cake—I could have changed into it. Everyone could have seen how generous and thoughtful you are, Antonio.'

'Black is not a colour for weddings,' he said simply. 'And

now I have one last present to unwrap. That is you!' He put the dress aside, his dark eyes flashing an invitation. Lifting her into his arms, he kissed her lightly before carrying her over the threshold of their room.

'No—wait, Antonio. We have to talk.'

'This is not a time for speech. It is a time for presents and—' He laughed, a deep, melodious sound from the depths of his broad chest. 'There is a parcel on our bed! Who is it from?'

'Me, of course. But Antonio, you must listen to me before you open it—'

'But you have already given me my present, Rissa.'

'This is another one. But—'

He reached the bed, but could not put her down, because the large box wrapped in silver paper and trailing ribbons was sitting squarely in the middle of their coverlet.

Antonio set her on her feet, clicking his tongue as he dragged the heavy thing towards him.

'The new laptop was more than enough, Larissa—I didn't expect anything else. I know you are as poor now as you've ever been, and will be until the...' he hesitated '...proceeds of the sale go through.'

'I should hang on to your gratitude until you hear what I have to say. Antonio, listen to me. I had to know for certain if your feelings were for me or this house. The Palazzo Tiziano was never for sale. I lied to you. It was a spur-of-the-moment thing, to see if your proposal was genuine, and now I regret it.'

Antonio's hands slid away from the ancient wooden box he had been unwrapping. He stood up straight. Not for the first time Rissa felt a shiver of apprehension as she saw exactly how big and powerful he was. She began to back away from him.

'That was a risk,' he said slowly. 'When I left you so suddenly, you must have thought your suspicions were right.'

She nodded, her head drooping.

'Then I am sorry, Rissa.'

Her head jerked up. '*You're* sorry? But I was the one who lied—'

'You did that only because you were feeling insecure. Your background with Luigi Alfere had destroyed your self-esteem. I should have realised that, and made my feelings for you unmistakable.' His voice was as soft and caressing as the hand he moved gently over the skin of her cheek.

'Then you accept my apology?'

'None was needed.' His fingers played beneath her chin, lifting it so that he could kiss her. 'Now, are you going to help me unwrap this present, Mrs Michaeli-Isola, so that we can move on to more…intimate treats?' he whispered eventually.

'I hope you did not spend too much on me,' he chuckled as they tore at the paper and ribbons to expose the present.

Rissa slipped her arms mischievously around his waist and hugged him. 'It didn't cost me a thing. Unless you count sleepless nights, scraped skin and broken fingernails, that is!'

Standing behind him, her face pressed against the broad expanse of his back, Rissa could not see what he was doing. His movements became slower, then stopped. She heard the box lid fall from his fingers, and gave him a squeeze.

'Well?'

He did not answer.

'Do you like it?'

'I don't understand.' He turned in her arms. In one hand he held a sheaf of dog-eared, yellowing papers. 'These are deeds to a property.'

'That's right. They are the deeds to *this* property. The Palazzo Tiziano—it's all legally yours.' Rissa smiled up at him. 'The house, the estate—all the bills, all the problems. As they said in the wedding ceremony—for richer, for poorer.'

'But…I thought you said you weren't selling it?' His brow contracted, as it always did when he was trying to puzzle something out. 'So you contacted my people again and arranged to sell it to me? That must be where you got the money for the laptop…'

'No money was involved. It's a present from me to you, Antonio. To keep for ever, with no strings.' She picked up a trail of silver ribbon and let it fall from her fingers, but her smile faded as she realised his expression was not showing the instant delight she had expected. 'I seem to have done the wrong thing, Antonio, and I'm sorry. When you proposed, my reaction was to think you were only after Tiziano. It was an instantaneous thing—I wanted to know for sure that your love for me was real, and not just an excuse to get your hands on your ancestral lands—'

He stopped her words with a kiss.

'Never doubt me,' he said, releasing her from the kiss but not from his arms. 'It was true that when we first met my thoughts were centred on getting my house back. Then I fell in love with you, and suddenly nothing else mattered. I would have seen you give away this *palazzo* without a word. I would have packed my bags and followed you to the ends of the earth. Instead, you have brought me home.'

'It is where we both belong,' Rissa breathed.

Taking her hand, Antonio led her over to the windows opening out onto their newly restored balcony. Down in the garden, celebrations were still going on. Strings of coloured lights threaded through the olive trees blinked in a gentle breeze. From here they could make out the newly planted rose bushes on the edge of the first terrace.

'Just think,' she breathed, 'we are the last of the Michaeli-Tizianos.'

'Ah—there I must correct you, Mrs Michaeli-Tiziano-Isola. I am not the last of my line. I intend to be the first in a new dynasty. Mind you, we may have to consider building a new wing, simply to house all the portraits we will have to get painted.'

Rissa laughed and slipped her arms around him. At that moment, the warm protection of his body was all she needed. 'At least we don't have to worry about any old curse, or the likelihood of earthquakes now that there's a legitimate heir in the house. This *palazzo* should stand for a thousand years.'